Stealth Antennas

Second Edition

by

Steve Nichols, G0KYA

Published by the
Radio Society of Great Britain,
3 Abbey Court, Frazer Road, Priory Business Park, Bedford, Bedfordshire. MK44 3WH, UK

First Edition Published 2010

Second Edition Published 2014

ISBN 9781-9101-9305-1

Cover design: Kevin Williams, M6CYB
Editor: Steve Telenius-Lowe, PJ4DX
Typography: Chris Danby, G0DWV
Production: Mark Allgar, M1MPA

Printed in Great Britain by Page Bros of Norwich, Norfolk.

Publisher's note
The opinions expressed in this book are those of the authors and not necessarily those of the RSGB. While the information presented is believed to be correct, the authors, the publisher and their agents cannot accept responsibility for the consequences arising for any inaccuracies or omissions.

Contents

Foreword

I can't believe it has been four years since the first edition of *Stealth Antennas* was released. Doesn't time fly when you are working DX?!

This book was originally written with 'the rest of us' in mind: those of us without 10 acres of prime real estate in the middle of nowhere, without optimally-placed pine trees to support low-band antennas and without giant masts for multi-element beams. No, we have to make do with much less – so-called 'compromise' antennas hidden in attics, or strategically placed bits of wire taped behind guttering.

I wanted to show that you *can* work DX from seemingly impossible locations and that yes, you can gain your DXCC or whatever other award you set your sights on. Above all I wanted to show that you can enjoy our wonderful hobby from just about anywhere.

As I started to research the original book I was struck by how many hams were more than willing to share their experiences with me. From home-made magnetic loop antennas to energised guttering, there were plenty of ideas out there.

I also wanted to save people a lot of time and trouble building antennas that wouldn't work as well as they'd hoped. That's why there are plenty of tales of home-brewed antennas and how well they work.

Above all I wanted to create a book that you would enjoy reading; a book that you can dip in and out of of, full of ideas, hints and tips.

This revised edition contains new chapters on receive-only and topband antennas, a host of new reviews of commercial designs, plus some more antennas for you to build at home.

I hope you enjoy it.

Steve Nichols, G0KYA / AB8ZV
August 2014

Dedication

To my dear wife Toni, who has to put up with this strange hobby, and random bits of wire strung around her otherwise immaculate garden, for far too long.

Steve Nichols, G0KYA

1
Introduction

THINK OF amateur radio antennas and you might expect to see a 100ft steel lattice tower bristling with polished aluminium beams. At the bottom the ham resides in their purpose-built shack with the glow of a 1kW linear amplifier to keep him or her warm. Just one CQ call and the ionosphere buzzes into life as the ham creates their own propagation with their mega signals. The world is this amateur's oyster as the QSL cards on the wall show.

Actually, reality is usually somewhat different. Most hams operate from urban and suburban properties, often with limited or no garden space and with the ever-present fear of interference being caused to televisions, telephones, hi-fi systems and anything else with a plug on it.

But that doesn't mean that you can't continue to be a radio amateur. There are plenty of ways of getting on the air from the most difficult of locations. And it doesn't mean you can't work decent DX either. You don't need a beam, tower and / or linear amplifier to work most DXpeditions and you can make do with attic-mounted dipoles, stealthy verticals built into your tree or dipoles hidden in your gutters. Or you could set up a temporary antenna in your back garden, just for that favourite contest.

And what if you are strapped for cash? A commercial vertical antenna can cost more than £250. But a long-wire or dipole antenna can be put up for less than the cost of a cup of coffee and will probably work as well or even better than its commercial counterpart.

Don't have an external ATU? Not a problem - build a small unbalanced-unbalanced (unun) transformer for about £10 and your rig's internal tuner will tune up your long wire on all bands no problem.

But what if you have virtually no space at all? Well, in this book you'll find discussions on magnetic loops, EH antennas, the 'Microvert' and other small antennas. They may not work quite as well as external antennas mounted high and in the air, but that is missing the point. As long as you can radiate a signal, and someone else can hear it, you are going to have some amateur radio fun.

I know what you're thinking – this is all OK, but I'm not going to be able to work anything of interest. Oh yes? I used to think the same, but the truth is that you can work the world using stealthy antennas. It just takes a little more time and a little

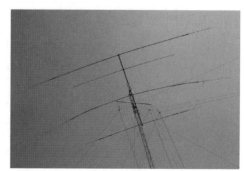

You don't have to have a large beam antenna to work the world.

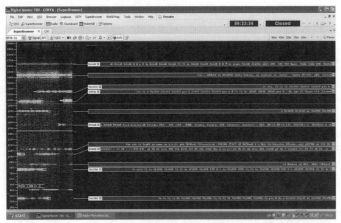

20m PSK31 running in the DM780 program's Superbrowser mode. You can see 11 QSOs taking place – all received using a loft-mounted dipole.

more dedication. The mode and band you use will make a big difference as well. CW and PSK31 will get through when you can barely hear a station on SSB. And contacting that rare DXpedition on 30m (10MHz) is going to be a lot easier than slugging it out on 20m (14MHz) with all the big guns.

Just flicking through my own log I see that I worked VP6DX (Ducie Island) on 80m using 100W to an 85ft long wire lying over the roof; TS7C in Tunisia on 40m using 40W to a magnetic loop in the attic; 3B7C (St Brandon Island) on 20m using an attic-mounted dipole, and 5A7A in Libya using 25W to an experimental EH antenna in the attic.

You don't need to have a beam antenna to work the four corners of the earth, although it certainly helps. In fact, so-called compromise antennas can work a lot better than you might expect. Let me tell you a story.

About 10 years ago I decided that it was about time I invested in some better antennas. All I had at the time was my multi-band dipoles in the attic (more of them later in the book) and an 85ft W3EDP end-fed wire that went up into an oak tree in the back garden. I ordered a 10m two-section tubular steel mast, a two-element mini-beam and a rotator. I won't say what make the beam was to spare any embarrassment, other than to say it cost nearly £500. My friendly local builder helped me dig out a one-metre cube of earth and we concreted the mast into place. Then there was a day's work to add the rotator and the beam, lay in the coax and rotator control leads and tune the whole thing up.

Just some of the QSL cards you could collect with your stealth antennas.

I cranked the mast up to its maximum height, stood back to admire my handy work (although my wife was less impressed) and went inside to see how well it worked. What I found was that on 20m (14MHz) the brand new beam was either the same or worse than the 'el cheapo' dipoles in the loft. I was livid – around £1000 expenditure and countless hours of work and the new installation was being beaten by about £5-worth of wire!

I spoke to the manufacturer who said that I really needed a balun, so £40 and a day's work later the beam went back up to 30ft.

Guess what? It was no different. The beam was about one S-point better than the dipoles on 10m and did show some directivity on that band only, but was it worth the effort?

Two years later, when I took the beam down to replace some of the tuning spokes, I put a five-band commercial vertical back up in its place at 30ft for a few months. Once again I found that the loft-mounted dipoles beat the vertical on 20m, where it was actually quite short (electrically). This story has been repeated over the years with a number of commercial and other antennas in three different locations, so it wasn't a fluke.

Now, admittedly you are less likely to cause TVI with an external antenna and noise levels are likely to be lower, but it does show that you can produce good results with stealth antennas and for very little expenditure too. The subject of avoiding interference and other EMC problems when using loft-mounted and other stealth antennas is covered in Chapter 10 of this book.

Don't get me wrong. A local ham friend has a SteppIR beam at 110ft and he can work things I just can't even hear, but the reality is that there is no way I could justify that level of expense, or persuade my wife and neighbours that a 110ft tower in a suburban garden is a good idea. It is also getting harder to get planning permission for external permanent antennas and neighbours seem ever quicker to complain about that "metal monstrosity" in your back garden.

And while I wouldn't encourage you to operate without knowing if you were causing interference or not, you are less likely to get complaints if your neighbours don't even realise that you are on the air! I know one ham who gets the blame for any interference, loss of signal, pop, bang or squeak on their TV by his neighbour – even if his station is switched off. Why? Because the three-element tribander at 60ft in his back garden just begs the neighbour to complain.

When it comes to interference issues get your own house in order first and the chances are that your neighbours will be fine. And with loft-mounted antennas you get the added bonus that:

a) you can work on them all year round in any weather;

b) you don't have to worry about the effects of high winds;

c) you don't get rain static, and

d) you don't have sleepless nights every time a thunderstorm rolls through town (although I still recommend that you disconnect the antenna and power supply from your rig when storms are around as the levels of induced pulses can be enough to fry delicate electronics. I know, we lost an answerphone and personal video recorder in one storm after lightning struck a building about 100m away).

Having stealthy antennas means you are less likely to be worried about direct lightning strikes. Photo: NOAA

What I have tried to do in this book is encourage you to try some different antenna ideas, even if you think that your situation is hopeless. I have also tried to describe antennas that haven't been discussed in other RSGB books. I have tried to dovetail the information in this book with the others that are available so that there isn't too much overlap. If you are looking for books that complement this one I can thoroughly recommend the excellent *Backyard Antennas* [1] by Peter Dodd, G3LDO. Also, the classic *HF Antennas for All Locations* [2] by the late Les Moxon, G6XN, is worth having in your library, as is *Successful Wire Antennas* [3], edited by Ian Poole, G3YWX and Steve Telenius-Lowe, 9M6DXX. There is also the excellent range of antenna books available from the ARRL.

But that's enough from me. Let's take a look at a few examples of amateurs from around the world who have overcome space limitations and put together effective radio stations.

CASE STUDY: JULIAN MOSS, G4ILO, AND HIS INDOOR ANTENNAS

Julian Moss, G4ILO, writes: "In 2001 I moved to a new development where the only permitted antennas were a TV aerial and a Sky satellite mini-dish. Therefore my antenna farm had to be in the loft space of the small three-bedroom property. My first loft antenna was a horizontal loop running round the perimeter, approximately 5m x 5m, fed in the centre of one side using a remote SGC auto-tuner. This worked quite well on 20m and up, even getting me DX contacts running QRP, but it became apparent that performance was poor on lower frequencies.

"With solar activity falling and the appearance of a severe noise source from one of the neighbours, I decided to try an MFJ-1788 magnetic loop covering 15 - 40m. This was a definite improvement on 30m and 40m, and gave similar results to the wire loop on 15, 17 and 20m. A magnetic loop has a sharp null axially through the centre which I thought would help with eliminating the noise, but in practice this was not as effective as I had hoped.

"When the sunspot cycle hit rock bottom I searched for ways to get on 80m, though I knew this would be a challenge with so little space to play with. I initially tried a 'Slinky dipole' using two steel Slinky toys soldered together per side, stretched round three sides of the loft and fed in the centre with a balun. This gave a good SWR across the entire 80m band, but signal reports received were poor. Contrary to claims that the Slinky dipole is a multi-band antenna, I found performance to be even worse on other frequencies.

"I then decided to try a commercial antenna, the Watson '80plus2' from Waters and Stanton. This is a compact antenna covering 80m, 40m and 20m that uses a combination of linear loading and inductive end loading to get the total length to just 52ft. I installed it in the apex of the loft with the

Julian has made use of loft-mounted antennas to get on the air.

feed point at the centre, folding the rest of each element into a dog-leg slanting down to one corner and then back towards the other. Considerable pruning was needed to make the antenna resonant on all three bands. The '80plus2' performs slightly better than the magnetic loop in most directions on 20m, but is slightly worse on 40m. Only a narrow section of the 80m band is covered with a usable SWR. As my main interests are digital modes and QRP CW I have tuned the antenna to cover that part of the band and the reports I get seem comparable to those received by others running similar power to a dipole. For most of the phone section and the low end of the CW section the SWR is too high for my ATU to match the antenna. I added dipole elements for 10m and 6m to the '80plus2' feedpoint balun, slanting away from the main element as in a 'fan dipole'. They had no effect on the existing coverage and have allowed me to make many Sporadic-E contacts on those two bands during the summer. My ATU provides an acceptable match on 12m and 15m, on which the dipole performs almost identically to the MFJ magnetic loop.

"I think the '80plus2' with extra 10m and 6m elements is the best solution I have found for multiband coverage from a very small loft. It covers part of 80m plus all of 40m, 20m, 15m, 12m, 10m and 6m and I am never conscious of using a compromise antenna. The MFJ magnetic loop also works very well on the bands it covers, 15 - 40m, giving similar performance to the dipole. Its small size makes it practical for use when there is no space for an HF dipole and it also allows coverage of 30m and 17m which are generally considered to cause too much interaction to be combined with other bands in a fan dipole."

CASE STUDY: MIKE ZINGELMANN, VK4AMZ, AND HIS THREE-BAND MAGNETIC LOOP

I'm not sure whether you could really call this antenna stealthy, but Mike's, VK4AMZ, magnetic loop antenna lets him work on topband from his Caboolture, Queensland, home in Australia when a full-size antenna for 1.8MHz would be impossible. Mike's three-band copper tubing loop took a lot of planning and research.

"Moving from a large semi-rural area to a small residential block has its drawbacks, more so if you love topband," Mike said. "A few years after the move I decided to get back into amateur radio. I tried verticals of all kinds: base-loaded, top-loaded, centre-loaded, helically wound, top hats, inverted-L and even a dipole of sorts. I managed to get three 33m radials down and I tied my 6m x 9m shed and my 6m x 6m carport into the earth system, but every time the results on 80m and 160m were hopeless. Most stations could hear me, some only just, but receiving was an even bigger problem. The noise in suburbia meant that I could hardly hear anything below S9. Most nights I had S9+20dB noise with carriers and interference on the net frequencies. I almost gave it away as a bad joke - a 30ft height limit on any aerial by the local council didn't help.

"I then tried a small electrostatically-shielded receiving loop on 80m and

Perhaps not so stealthy, but can you think
of an easier way to get on topband in a small
garden?

the results were amazing! I could null the interference and stations buried in the noise were now readable. However, a lot of the net participants had trouble hearing me on my vertical or inverted-L. I was one of the weaker signals.

"I decided to try a magnetic loop antenna to see if it could work as well as The *ARRL Antenna Book* [4] and data from Ted Hart, W5QJR, suggested. The trouble is most of the websites I visited were building small loops, running them on the desk inside the shack and then telling us how far down the loop is in performance when compared to the dipole at 40ft in their back yard. What's the point?"

Mike then spent time actually planning the design of his new antenna and ended up with a 12ft (3.6m) wide octagonal loop with a total circumference of just 1/13 of a wavelength on 160m. It consists of 3/4in (20mm) hard-drawn copper and every joint is brazed. Tuning is accomplished by way of a 1000pF vacuum variable capacitor and gamma match feeding. Mike also incorporated a stepper motor and controller to tune the 20-turn vacuum capacitor and used a timber frame to support the loop.

"I have used this loop for over six months on nets with around 10 or more stations. I have three to four stations within 15km of me and another four within 100km. The result that almost blinds you with its never-changing consistency under all band conditions - especially when propagation is poor - is this loop's transmit performance on 160m, especially over long distances," Mike said.

"This loop really competes with full-size dipoles on 40m and consistently outperforms them on 80m and 160m. A lot of these dipoles are well built with open wire feed and a few mounted over a ground plane to help minimise the loss of low height induced currents. How many of us can get a full-size dipole up over 120ft in the air on the 160m band? I am often the strongest signal over distance and sometimes the only signal heard inter-state in bad conditions on the net. My location is low with poor ground and S9+20dB local noise - I have tried numerous aerials at this location over the past two years and this loop has unbelievable performance.

"There is a TV aerial 2m away from the loop, just below the bottom of the loop. There is no interference on the weak TV reception from this aerial. The main aerial in the house fires straight through the loop, there is no interference on digital or analog TV reception and it has a mast head and distribution amplifier."

Mike's 1000pF Jennings vacuum
variable capacitor and a 100pF version
for comparison.

So Mike is able to work 40, 80 and 160m with a single 12ft-wide antenna. But is it stealthy? "Visiting hams have had trouble finding my QTH and have not seen the loop even though they are looking for it," said Mike.

You can find out more about Mike's loop by Googling "VK4AMZ".

CASE STUDY: BILL STEVENSON, G4KKI, AND HIS INDOOR MAGNETIC LOOPS FOR 10 - 80M

Sadly, since the first edition of Stealth Antennas was published Bill Stevenson, G4KKI, has become a silent key. As a tribute, I have left his original report on magnetic loops in this edition as an inspiration to other hams.

Bill Stevenson, G4KKI, lives in Swinton near Manchester and was a radio operator in the Army's Royal Corps of Signals until 1972. He took his amateur licence exam in 1980 and operates mostly HF, about 99% of which is CW (Morse). "I have lived at this QTH which is in the middle of a small row of terraced houses, right in the centre of town, with a public car park at the front and a bit of grass at the back, for 31 years," said Bill. "When I was first licensed bits of bent wire got me out, but it was always a struggle. My back yard measures 20ft x 15ft and my front door opens on to the pavement. I erected a half-size G5RV and even that had to be bent and placed over the rooftop. It never worked very well and I resigned myself to the fact that I would never put out a decent signal from here.

"Then I read some articles about magnetic loop antennas and I decided to make one and see how it would work. I read several articles before I made one. One of the most informative was by Roberto Craighero, I1ARZ, and was published in *RadCom* in February 1989 entitled 'An Electrically Tuneable HF Loop'," [this antenna also appears in *Backyard Antennas* [1] by Peter Dodd – *Ed*].

Bill then built a loop using 22mm copper tubing, a wide-spaced 100pF variable capacitor and a 1.5V barbecue spit motor, which he bought for £3 from his local garden centre. He also fitted a 6:1 reduction gearbox to slow the rotation speed down.

All of his antennas are now magnetic loops and are located in the roof space of his house. He currently has a 6.5ft (2m) loop for 80 / 40 / 30m and a 3ft (91cm) HF magnetic loop, which covers 20 – 10m (14 - 28MHz). He has also experimented with what he calls his 'Baby Zilla' - a 20 – 10m loop that is 900mm across and made with 75mm aluminium tubing.

Bill said: "The 80 – 40m magnetic loop has exceeded my expectations. All of the UK has been worked and out into Europe. The most unexpected QSO of late was when I worked Rob, W1MK, in Boxford, Massachusetts, on 80m (3.5MHz). I was running 70W with my TS-530S on 3.508MHz. Rob was 599 and gave me a 559. I admit his

Bill's, G4KKI, loft-mounted magnetic loop.

Bill with one of his experimental EH antennas.

antenna, which he described as a four-element beam on 80m, did the work, but when he said that a lot of EU [stations] were not audible because of the high noise level I think the magnetic loop proved just how well it works.

"I have since worked W1MK several times using the magnetic loop and with QRP power of only four watts. I have also worked several other stations in the USA on the east coast. Also out into UA9 with good reports on several occasions. The best DX on 40m was working the VP6DX Ducie Island DXpedition in 2008 at 0830 one morning towards the end of the operation. I have worked VK, ZL and most USA call areas, VE and all over EU and out into Asia with the 1m HF loop. All the UK and EU has been worked on 40m and Stateside has been worked on 30m."

Bill has also experimented with EH antennas and worked G4OYC 217 miles away in Paignton, Devon, on 40m using just 20W with the two-foot high EH antenna hanging from the ceiling in his shack. "I also built a version for 20m that was only 1ft high. They are very small but I have been very surprised at just how well they work," Bill said. "I will admit that the little EH antenna is not the most efficient going, but it does work and if you can't put up an outside antenna then the EH will still get you some QSOs."

Bill has also experimented with an army-type magnetic loop tuner that you can use at the operating position. "I built a circuit / tuner and it is working really well. With just 12ft of wire in a loop I worked several stations over a few days on 40 and 20m with 5W on CW with my FT-101ZD. I have added a meter to read the current. I first peak the loop on receive and then with a low power of about 5W peak both capacitors for maximum current. This will also correspond to a low SWR.

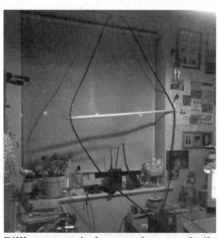

Bill's magnetic loop and tuner, built according to the US army design.

"I could achieve a 1:1 SWR on both 20 and 40m with a loop consisting of 12ft of wire. I found the same length of RG213 coax using the braid gave the same results but the tuning was a little sharper and so a better Q. With the RG213 coax loop I worked OK4RQ on 40m with just 5W," Bill said.

Bill shows that you can still work the world with all your antennas hidden from view in your attic.

CASE STUDY: JOHN SMITHSON, N8ZYA, AND HIS INDOOR ISOTRONS FOR 80M, 40M AND 20M

John Smithson, N8ZYA, is based in Charleston, West Virginia, USA, and really epitomises what can be done with stealth antennas. "I really don't have a 'shack' for my simple station," John says. "I keep the radio, my key, and a small GMT clock on a table underneath my Isotron 80-40-20 combo that I use for my 'antenna farm'. I keep it this way because (if I choose to do so) I can pack it up in a matter of minutes and be on the road where I can use a 4000ft radio tower - one of the nearly one hundred mountain tops in West Virginia above 4000ft!

"I'm forced to use the Isotron antennas because I live in a 'historic district' near the state capitol building here in Charleston," said John. "It's a horrible radio location with the hills on both sides of me and an apartment building next door - I jokingly kid others about bouncing signals off the gold dome of the state capitol building just up the street!"

John says that he realises that his simple station is at a great disadvantage because of his location and the fact that the antenna is mounted indoors on a painter's pole, bungee-corded to the bedpost in his spare room. He uses an Icom IC-703 at 5 - 10W output. "But I have fun with it . . . and to me . . . that's all that matters," John said. "I manage to do pretty well with these

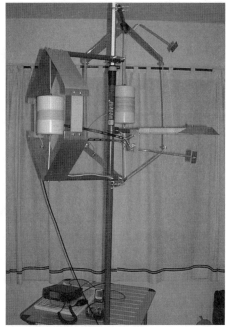

John's 80-40-20m combination Isotron antenna.

antennas. Most of the neighbours have no idea I'm a ham radio operator unless they see the 'tag' on my automobile. I have a good feeling when I meet another nice person on the air. Many of the people I've worked have become good friends and I feel especially close to those that drop by and comment on my blog. It lets us all learn about our hobby and our native countries.

"I've only been seriously active since retirement two years ago, but have made hundreds of contacts, the majority being on 40m (7MHz). I've worked 'coast to coast' here in the US on 40m and have worked 28 DX stations, mostly on 20m, with QRP power. The vast majority have been with the Isotron antennas. My recent '1000 Miles per Watt Award', when I contacted LZ2BE in Bulgaria, was made with the little 20in Isotron antenna. I've also earned some other awards with both the Fists and NAQCC clubs. I promote the NAQCC club especially since it's all QRP operators," said John.

John says he is especially fond of both the Fists and NAQCC clubs as they actively promote CW, which he thinks is a great mode and allows him to make good contacts under more than difficult operating conditions. He

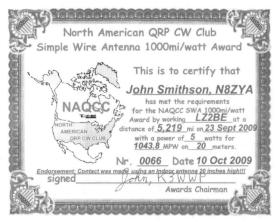

John Smithson's, N8ZYA, 1000 Mile per Watt award, earned using an indoor Isotron antenna.

also likes to go out portable, using the same antennas. "The biggest advantage I have with Isotron antennas is their portability and the low noise levels in the hills when I go portable. When I get out in the field (and away from all this electrical noise) I can literally work stations that don't move the meter," he said.

CASE STUDY: JACK CIACCIA, WM0G, AND HIS RAIN GUTTER ANTENNA

Jack Ciaccia, W0MG, lives in Boulder, Colorado, and has perfected the art of using house guttering as an antenna. He is now on version three of his RAINGUTTir antenna (no doubt playing tongue-in-cheek homage to the SteppIR range of antennas!). Jack takes up the story: "After I moved to a new QTH in Lafayette, Colorado, I tried to put up my trusty old Butternut HF6VX vertical. I was located in a covenant-controlled neighbourhood and thought the vertical would suffice as it is ground-mounted and is not taller than my house. But, the local neighbourhood Home Owners' Association (HOA) 'watchdog' showed up at my front door about one week after I put it up and reminded me about the HOA rules of *no outside antennas*! It turns out she lived in the house directly at the back of me and could see the antenna from her dining room window - my typical luck! Well, not to put the nice radial system I had recently 'planted' to waste, I started to think about some alternative, stealthy antenna designs.

"I noticed the rain gutters and downspouts of my house. They were aluminium and brand new so they probably made contact continuously. The downspout section is about 25ft high and it connects to a horizontal gutter run which is 35ft long.

"Hmmm . . . 60 feet of conductive material in an inverted-L Marconi-type design and ready made! I'd heard of hams loading up their rain gutters before, but never thought that I would be relegated to this option myself. I ran a 50ft piece of RG-8X out from the 'shack' to the bottom of the drain spout. I drilled a hole in the drain pipe and attached a sheet metal screw. To this screw I attached the centre conductor of the RG-8X coax. The shield side of the coax was then soldered to the ground radial leads. The ground radial system consisted of 10 random lengths of four conductor antenna rotor cable buried in the lawn and the ends of three of these radials were also screwed into my basement's metal window wells too.

Spot the antenna – Jack Ciaccia's, WM0G, raingutter antenna is totally invisible.

"I tested the stealth antenna with my MFJ antenna analyser to see if there were any inherent resonant points on this system. There were a few spots where the 'rain gutter antenna' was under 2:1 SWR. Coincidentally, these occurred at the top of the 75m band (3.8MHz) and again in the middle of the 15m (21MHz) band. Jack found that the antenna worked well and he received similar reports on an 80m net to another local ham with a commercial antenna. He then tried working HF in a contest.

"I worked 41 different countries in five hours of operating time on all bands. I was selective in who I called too. I worked 78 total 'band countries' and made 97 contacts. Most of these stations answered on my first call. I also made sure to zero beat right on top of their frequency before I called. I spent about half of my five hours on 40m (7MHz) and worked 28 different countries there in the evening. In one hour on 20m (14MHz) I worked 20 more countries; one hour on 15m (21MHz) yielded 14; 15 minutes on 10m (28MHz) another nine countries; and about 15 minutes on 75m (3.8MHz) with seven more. The total number of different countries worked was 41. If I had known this antenna was going to perform so well, I would have planned to work the entire contest and attempt to achieve a DXCC country count!"

The feeder's connection to the gutter and radials.

Jack has since moved to another house, but his stealth antenna idea went with him. "We moved into a new house in a golf country club community and of course, it has Home Owner Association CCRs (Covenants, Conditions and Restrictions) regarding ham radio antennas, just like the other developments we have lived in here near Boulder, Colorado. But, this time I have a home with a nice tall rain gutter on the south-east corner of the house. The home is built into a hillside and the rear of the house has gutters that are over 25ft tall," he said.

Jack says that the radio shack is located in the basement and he was able to drill a couple of discreet holes through the wall to get the lead-in antenna and ground wires to a new SGC-230 automatic antenna tuner. "I laid out a series of radial wires extending about 60ft, each radiating from the corner of the house, as I had in my previous installations and I am still using the same transceiver, an old Icom IC-745 running about 80W. I can work any DX that I can hear, and I am able to work on the WAS nets as I had before, with approximately the same signal reports (plus or minus propagation and conditions).

"I managed to work the 160m contest and logged 80 QSOs from the east to west coast as well as three DX countries in the Caribbean in just five straight hours of operating time. Not a great contest 'run rate' by any means, but at least I was participating. Again, I'm sure most of the work is being done by the other station's antenna but . . . you still have to put out some sort of signal on the band to be heard."

Jack said that the only interference he has noticed is with his fax machine in his home office. The RFI played havoc with it at first, but a couple of well-placed RF chokes on the power cord and telephone line cured that fairly easily. "I haven't noticed any other interference nor have I received any complaints from my new neighbours," said Jack. "Of course, they don't even know I have a ham radio station as there aren't any tell-tale signs outside! I am operating a stealthy, yet effective, amateur radio station and everybody is happy."

Jack said that he has been thinking about moving into a smaller home and this could be his last rain gutter antenna. "Of course, I could go out and spoil all of this fun by building in a non-CCR subdivision and put up a tower, beam and verticals like other hams do, but what's the challenge in doing that?" he said.

Editor's note: In the UK we seldom have metal guttering, but you could lay an insulated long wire in the plastic gutters or behind them, and drop it down the back of the down pipe. If you use black insulation tape to hold it to the pipework it would be almost invisible. You could then use an ATU, either a remote one such as the SGC mentioned above if your shack is quite a way from the down pipe, or use an un-un (see the chapter later) and a length of coax back to the shack.

CASE STUDY: TOM GARRISI, W8BNL, AND HIS STEALTHY ANTENNAS

Tom Garrisi, W8BNL, lives in a mobile home community in Michigan, USA. He originally put up an inverted-V antenna, but his neighbours made him take it down. So he looked for a better solution. Here's what he found: "Thanks to the kind helpfulness of some local hams, I managed to get my hands on three 'Hamstick' antennas. They are for 75, 40 and 20m. Using a triple mag-mount, and a bracket made from some scrap in the toolbox, I now have nearly all-band coverage of those three bands through the fantastic internal auto-tuner on my Kenwood TS-850SAT. It will even load up on 12, 15 and 17m, but I haven't tried a QSO on those bands yet," Tom said. Tom just had to bring his coax in from the car parked outside – that's a great idea if your neighbours don't like antennas!

He then looked at how he could put up a stealthy antenna for 40 and 80m. He ended up with a thin wire full-wave loop for 80m that goes up and over the roof and around the back of his property, as shown in **Fig 1.1**. It uses loading coils to resonate and Tom has connectors so that the antenna can be switched from a full-wave loop on 80m or a half-wave dipole for 80m.

He has since added a 40m OCF (off centre fed dipole), which is just lying along the peak of the roof. As he said: "Just finished a QSO with Bob, KI4HEE, who is located near Myrtle Beach, South Carolina. Not bad for some black wire on a black roof which is nearly invisible."

Tom Garrisi, W8BNL, uses antennas mounted on the roof of his car as base station antennas.

STEALTH ANTENNAS AND BAD PRESS – BUT IS IT ALL JUSTIFIED?

Stealthy and compromise antennas have generally received some bad press over the years. The terms "expensive dummy load" and "waste of money" have often been directed at them, often with some justification.

Steve Yates, AA5TB, always says that an antenna may have any two of the following attributes:

*   Small
*   Efficient
*   Broadband (work over a wide frequency range without retuning)

. . . but never all three.

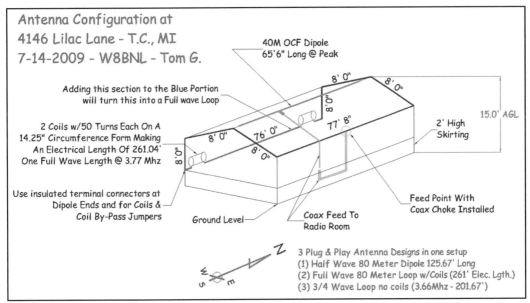

Fig 1.1: Tom's stealthy antenna is made of thin wire so as to be almost invisible.

I have also seen some antenna designs that were small, but had transmit efficiencies of less than one or two per cent. I once built a small four-turn loop antenna from a design from a long-deceased ham. While it would receive OK I never managed to work anyone with it. What I did get though were some very effective RF burns, even when running just 10W. The antenna made everything hot with RF. With hindsight I should have used a more effective earth or attached a quarter-wave counterpoise, but I was 'green and keen', as they say. I eventually gave up and used the wooden frame for a medium wave loop antenna. The tuning capacitors probably ended up in another project.

I have often heard a lot of criticism aimed at the Joystick VFA ('variable frequency antenna'), which was made in the UK by a company called Partridge Electronics in the 1960s. The Joystick was used as an all-band HF vertical antenna under restricted space situations and would cover from 80 to 10m with a tuner.

Many hams world-wide used it for many years but, over time, like other commercial antennas, the Joystick antenna faded from existence on the commercial market. I have heard people scoff at it and say it was a waste of time, while others say that that it worked. Can both groups be right?

The Joystick consisted of a spiral-wound coil on a wooden former and a small matching ATU. That doesn't sound very spectacular and you wouldn't expect it to work terribly well. At 8ft long it was supposed to sit in the corner of the room and be fed with a single wire. The manufacturers cheekily suggested that it could be mounted on the chimney and fed with a wire from there – effectively giving you a 30 - 40ft long wire with end loading. However, people did report that they were able to work stations with it when used indoors – even on topband (160m).

Now here's the interesting bit. While researching this book I found that

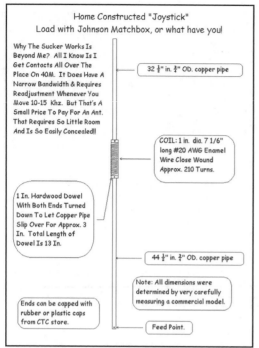

Home Constructed "Joystick"
Load with Johnson Matchbox, or what have you!

Why The Sucker Works Is Beyond Me? All I Know Is I Get Contacts All Over The Place On 40M. It Does Have A Narrow Bandwidth & Requires Readjustment Whenever You Move 10-15 Khz. But That's A Small Price To Pay For An Ant. That Requires So Little Room And Is So Easily Concealed!!

32 ¼" in. ¾" OD. copper pipe

COIL: 1 in. dia. 7 1/6" long #20 AWG Enamel Wire Close Wound Approx. 210 Turns.

1 In. Hardwood Dowel With Both Ends Turned Down To Let Copper Pipe Slip Over For Approx. 3 In. Total Length of Dowel Is 13 In.

44 ½" in. ¾" OD. copper pipe

Note: All dimensions were determined by very carefully measuring a commercial model.

Ends can be capped with rubber or plastic caps from CTC store.

Feed Point.

Fig 1.2: The Canadian ARES version of the British Joystick.

a Canadian ham, Bob Morden, VE3EIM, remembered the Joystick and wanted to see if he could make a modern-day equivalent. His design consisted of a one-inch dowel about 22in (56cm) long holding a centre loading coil comprising 97 turns of #12 copper wire. Fitted into either end of the wooden dowel were two pieces of half-inch copper pipe – the top one 31.5in (80cm) long and the bottom one 43.75in (111cm) long.

The antenna was fed at the top via a tuner and against a simple cold water pipe for an earth. Bob reported that his son was able to have RTTY and CW contacts from his basement shack across the Atlantic to Europe and down into South American using 160W on 20m (14MHz) and 15m (21MHz). That's from a shack that was below ground level. He was also able to have regular skeds with his father using CW on 40m over 180 miles with reports of 579 and 589.

In another design by the Niagara branch of the Amateur Radio Emergency Service (ARES) their Joystick replica (**Fig 1.2**) is fed at the bottom of the copper tubing. They also reported that the antenna worked with contacts all "over the place" on 40m. I'm not saying that you go and build a Joystick antenna – just pointing out that for every one person who says an antenna is rubbish there'll often be someone else who uses it and gets the results they want. Yes, you would get better performance out of an outdoor half-wave dipole, but that's missing the point. If you don't have a garden or an attic then something like the Joystick might just work for you.

In another famous test [5] Thomas Schiller, N6BT, connected a 150W light bulb to his TS-850S transceiver and proceeded to work a large number of stations in the ARRL's DX CW contest, including 14 countries on 10m (28MHz). He estimated that the performance of the light bulb (or 'Illuminator' as he called it) was about 18dB below a dipole. But it did work. The moral of the story is this – if you have an idea for an antenna try it. Better to get on the air with an inefficient antenna than not being on the air at all. And far better to prove to yourself that your design works or doesn't than believe so-called experts who have never tried anything in their lives. If you connect a radio transmitter to a metallic object it will radiate – it is just a question of how well.

WHAT CAN YOU EXPECT TO ACHIEVE?

As you have seen in the case studies, there is no reason why you shouldn't be able to put a viable HF station on the air, whatever your circumstances. But let's put this into perspective. In my experience loft-mounted half-wave dipoles for HF tend to be either equal to or no worse than about 1 - 2 S-points down on an equivalent antenna outside. Half wave dipoles for 20 - 10m in the attic will pick up more noise too, but it shouldn't be impossible to work DX stations. There are plenty of hams around the world who gained DXCC using compromise antennas and you could be one of them.

Forty metres (7MHz) is a little bit more a problem as a dipole for the band would really need to be about 66ft long to be wholly effective. But as I'll show later there are techniques for shortening the antenna, including zig-zag (non-inductive) loading and the use of loading coils (inductive loading). In my tests a zig-zag loaded dipole for 40m was certainly no noisier than external antennas and its performance was better than an 85ft end-fed wire and roughly equal to an external 132ft Windom.

Eighty metres is more of a problem again, as a half-wave dipole for the band would really need to be 132ft long. Loading and zig-zagging is the order of the day, but don't expect miracles out of a loft-mounted dipole. Experiments with a 1.7m magnetic loop antenna on 80m showed it to be down around 10dB on an external dipole and perfectly useable. Using the late Reg Edwards, G4FGQ, *MAGLOOP* program confirmed that a 1.7m magnetic loop for 80m would be around 12dB (2 S-points) down on a dipole. This sounds bad, but given most UK signals on 80m are around the S9 - S9+20 mark, the antenna will let you talk to locals with few problems. The only problem is the constant retuning: typically, you will only be able to move around 1.5 - 2kHz before you need to retune the antenna.

Unfortunately there are very few commercial magnetic loop antennas available for the lower-frequency bands, which means you are going to have to build your own. This isn't the end of the world, but sourcing the necessary low-loss capacitors, arranging for a motor-driven remote tuning control and handling the required 'plumbing' seems to put many people off.

On HF, there are commercially-made magnetic loops available and they tend to perform better than those made for lower frequencies. On 28MHz (10m) an 80cm diameter loop can be almost 95% efficient and offer dipole-like performance. On 14MHz the same loop gets within about 0.5 - 1 S-point of a full-size half-wave dipole.

When it comes to external wire antennas, it really depends on whether you can get them high and in the clear. Obviously, the higher the better for DX, but lowish full-size wire antennas for 80m will be very good for local contacts using NVIS (Near Vertical Incidence Skywave) communications. We have one ham in our local club who puts out a very competitive signal in the RSGB 80m Club Championship contests, but his dipole is only 15ft high. I think the secret is that it is relatively in the clear and the ends are as high as the middle.

If you are using vertical antennas their efficiency will be directly proportional to how much effort you put into establishing a decent ground plane. Planting a quarter-wave or trapped vertical on a 4ft ground post and then admiring your handiwork won't get you very far. But establish a good network of ground radials (hidden of course) and you could have a potent DX antenna.

WHAT IS THE BEST MODE TO USE?

What has mode got to do with antennas, I hear you cry? When you are operating with less than ideal antennas and low power the mode you use can make quite a difference. Let's look at my suggested top modes for stealth antenna success.

CW (MORSE CODE)

When writing this book what really came through is that the most successful stealth antenna users use CW or Morse code. In fact, they are able to work just about every DXpedition that comes on the bands and often work countries that are otherwise inaudible on SSB. This doesn't really surprise me as I have had the best success using CW as well.

If you are a fairly new licensee who didn't have to learn Morse code to get your ticket you might find that statement pretty depressing, but it is true: "a CW signal will get through when SSB fails miserably".

I saw a perfect example of this at the Marconi Centre in Poldhu, Cornwall, a few years back. It was 4.00pm on 12 December. Each year the centre makes contact with the Marconi Radio Club in Newfoundland to commemorate Marconi crossing the Atlantic with his signals in 1901. We were using 20m (14MHz) SSB and Joe Craig, VO1NA, of the Marconi Radio Club was on the other end of the contact. We were really struggling as it was close to sunspot minimum, mid-winter and band conditions were far from ideal. In fact, we nearly gave up as Joe was pretty inaudible. But we decided to switch to CW and lo and behold Joe was a perfect copy. The contact was kept up for a further 15 minutes and was perfectly readable for the whole time.

A CW signal can have more than a 10 - 20dB advantage over an SSB signal (depending on which book you read). An SSB signal will usually occupy about 2.5kHz. An FM signal will take up about 10kHz, but a CW QSO can take place in a bandwidth of about 300Hz. As you are only listening to a single tone in a narrow bandwidth, it is a lot easier to filter out QRM and electrical interference. This is vitally important in urban areas and with stealthy antennas which are more prone to picking up noise from nearby electrical wiring, domestic TV sets, power line transmission (PLT) and a host of other pieces of equipment.

Morse will get through when SSB fails miserably.

This is a two-way street as well. If you can reduce your power and use CW you are far less likely to cause interference to both you and your neighbours. I could go on, but it is up to you to decide if CW is for you. I know that CW has allowed me to make contact with just about every DXpedition I have ever chased when SSB contacts have been impossible.

If you do decide to go ahead with CW, Roger Cooke's, G3LDI, excellent book *Morse Code for Radio Amateurs* [6] is worth buying. Ray Goff's, G4FON, Koch Morse training program [7] is free and will also help no end – I wish there had been such things when I learned the code 20 years ago. Couple this with the RSGB's GB2CW transmissions or the ARRL's slow Morse broadcasts from its W1AW headquarters in Connecticut (2100UTC usually, but check the ARRL website [8] for the latest schedule) and you are well on your way. Incidentally, depending on where you live the weekday evening (UK time) slow Morse transmissions from the ARRL are a good test of your antennas. Check out 7.0475MHz and 14.0475MHz – one of them is sometimes audible depending on the time of day and year.

If you can't or don't want to use Morse code I suggest you take a look at PSK31.

PSK31

PSK31 is a data mode (**Fig 1.3**) which will get through when you can barely hear a signal. In fact, I have had perfect copy from a station in VK (Australia) when the signal had vanished into the noise. For this reason it has become a firm favourite for QRP and stealth antenna operators.

PSK31 was developed by Peter Martinez, G3PLX, and introduced to the amateur radio community in late 1998. The mode was enthusiastically received and has since quickly spread into world-wide use. PSK31 can often overcome interference and poor propagation conditions in situations where voice or other data methods of communication fail. The mode works well with propagation paths that preserve phase, and can be adversely affected by those that do not, such as transpolar paths, where auroral influence can disrupt the signal phase continuity.

Contacts can be conducted at less than 100Hz separation, so with disciplined operation at least 20 simultaneous PSK31 contacts can be carried out side-by-side in the bandwidth required for just one SSB voice contact. Typically, you can make good round-the-world PSK31 contacts with 10 - 25W.

There are a few downsides to PSK31. One is that many contacts tend to be 'rubber stamp' QSOs with amateurs just sending pre-prepared texts or macros. Some of these leave a lot to be desired as many operators seem to think that you are interested in what sound card and other computer equipment they are using. If you are a DX chaser the other limitation is that many DXpeditions don't operate much PSK31 (if any) - you might be better off adding CW to your arsenal.

But if you are limited in terms of what antennas you can put up PSK31 will let you make guaranteed contacts when SSB would be virtually impossible.

SSB

Third on my list is SSB, which will work for you, but I predict that you won't work as much DX as you will with other modes. You'll be fine with SSB for contacts around Europe (or your locality if you live elsewhere) and you will get better results on DX on the higher bands, especially on 10m at the peak of the sunspot

Fig 1.3: PSK31 will also get through under poor conditions or when your antenna is less than perfect.

If you have trouble working SSB from your location why not take part in a special event station, such as this one from the North Norfolk Railway for the Railways on the Air event?

cycle. Ionospheric absorption decreases as the inverse square of the frequency, which means that absorption on 28MHz is going to be a quarter of what it is on 14MHz. That, plus the lower noise levels on 28MHz, explains why it is such a good band for DX contacts, but only when the sun is playing ball.

So if you are using stealthy antennas on say, 20m (14MHz), please feel free to use SSB. If your antennas are less than efficient you may struggle if the station you are trying to contact is weak, say S4 or less. But if they are S8 - S9 you should be able to get through. Bear in mind that you will be able to work across the Atlantic, but it helps if the station at the other end is using a beam. Many of the US stations you come across on 20m (14MHz) are using 1kW and beams - sometimes stacked multiple beams. They will be more than happy to make contact with you. I have contacted stations in the US who are using compromise antennas while using stealthy ones myself, but these have generally been on 10m when using SSB.

At sunspot maximum on 10m (28MHz) the world is your oyster. During these halcyon days you can work just about anyone on 10m using just a handful of watts and a loft-mounted dipole (which is only about 16.5ft / 5.2m) long. Back in October 1999 I wanted to join the American 10-10 International Club. To be eligible to join you had to work 10 other 10-10 members on 28MHz. My log shows that this took less than two hours to achieve using about 25 - 50W to an attic-mounted dipole. Some of the reports were 52 or 53, but with such low noise on 10m these were very solid contacts.

I have to admit that I actually got bored working Stateside stations on 10m! Don't let that happen to you – once the sunspots declined I didn't hear another US station for at least seven years.

To whet your appetite for what you can work using SSB on 10m when the sun spots are playing ball my log shows 9K2OD (Kuwait), ZS6WPX (South Africa), AP2JZB (Pakistan), VP5/WA5AO/P (Turks and Caicos) and N9APA/HI (Dominican Republic) over a five-day period in 2002. At that time the solar flux was in the range 150 – 169, according to the indices at http://www.swpc.noaa.gov. At solar maximum the flux was up around the 280 mark and at sunspot minimum the flux was more like 68 – 75 so you can see what a difference the sun makes to 10m.

I usually find that a solar flux of around 120 - 130 or more is needed for transatlantic paths to open up reliably from the UK in the spring and autumn. It will open with lower flux levels but they will be quite sporadic.

VHF / UHF FM

You might think FM would be an odd mode to include in a book on stealth antennas, but it actually has its uses. Obviously, it is of great use on 2m (144MHz) and 70cm (430MHz), but there is also a lot of activity on 6m (50MHz) and 4m (70MHz) – at least in countries where that band is permitted. All of these bands can easily be worked using loft-mounted vertical antennas, or with whips or 'Slim Jims' attached to balconies or in room corners. A five-eighths-over-five-eighths wave collinear for 70cm (430MHz), which is about 1.15m / 3.8ft long, mounted in the loft also seems to work well and can easily get into a number of repeaters in the area.

FM is also very resilient to causing interference to audio equipment. The worst you may get is a click as you transmit and / or a slight buzz. It is, however, quite capable of interfering with TVs, especially the newest digital transmissions – see the section later on preventing interference.

10FM

The segment of the 10m (28MHz) band between 29.5 and 29.7MHz is where you'll find FM operation. FM operation is centred around 29.6MHz, which is used as a calling frequency. Although when the band is not open this is used by many as a local chat frequency, it is courteous to move off once contact has been made.

10m FM is ideal for local communications as ranges up to 25 - 30 miles are possible with just a few watts to a half-wave vertical antenna. You can easily make a stealthy end-fed half-wave 10m vertical antenna that you can hide in a tree – this is described later. While a vertical is handy for local 10FM work and for low-angle DXing, you don't need a vertical to work far-off stations as the polarisation of radio waves change as they pass through the ionosphere. This means your horizontal antenna will work well when DXing on 10FM.

You find FM simplex operations on the odd numbered 'channels' above and below 29.6MHz, such as 29.590, 29.610 and 29.630MHz. The 'even' frequencies above 29.6MHz are the repeater output frequencies, such as 29.620MHz, 29.640MHz, 29.660MHz and 29.680MHz. These have corresponding inputs 100kHz lower. So if you want to work a repeater on 29.640MHz you transmit on 29.540MHz. Many 10-metre repeaters now require a CTCSS sub-audible access tone, and while many modern radios include CTCSS on 10m FM, some older monoband 10m radios do not.

All 10m repeaters have some form of identification, usually a combination of CW or spoken idents. The repeaters enable you to work countries that might not be possible using SSB and poor antennas. There are literally hundreds of 10m repeaters around the world and your less-than-perfect signal should be able to open many of them when the sunspot cycle is in full swing. Just Google "10m repeaters".

Typical signal strengths can be S9+ even on poor antennas. To give you an idea, a typical autumn afternoon near sunspot maximum might start with you hearing KQ2H in New Jersey on 29.620MHz. If you are lucky you might then pick up NP2Y in the Virgin Islands on 29.660MHz or even NP4VG in Puerto Rico on 29.680MHz.

A simple 10FM transceiver like this Albrecht, a half-wave dipole just 16.5ft long and a few sunspots will give you a lot of fun.

In the summer, with Sporadic-E conditions you might hear repeaters closer to home, such as HB9HD on 29.660MHz.

One problem with 10FM is that you do get phase distortion

as the signal tumbles through the ionosphere. Fading (QSB) can also be a problem. But for stations with compromise antennas, the 10m repeaters can be a godsend.

OTHER MODES

Feel free to try RTTY, but I would guard against using AM. This has a nasty habit of being rectified by some pieces of hi-fi gear, which means your voice may come out of your, or your neighbour's, stereo system with absolute clarity – not what you are trying to achieve with a stealthy set up!

REFERENCES

[1] *Backyard Antennas*, Peter Dodd, G3LDO (RSGB).

[2] *HF Antennas for All Locations*, Les Moxon, G6XN (RSGB).

[3] *Successful Wire Antennas 2*, Ian Poole, G3YWX and Steve Telenious-Lowe, 9M6DXX (RSGB).

[4] *The ARRL Antenna Book*, 21st edition (ARRL).

[5] *Simple and Fun Antennas for Hams*, ARRL, ISBN 0-87259-862-4.

[6] *Morse Code for Radio Amateurs*, Roger Cooke, G3LDI (RSGB).

[7] Koch Morse training program, Ray Goff, G4FON: www.g4fon.net

[8] ARRL website: www.arrl.org

Electrical and other safety issues

I THINK IT IS very important to think about your own and other's personal safety when it comes to installing stealth antennas, so I make no apologies for including this chapter at the beginning of the book. One thing: it is always a good idea to tackle antenna erection work with a friend. That way if there is an accident there will be someone to help. There are always risks involved with any antenna installation, but let's look at the particular problems that you might face.

OVERHEAD POWER LINES

Family Electrocuted After Antenna Strikes Power Line

PALM BAY, Florida, USA - A family was torn apart and two neighbourhoods were hit hard by the electrocution of three people Monday night.

A man, woman and their 15-year-old son died trying to install an antenna on a roof. On Monday night, the parents and their son were trying to install a ham radio antenna at their home.

It fell on a live power line and killed all three of them when 13,000 volts of electricity shot through the pole they all were holding.

Authorities say rescue crews responded to a 911 call about the electrocution Monday evening when they found the three on the ground not breathing.

The mother was pronounced dead at the scene. The father and son were taken to a hospital where they were pronounced dead.

Please don't become a statistic. Check carefully before erecting any antenna.

I'm always saddened when I hear of a death after an accident including antenna erection and overheard power lines. These are so avoidable.

In the USA, CPSC (Consumer Product Safety Commission) statistics show that between 1990 and 1998 more than 300 people in the US were electrocuted when an antenna or pole they were holding touched a high-voltage power line. During this same period nearly 150 electrocution deaths were also recorded due to ladders coming into contact with an electrical line.

If you are installing antennas check the area around your property for power lines. If you have what you think are telephone lines it is worth double checking – treat every line as potentially lethal. Also be aware that you don't even have to touch high tension lines to be killed – at sufficiently high (kilovolt) levels the current can jump across the air gap. At these power levels you are unlikely to survive as there are major burn risks as well as shock effects.

The golden rules are:

* Keep all objects - including masts, poles, ladders, tools and antennas - far away from power lines at all times. If in doubt consult an expert or leave well alone.

* If you are taking down or moving an antenna, be aware of new power lines that may have been put up since the antenna was first installed.

* Never assume that an overhead power line is electrically insulated; always assume that contact with any line can be lethal.

* Don't rely on fibreglass fishing rods (roach poles) or wooden poles being insulators.

* Keep the distance from an antenna or pole to the power line at least twice the height of the antenna or pole.

* Be aware that you can be electrocuted by touching a power line directly or by touching a conductive material (such as a metal ladder, antenna or pipe) that is in contact with it.

* Keep away from all downed power lines. A power line that touches the ground can shock or kill you even if you do not touch it. The electric current can travel through the ground and into your body.

* If your co-worker does contact an electrical wire, do not touch them. Instead, cut off the power if you can or use an insulated pole to knock the energised conductor away from them. If the person is not breathing, immediately start CPR and call for emergency assistance.

It might be a good idea to invite a first aid speaker to your club to talk about resuscitation techniques. Please don't become a statistic.

ELECTRICAL SAFETY IN THE HOUSE / ATTIC

Installing stealthy antennas invariably means drilling holes through walls and ceilings. If you are doing this make sure that you are not about to drill through an electrical wire or water / gas pipe. If in doubt, don't do it, or seek professional advice. You can get detectors that will help you find wiring or copper pipework, but don't rely on these. They won't spot plastic pipework anyway.

If working in the loft bear in mind that there could be bare wiring or junction boxes. If the builder has done their job properly there shouldn't be, but don't take any chances.

If you use a detector to find pipes and wiring, don't rely on it.

PERSONAL SAFETY IN THE ATTIC

We've all seen comedy sketches where someone puts their foot through the ceiling, but it isn't actually very funny – and your partner will take a dim view of your hobby after that point!

When working in a loft or attic make sure that you have adequate lighting. I have permanently installed lighting in mine, but have used a mains-powered lead lamp in the past. Take a spare torch for emergencies by all means, but don't rely on a battery-powered torch as they have a nasty habit of going flat – usually when you are 30ft away from the loft hatch!

While a torch may be useful they have a nasty habit of going flat – use mains lighting in the loft.

When working in the loft it is a good idea to have someone else in the house at the same time. That way, if you get stuck, become ill or fall out of the loft there will be someone to help.

Do not attempt to walk on the joists themselves. This can be dangerous and you could cause substantial damage to the ceiling of the room below (and you) should your footing slip. You could use a plank of wood to slide over the joists that you can lean / stand on to support your weight. If you are in any doubt as to your ability to do this have the loft boarded out.

A builder's hard hat might save you from a nasty injury when working in the loft.

The attics in all of my houses have been boarded and it makes life a lot easier (and safer). It also turns an otherwise useless area into a good storage space.

The glass fibre insulation used in lofts is an irritant. If you find this a problem, or have to rummage around in the insulation, gloves, covered arms and legs and a face mask will help a lot. Sturdy shoes will help as well. Lightweight disposable overalls are available to people fitting loft insulation and these can be invaluable. It might also be a good idea to wear a builder's hard hat as nails and screws can often be sticking out of beams and rafters.

If you are going to be going up and down into the loft on a regular basis a permanently-fixed loft ladder will help too. These make it a lot easier to get into an attic and can't fall over as you ascend or descend. Having been left dangling out of a loft trap door once I am unwilling to repeat the experience!

WORKING AT HEIGHTS

Again, if fitting antennas do so with a buddy. If using ladders make sure they are up to the job and have someone steady the ladder at the bottom. Do not crawl on to a pitched roof without suitable equipment. I once climbed on to my roof on a damp February morning before realising how wet, slimy and slippery it was. At this point I started to slide down the roof and only stopped when I was able to stick a foot into the guttering. Never again.

It is worth getting a professional antenna installer to drill the holes through your wall for you.

I have found that the safest thing to do is get your local TV aerial contractor in to do the work for you. This doesn't cost a fortune if you have everything ready for when they arrive. They usually relish the chance to do something a little different and have all the necessary equipment with them. Twice now I have needed holes drilling through brick walls for coax and they have the requisite long drills to do the job.

If you need cable clips I would buy these yourself as TV coaxial cable is usually a different size to the RG58 and RG8 cables that amateurs use. I have bought 10mm cable clips for RG8 / RG213 coax off eBay for only a few pounds a box.

SAFETY WHILE USING CATAPULTS

In a later chapter you will see that I recommend using a catapult for putting wire antennas across roofs and into trees. Before using a catapult make sure that you are wearing eye protection and ensure that there is no one else around that

A bright yellow tennis ball with a loop of fishing line attached can be useful when catapulting antennas over roofs.

could be injured by your antics. Also make sure that your line could not cross any electrical or telephone cabling, especially if it goes off course. If shooting a line over a house I recommend the use of a bright yellow tennis ball rather than a lead weight. This is less likely to destroy a window and marital harmony if your antenna antics go pear-shaped. They are easier to spot too once they land and less likely to cause damage if they hit anyone.

Always make sure that you tidy up after yourself and remove any fishing line that is lying around in your garden – it is virtually impossible to see, but makes a very efficient man (or wife) trap.

ANTENNA CABLING

Don't leave coax cable loose on lawns for any length of time. And if you are fitting ground radials make sure they are buried, or if they are temporary make sure they are a bright colour, so that people don't trip over them.

Any lightweight antenna guys should also be colourful and not placed in a position likely to injure someone.

RF BURNS

If you are fitting antennas where they could be touched make sure that you have warned people of the dangers of RF burns. Any transmitter is capable of causing a painful RF burn or electrical shock at powers in excess of a few watts.

At higher power levels these can be serious. Ungrounded metallic objects within the station or nearby can also be a risk.

If you have small children do not put antennas where they can reach them – mount the antennas high above the ground. Note that tuned elevated radials can also have high voltages on their ends. Also bear in mind the RF safety issues outlined in the following section.

RF SAFETY

Both the RSGB [1] and ARRL [2] have extensive literature on their websites that deals with the issue of RF safety and humans. As radio waves are invisible, these issues are often overlooked, but they shouldn't be.

Stealth antennas by their nature are likely to be closer to the people using them (and others in the house). The golden rule for antennas is usually the higher they are and the further away from the house they are, the better. But if you must use indoor or attic-mounted antennas, you need to look very closely at your exposure to RF fields. You need to ensure that your station is RF safe. In this context 'RF safe' means that no known harm will be caused to the station operator, or to persons who may visit the station or come within the vicinity of apparatus or antennas.

The effects of HF electromagnetic waves on the human body are not completely understood, but that shouldn't stop us from completing a check of our station to see if it is compliant with current requirements.

The minimum health and safety requirements are set out in the European Commission Directive 1999/519/EC3. This uses guidelines established for safety in general public situations. Guidelines, which are more applicable to those frequencies authorised for use by amateur radio stations in the UK, have been issued by Ofcom.

What we need to concern ourselves with is what is happening in the 'near field' of the electromagnetic wave - the region where the distance from a radiating antenna is less than the wavelength of the radiated EMF.

If an antenna is suspended and well away from anyone, it can be considered safe, but an 80m loop antenna wrapped around the gutter of a bungalow - or in a loft above the shack - is "not recommended" unless you are running low power.

The actual 'near field' is an area that depends upon the type and location of the antennas employed at the station. For the sake of this book and simplicity I will assume that you are using zero gain non-directional antennas, such as dipoles. If you are using beams of any description the following will not be correct and you are urged to read further material.

Download a free copy of *RF Safety and the Radio Amateur* from the RSGB for more information.

The RSGB has a free leaflet called *RF Safety and the Radio Amateur* which can be downloaded from its website [1]. Likewise, the ARRL has an extensive section on its website, at [3]. The following information is taken from *RF Safety and the Radio Amateur*.

If we assume that you are using zero gain antennas, to arrive at safety distances it is necessary to understand the power delivered to the antenna and the frequency. For HF, the recommended safety distance in feet (ft) for a horizontal half-wave dipole wire antenna is shown in **Table 2.1** (data based on FCC Bulletin ET65B supplement B).

This table errs on the side of caution. For example, the power delivered to the antenna will be somewhat less than the 100W generated by the typical transmitter by virtue of feeder losses, and the table assumes that this is a CW transmission, key down, 100% duty cycle. In practice the 'continuous' near-field power will be considerably less, depending on the mode being used.

Transmit power (watts)	3.5MHz	7MHz	14MHz	21MHz	28MHz
100	2	3.5	7	11	14

Table 2.1: Recommended safety distance (in feet) for a horizontal half-wave dipole wire antenna on HF amateur bands.

Mode	Duty factor	Comment
SSB QSO	20%	Factored for voice and syllabic characteristics
SSB QSO with compression	50%	As above, but with heavy speech processing
Voice FM	100%	
AFSK / FSK / RTTY	100%	
CW QSO	40%	Normal QSO operations
Carrier	100%	Full output power for tune-up

A CW station has the key down for only a fraction of the time during normal operation, and an SSB transmitter, even with heavy speech processing, has a much lower duty cycle than the key-down situation.

Having a detailed understanding of the radiation pattern of a particular antenna is not essential; the power delivered to it is the important issue. For example a dipole, which has been bent to fit into a small garden, will still require the same safety distance as for a regular dipole. The radiation pattern may be distorted but the field generated will be the result of the power input. It will still be 100 watts.

The safety distance is directly related to the square of the power applied to the antenna. Increase the power four-fold (6dB power) and the safety distance halves. One consequence of being in the near field is that the actual field may be magnetic or electric, but in both cases the signal falls rapidly with distance or with frequency. The effects of altering the frequency or the distance are in reality the same since both change the number of wavelengths from the antenna to the boundary of the safety distance. If the safety distance around an antenna is doubled, the incident near-field power is reduced by a factor of four, making it at least four times as

If RF exposure is an issue for you why not stick to QRP, such as the 5W output from this Yaesu FT-817?

safe. In practical terms, a station set-up running moderate power (100W) with wire antennas with separations of more than 33ft (10 metres) from surrounding objects or persons can be considered safe.

There are numerous RF exposure calculator packages available for the PC on the Internet. One such calculator is 'MPE Calculator' by W0JEC. At the time of writing it was available as a free download [4].

ANTENNA HEIGHT

The height of an antenna above ground must be taken into account, in general the higher the antenna the better, since it ensures that the safety distance requirement is easily met. A dipole antenna that is 15 metres above ground and clear of buildings by the same distance is safe on any of the HF bands with up to 400 watts.

ATTIC-MOUNTED ANTENNAS

If you have been following this carefully you will realise that attic-mounted and indoor antennas bring particular problems due to their inherent proximity to living areas. This is why if you do use loft-mounted antennas I advocate that you mount them as high as you possibly can in the apex of the roof, in order to maximise the distance from you and other household members.

If we take my house as an example, my loft roof is about seven feet high from the attic floor. But using inverted-Vs in the loft means that the average height of any one antenna is more like five feet off the attic floor. Now, the attic floor is likely to be around two feet higher than anyone else in the house, so we end up with a total of seven feet separation from the antenna and anyone in the upstairs bedrooms. So going back to our original chart seven feet separation means that, theoretically you could safely run 100W on 3.5, 7MHz and 14MHz without exceeding the recommended guidelines. Factor in the required duty cycle adjustment and you find that it could be borderline for operation at 100W on 21MHz and 28MHz.

If you operate from a downstairs shack and no-one is upstairs you could argue that you could operate at high powers and still be within the safety guidelines. I suggest that you don't. So, as far as loft-mounted antennas and RF safety are concerned I feel that 100W at HF should be considered an absolute maximum and wherever possible the power should be turned down at every available opportunity.

You might like to try 25 or 50W or even less. If you can make the contact at 10W then do so. If you can make it at 5W then join the GQRP Club [5] and enjoy yourself!

If you are operating with the antenna right next to you then you may have to think again. These situations are really only suitable for QRP levels of 5W or less.

On VHF and UHF I think 10W - 25W to indoor antennas is more than enough and the lower the power the better.

To be honest, RF safety concerns are one aspect that you have to consider when using indoor or stealth antennas, but EMC concerns are equally as important. These are covered in Chapter 10 of this book.

REFERENCES

[1] RSGB website: www.rsgb.org

[2] ARRL website: www.arrl.org

[3] ARRL RF safety: www.arrl.org/news/rfsafety

[4] 'MPE Calculator' RF exposure calculator by W0JEC: www.qsl.net/w0jec

[5] GQRP Club: www.gqrp.com

3

Using your roof space

IF YOU DON'T have a garden big enough for HF antennas, or don't fancy upsetting the local planners or your neighbours, look to your roof space. As outlined in the introduction, loft or attic mounted antennas (especially dipoles) can work extremely well and outperform external compromise antennas. There are additional bonuses, such as:

- Having a completely stealthy antenna set up – the neighbours will never know that you are operating.
- You can work on the antenna system in all weathers and at any time of the day or night.
- The antenna will never deteriorate.
- Your antennas may get an instant 30ft height increase automatically. Mounting antennas in your loft may hide them, but it does bring additional problems. The main problem is the risk of interference – interference that you may cause to other people and interference that you may pick-up from electrical devices and wiring in your house. A lot of these issues are dealt with in Chapter 10, but to reiterate:
- Make sure that you mount your antennas high in the loft away from the mains wiring.
- Reduce your power to reduce the risk of interference.
- If using dipoles in the loft use a balun to minimise the risk of current flowing on the outside of your coax and causing EMC problems.

A balun might also help reduce the risk of interference being picked up on your receiver. Houses and lofts are noisy environments and typically you can expect noise levels to be 2 - 3 S-points higher than if you were using an outside antenna.

This doesn't mean that loft-mounted antennas can be inefficient. I consistently get stronger signals on my loft-mounted parallel-fed dipoles than I do on a number of external antennas that have been tested. For example, the 20m loft-mounted dipole is usually 1 - 2 S-points louder than a vertical mounted between the outside wooden shed and a tree. Why? Well, the vertical is a trapped quarter wave antenna and inherently about 3dB down on a dipole at a reasonable height. Secondly, to work efficiently it really needs a good ground plane of about 30+ radials. I only have a ground stake and six radials. It is also screened a little by the shed and tree, which may rob it of an S-point or more.

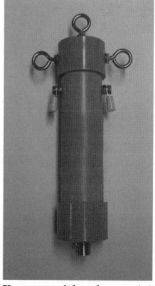

You can either buy a 1:1 balun or make your own.

If I really wanted to improve the performance of the vertical I would try to place it in the clear (difficult) and give it a decent ground plane. As it is, a dipole in the attic is simpler and less obtrusive.

If you want to run 100W with impunity an external antenna is probably a safer bet in terms of causing RFI, but I normally turn the power down to more like 20 - 25W and the loft-mounted dipoles don't cause problems.

There is another thing to bear in mind – vertical antennas are inherently noisier than horizontal ones anyway so sometimes the difference in noise levels isn't as much as you think. Now let's look at some of the other issues.

TILE / ROOF ABSORPTION

I must be lucky, but in the four houses that I have lived in every one has given excellent results with loft-mounted antennas. However, I have heard of people who have had a virtual Faraday cage effect in their lofts, possibly caused by the type of roof tile or slate that they had. My houses have all used typical red / grey roof tiles of the types used in the UK building industry for the last 20-odd years. The roofs have all been of a roofing felt and tile construction and do not appear to attenuate HF signals to any great degree. Likewise, VHF and UHF antennas have also worked quite happily in such an environment.

Some tests by TV companies have estimated losses at UHF to be around 3dB for a typical asphalt / tiled roof. Slate tiles can also be far more lossy due to their metallic content.

ATV (Aerials and Television) of Sheffield did some tests with TV antennas at UHF and found attenuation levels of around 8dB at UHF with a roof made of Welsh slate. Ofcom also says that some concrete tiles, for example, can reduce UHF television signals by as much as 20dB because of their high metallic content.

The losses around the HF bands should be much lower – probably around the 1 - 3dB mark for a typical tiled roof.

Logic also says that rain and snow lying on a roof will also increase attenuation, although in practice I have not noticed the effects to be too large.

I once erected a three-band trap dipole for 20m, 15m and 10m at about 30ft in the back garden for testing purposes. On back-to-back tests with the loft-mounted dipoles there was little to choose between them, proving that the roof does not absorb too much RF at those frequencies. Having said that, the external antenna was about two S-points quieter in terms of electrical noise.

Back to back tests showed that my roof does not absorb too much RF at HF frequencies, but do test yours.

Before you go ahead and expend a lot of effort on erecting an antenna in the loft there are a few steps you can take to see if it will be worthwhile.

Firstly, check to see if your roof is lined with aluminium foil-covered insulation. If it is, this will make a very efficient screen and you are wasting your time. Secondly, take a small transistor radio and while outside tune it to a weak foreign station on medium wave. It is probably better to do this at night when medium wave signals are likely to coming in via ionospheric skip and relatively high angles. Now go up into the loft and see if the signal vanishes. If it remains the same or gets louder this is a good sign that HF signals will not be attenuated too much. If the signal vanishes you may need to look elsewhere. This is a rough and ready test as you are really checking the roof's transparency to signals of about 1 - 1.5MHz, which is similar to the 1.8MHz amateur band (topband). If you have a portable short-wave receiver you can repeat the experiment at higher frequencies, such as the broadcast bands at 13 and 15MHz. Finally, you can also check at VHF – around 100MHz – although the mere fact that you are much higher (in the loft) can mean that you receive signals more strongly from your local transmitter anyway.

As a final test, take your VHF handy-talky into the loft and try accessing your local repeater to talk to a friend. If this all checks out you can move on to actually building a loft-mounted antenna.

So in conclusion, yes you will get some level of attenuation in your roof, but you can actually get close to quantifying this with a receiver before you start.

DETUNING / INDUCTION EFFECTS

A loft is a pretty inhospitable place for an antenna. It will definitely have mains cabling running around it and possibly TV antennas. You may also have copper pipework for your heating system and even a large copper water tank (although increasingly these are plastic nowadays).

All this adds up to a nightmare when it comes to putting up a transmitting antenna. As you transmit you *will* induce currents in nearby cabling, especially if it is running parallel to your antenna.

There is no easy solution to this other than:
a) Keeping your antenna as far away from metallic objects and cabling as possible;
b) Trying to avoid having antennas parallel to cabling or pipework.

If you find that you are unable to get a low SWR when tuning your antenna this can be a sign of coupling between the antenna and metallic objects – try moving the antenna to a different spot.

While we are on the subject of coupling a word of warning. Wherever possible only have one antenna for each band that you wish to use, otherwise they will couple and detune each other

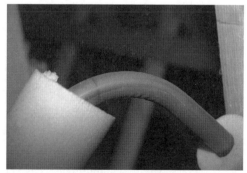

Copper pipework and cabling can detune your antennas, so keep away from them as much as possible.

A loft is not the best place for a magnetic loop antenna, but it does work.

or act as shields. I have an MFJ magnetic loop antenna in the loft, sitting amid the parallel-fed dipoles. When it is close to the 20m one in particular I find it impossible to achieve an SWR lower than about 3:1. If I move it to another part of the loft I get a similar problem with 10m. If the antenna is mounted outside I get no such problems, which just goes to show how coupling between antennas can be a problem.

I have also had a far more vivid demonstration! While testing a portable antenna for *RadCom*, Chris Danby, G0DWV, and I were pretty appalled by its performance on 80m. Signals that were S9 on his dipole were about S3 on the portable antenna. And therein lay the clue. The antenna had been erected *underneath* the 80m dipole. When we took the dipole down the performance of the portable antenna improved dramatically – the dipole had been acting as a screen.

If you do have antennas mounted above each other try to ensure that they cross at right angles, which will reduce the coupling effects.

Does wood reduce the efficiency of an antenna? This is an interesting question as I have always mounted my antennas direct to the wooden rafters in my loft. Some people suggest that this can be a problem as the wood can be 'lossy'. Dry wood, as found in lofts, actually acts as a lossy dielectric. I have never found a problem with wood detuning my antennas, but if you are bothered by this you could ensure that your antennas are strung up in free space in the attic area, or you could use insulators (such as those used for electrical fences) to hold the wire away from the wood. There is room for experimentation here.

One word of warning. In case you hadn't noticed wood is flammable – so make sure that you only use low power (less than 100W) when using loft-mounted antennas and let the ends of dipoles (which are at a high voltage when transmitting) hang loose away from the rafters.

TYPE OF WIRE

This isn't critical, but I do find that PVC-covered insulated wire works best. It is cheap, can be cut easily and lends itself very well to being tacked to rafters. I wouldn't use non-insulated wire in the loft – save that for external antennas.

FIXING ANTENNAS IN YOUR LOFT

I have found the easiest way to affix your antenna wires to your rafters is with a staple gun. These are very cheap to buy and work well in the confines of a loft where a hammer and nails would be cumbersome and a pain if you drop them.

It doesn't really matter what make the staple gun is, just make sure that you have loaded it up with staples before you enter the loft. The process is then simple – just hold the insulated antenna wire against the rafter, put the head of the staple gun across the wire so that the prongs of the staple go either side of the wire and pull.

How many staples you use is up to you, but one per rafter should be more than enough for a typical HF dipole. If you are worried about the antenna pulling free, just double it over at the end and put in two staples or, better still, bend the end of the dipole at right angles for the final two inches or so and staple again.

If you make a mistake it is relatively easy to pull the staples out, either with a dedicated staple remover or with a small screwdriver. I would recommend that you remove all unused staples as they can otherwise cause injury if you grab hold of a rafter with a staple sticking out.

A staple gun is the easiest way to fix wire antennas to rafters. Just put it across the wire so that the staple straddles it.

I usually find that this method of attaching wires is sufficient and there is no need to support the dipole centre, although simple string will suffice if necessary. If you are only putting up a single dipole or perhaps a trap dipole you might want to consider suspending the whole thing in free space. You might also want to think about the direction of the maximum radiation, which is at right angles to a half-wave dipole. Does this point in a direction that interests you? Or do you need two at right angles to each other?

If you are fitting a 2m ground plane or vertical in your loft you can either just stand it on the attic floor, wedge it in the rafters or support it with a string from the highest point in the attic. Once again, this is preferable as it gets the antenna away from the wiring and gets it nice and high – which is important for VHF / UHF.

Other antennas, such as magnetic loops, can be suspended with string, supported on rafters or mounted on brackets that are available from TV antenna suppliers.

I once had a 2m rotatable quad in an attic that was fitted on a small mount. It was fine, but did cause quite a lot of noise to resonate through the rafters when the rotator was used. The solution was to fit a rubber pad between the mount and the rafters, which helped no end.

Fix the centre of your dipole as high in the loft as possible. This one was made from an electrical 'chocolate block' connector fitted into a 35mm film canister. It feeds parallel dipoles for 40, 20, 17 and 10m.

BALUNS AND CHOKES

A balun's purpose is to allow us to connect a balanced antenna (e.g. a dipole) to an unbalanced line, such as coax which is not balanced, hence the name - balun. The 1:1 choke 'balun' is not actually a balun. Its function is to help eliminate RF currents from flowing on the outside of coaxial cable using the principle of choke action. In transmitting antennas, this is accomplished by presenting a high impedance (resistance), to RF currents flowing on the outside of the coax shield. This forces currents in each side of a driven element to be equal. In a simple dipole, the balun (choke), assures that the dipole, and not the feed line, is doing the radiating.

It is very hard with a loft-mounted dipole to ensure that the feeder comes away at right angles to the antenna. So unless care is taken you can end up with feeder radiation. The radiation characteristics of the antenna system will be seriously compromised and as the feedline becomes part of the antenna, currents can flow from the line into the mains and on TV cables, causing a variety of EMC problems that can be very difficult to trace. Frequently these problems are simply due to an imbalance - and the solution is the humble air choke. No costly ferrite-cores are needed, just a short length of 3 to 5in plastic pipe, about 25ft of 50Ω RG58 or RG8 / RG213 coax plus some nylon cable ties.

For 3.5MHz to 30MHz coverage, about 18 to 21ft of coax is needed. The number of turns is not critical because the inductance depends more on the length of the wire (coax) than on the number of turns, which will vary depending on the diameter of the plastic pipe that is used.

Steve Steltzer, WF3T, says that a 1:1 coaxial balun with excellent choking reactance for 10m to 20m can be made by winding just six turns of RG-213 on inexpensive four-inch PVC sewer pipe. For 40 or 30m, use 12 turns. He says that you shouldn't bunch the turns together. Wind them as a single layer. Bunching the turns kills the choking effect at higher frequencies.

To make an air choke or 'ugly balun' just secure the first turn of the coax to the plastic pipe with nylon cable ties passed through small holes drilled in it. It is best to leave a length of about one foot at either end to connect PL259 plugs to. Now wind the coax around the former, making sure that the turns are as close as possible and do not overlap. When you get to the end fit another cable tie. If you 'scramble wind' your balun without a coil former the end result may not work properly as it is difficult to keep the turns neat and tidy without overlap. So get yourself a former. Even a plastic drink bottle will do – empty it, take the top off and put it in the freezer for an hour. Then take it out and put the top back on. As it warms up the air inside will expand and you will end up with a fairly rigid structure to wind your choke on.

A choke balun (or 'ugly balun' as some people call them) just consists of 8 - 12 neatly-arranged turns of coax on a plastic former. They don't come much cheaper and will prevent currents flowing on the outside of the coax.

By putting a PL259 plug on either end of the balun you can then 'plumb' it into your coax run near your dipole feed point using back-to-back SO239 connectors. Or if you are clever you can incorporate it into your feedline run with no connectors whatsoever.

The additional losses introduced by using the choke balun will be negligible. On 20m (14MHz) the losses of about 25ft of RG8 are about 0.11dB. For RG58 they are about 0.33dB. On 10m (28MHz) the losses are about 0.45dB for the RG58 balun and 0.17dB for RG8. If you really conscientious I would use RG8 for your balun – losses for RG213 are higher than those of RG8, but less than RG58.

You can also buy baluns or fit clip-on ferrite rings to your feedline, but you do need quite a few to choke off the braid currents effectively. If you do buy a commercial balun make sure it is a 1:1 balun as you are matching 50Ω coax to the dipole centre which is around 50 - 75Ω. The 4:1 and 6:1 baluns are for more exotic antennas like off-centre fed dipoles.

You can use clip-on ferrites on your coax to choke currents on the feeder (common mode currents), but you will need quite a few – budget for about 10.

FEEDLINES

The simplest feedline to use with a loft-mounted antenna is coaxial cable. It is relatively cheap, very flexible and not too obtrusive. Although balanced feeder can offer lower losses under some circumstances (high SWR) it is harder to manage. For example, balanced feeder should be kept away from metal objects, which can be hard when you are plumbing feedlines into a loft area. What you shouldn't really do with coax is use it where the antenna represents something other than a 50Ω (SWR 1:1) impedance to the feedline. For example, using a 20m (14MHz) antenna on 10m (28MHz). The high resultant SWR will result in substantial losses with coax.

But as we'll show later there is an easy way to put up multiple dipoles and feed them with a single feeder that gets around the problem.

Your choice as to whether you go for balanced feeder or coax will depend upon your own situation. If your shack is upstairs, just below the attic and situated so that the balanced feeder could come straight down from the dipole to your station then it could work for you. But if, like me, the line has to take a tortuous route out of the loft, down the wall and then into my shack, coaxial cable is better. Also, bear in mind that if you do use balanced feeder you will either need a proper balun (not a choke balun) at the rig end of the feeder or an ATU with a balanced output. Coax is also more stealthy and harder to spot. If anyone does notice it you can pass it off as TV coax.

USING AN ATU

If you are using a loft-mounted dipole (or parallel-fed dipoles) you may not actually need an ATU. It should be possible to tune the antenna for a low SWR. However, on the lower bands you may find that you can't cover the entire band and an ATU will reduce the SWR at the band ends.

An ATU will also let you use a dipole cut for one band on another, such as a 20m dipole on 12m. But the end result will be nowhere near as good as using a dedicated antenna and should be thought of as a 'fudge' or a temporary measure until you can put up a dedicated antenna for that band. Expect signal strengths to be down 2 - 3 S-points.

For more information see the later chapter on maximising efficiency.

GETTING THE FEEDER OUT OF YOUR LOFT

Again, this will depend on your particular circumstances. I have had two shacks which were just underneath the loft. It was relatively simple then to bore a small hole in the ceiling (next to the wall) and feed the coax down into the shack. Before boring any holes make sure that there are no electrical cables behind it. If possible, make sure that you are not about to bore straight into a rafter as well.

Ceiling board is usually very soft and a simple screwdriver is all you need, but prepare for a lot of white dust and muck. To make the installation look very neat you can also buy white trunking from your local DIY shop and hide the coax in that. It is always better to get the wider trunking. That way you can add a couple more cables in the future.

If your shack is not upstairs you may need to think again about how you get your feedlines in place. With my last two houses I have employed a TV antenna specialist to drill holes in the end of my loft wall and then pass coaxial cable through them. He then used cable clips to neatly route the coax down the wall and into my shack via another hole. In my last house the coax disappeared under the garage roof tiles and then entered the shack via a hole between the garage and the shack.

I would guard against drilling your own holes as you will need a special long masonry drill and it is usually quite a task to support yourself up a ladder while you use it. A TV antenna specialist will probably do it for about £25 - £40 and take all the worry away from you.

If your antenna cable has to come in via a window you can just trap it in the window surround if you wish, but I don't really recommend this. The window will probably end up being draughty, you could cut the cable and it will never look neat. A hole in the wall is neater and can be filled should you ever sell the house.

Buy proper 10mm clips for RG213 coax. These will hold the cable much better than clips meant for 75Ω brown TV coax.

Stealth antennas for the loft

THE SIMPLEST (and probably cheapest) antenna you can build is a loft-mounted half-wave dipole (**Fig 4.1**). This is simply cut for your band of choice according to the chart and fed with 50Ω coax.

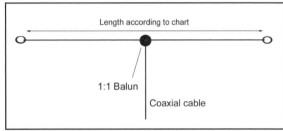

Fig 4.1: The half-wave dipole is a simple antenna, but very effective.

THE HALF-WAVE DIPOLE

A half-wave dipole is cut to length according to the formula: total length (in feet) = 468/f, where f is the centre frequency in MHz. The metric formula is total length (in metres) = 142.65/f. Typical dipole lengths for the bands from 40m to 6m are given in **Table 4.1**.

When I was first licensed I strung up a half-wave dipole for 10m in my attic. It worked a treat with a very low SWR across most of the band. What's more it worked stations with many contacts being made across Europe and the USA.

Just about any type of insulated wire will work and you don't need end insulators – just use a staple gun to tack the wire to the wooden rafters and let the final four inches or so dangle free away from the wood. This is a safety feature and prevents the antenna arcing to the woodwork, although that is very unlikely to happen if you keep the power levels down. I usually leave my power setting at about 25W and seldom use more than 50W. *Do not use a linear amplifier!*

A so-called 'chocolate block' electrical connector will let you connect the ends of the dipole to your 50Ω coax, which can then be led vertically away at right angles to the dipole to prevent RF pick-up and help keep the antenna balanced. If possible use a balun or choke as described earlier.

Once you have installed the antenna check the SWR in the centre of the band. Now check it at the band edges too. If the SWR is better at the lower edge of the band than the top end

Frequency (MHz)	Total length (ft in)	(metres)
7.100	65ft 11in	20.09m
10.100	46ft 4in	14.12m
14.175	33ft 0.24in	10.06m
18.100	25ft 10in	7.88m
21.225	22ft 1in	6.72m
24.940	18ft 9in	5.72m
28.500	16ft 5in	5.00m
29.500	15ft 10in	4.84m
50.200	9ft 4in	2.87m

Table 4.1: Half-wave dipole lengths.

this means it is too long. If it is better at the top end of the band it is too short. If it is too long don't cut it – just fold the ends back on themselves and either twist the wires together or use nylon cable clips. Electrically it will appear 'shorter' to your radio and have the same effect as cutting it.

Don't be surprised to find that you have to shorten the antenna slightly once you have it in position. The PVC covering of the wire and capacitative end effects will make it appear too long electrically and it is easier to shorten an antenna than lengthen it.

One you have the lowest SWR at or around the centre of the band, stop – as long as it is less than about 2:1 you will be fine. In reality you should be able to get it to 1.5:1 or better.

You may struggle to get the 30m and 40m versions in your loft – they may be too long. If that is the case see the section on the zig-zag dipole later on. Just about all of the others should fit within an average-sized loft.

It is best to mount the centre of the antenna as high as you can in the apex of the roof. This helps keep it away from electrical wiring and copper water tanks that might otherwise affect its tuning. It also helps with your radiated signal as it is the current portion of the antenna that does all the work and the current maximum on a half wave dipole is in the centre.

The dipole legs can either be tacked along the central apex with a staple gun or brought down in an inverted-V configuration - see next section.

A half-wave dipole is strictly speaking a monoband antenna, although a 40m (7MHz) version can be used on 21MHz (15m) albeit with a slightly higher SWR. You can use a dipole on something other than its design frequency, but you will need to use an ATU and the performance will not be very good. But as a 'get you going' compromise it will work. As explained in our later chapter on matched and unmatched losses using a long run of coax with a high SWR will result in high losses and is not recommended.

If you really want to use a single dipole in the loft on a band other than that of its design frequency you are better off feeding it with 300 or 450Ω ribbon cable, but this is less easy to handle than coax and must be kept away from metallic objects. Your dipole then becomes a *doublet*. If you do want to experiment with this, cut your dipole for the lowest frequency you want to use and then use it with open wire feeder on this and higher frequencies.

There are other coax-fed multi-band alternative that you can read about later.

THE INVERTED-V

The dipole doesn't have to be laid out in a straight line. You can, in fact, arrange one as an inverted-V with the centre at the apex of your roof and the legs coming down at an angle. In fact, there are a number of advantages in doing this. The first is that an inverted-V loses some of its directional characteristics. A dipole usually has its maximum radiation at right angles to the wire with little radiation off its ends, but when arranged as an inverted-V it becomes slightly more omnidirectional, as shown in **Fig 4.2**.

You will find that as an inverted-V a dipole will need to be up to about 4% shorter than if it is in a straight line. Don't worry about this. Cut it according to the chart and fold it back once installed to bring it to as close to a 1:1 SWR as you can.

Secondly, the impedance of a half wave dipole in free space is more like 70 - 75Ω, not the 50Ω our radio expects. This can result in an SWR of about 1.4:1 – 1.5:1. By narrowing the angle between the legs the impedance changes and the SWR is reduced to closer to 1:1.

But, and it is a big but, the angle between the legs of a dipole should not fall below about 70 - 80°. For best results with this type of antenna, the apex angle should be kept between 90 and 110°. Less than this and the radiators start to become parallel to each other and signal cancelling will start to occur. Above about 120° the antenna starts looking like a standard dipole, minimising any of the feed impedance and shortening effects. The optimum apex angle is 90 - 120°, but it isn't that critical.

Some pitched roofs are actually very steep and you should check to see what the angle is on yours. If you wish to fit an inverted-V you might be better off putting each leg across the side of the roof rafters to reduce the angle. That is, install it an angle with the rafters.

Inverted-V dipoles for several different bands can be connected to the same feeder, as shown in **Fig 4.3** to provide a multi-band antenna.

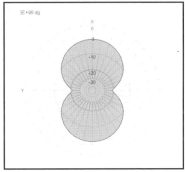

Fig 4.2(a): You can see that when erected in a straight line the dipole is quite directional.

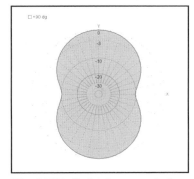

Fig 4.2(b): But when erected as an inverted-V you gain a couple of S-points (10 - 12dB) in the directions in which the dipole wires point.

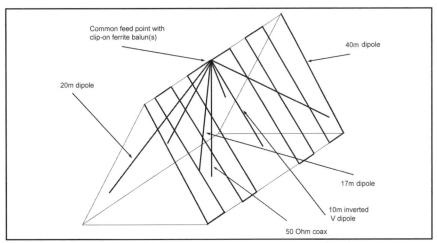

Fig 4.3: This five-band loft-mounted antenna has been used at two locations with great results.

MULTI-BAND PARALLEL-FED DIPOLES WITH ZIG-ZAG (NON-INDUCTIVE) LOADING

This antenna has nothing new about its design, but it does bring together quite a few useful ideas and characteristics. These are:

- Fully no-tune antenna system for five popular HF bands;
- Suitable for SWLs, QRP, M3 licensees and PSK31 operating plus occasional use up to 100W, but watch out for RFI at high powers. *Do not use a linear!*
- Uses non-inductive (zig-zag) loading for 40m.

Your actual mileage may vary depending on the type of loft you have, the tile type and the amount of metalwork in your attic. I have used this antenna at two different modern semi-detached and detached houses and it has always worked well. What surprises me is just how well it does work – so well, in fact, that I have yet to find another experimental indoor antenna that can beat it, including magnetic loops, crossed field loops and EH antennas.

It has been compared with the following:

- 85ft W3EDP end-fed that went up to the top of a 60ft oak tree in my garden with a 17ft counterpoise – the multi-band dipole beats it hands down on 20m and up and offers much lower noise level. On 40m they are fairly even.
- Capco and MFJ magnetic loops mounted in the loft and outdoors at a height of four metres – the multi-band dipole was consistently either equal or 1 - 2 S-points better.
- Commercial five-band, no counterpoise, vertical at 30ft – the multi-band dipoles beat the vertical on 20m by 1 - 2 S-points. But the vertical beat the dipoles on 17m on 15m by the same amount. They were very similar on 10m, although the vertical also tuned 12m. The SWR was flatter on the multi-band dipoles. While trying to read weak CW from the 3Y0X Peter 1st Island (Antarctic) DXpedition signals were inaudible on the vertical and S1 - S2 on the dipoles on 20m.

The antenna consists of separate half-wave dipoles for 40, 20, 17 and 10m (as shown in Fig 4.3), cut to a length of 468 (feet)/frequency. Only the resonant dipole will accept current at the desired frequency – the others are effectively ignored and offer a high impedance. These are fed via RG58 50Ω coax at a common feedpoint at the very apex of the centre of the loft – just buy an electrical chocolate block connector. The original version was potted in a 35mm film canister with fibreglass resin as it was going to be put up outside.

Three or four large clip-on ferrites (of the type used to get rid of RFI) are clipped on the coax at the feed point. This prevents interference flowing up the outer of the coax and makes the antenna very quiet electrically. Or you can use the choke balun described earlier.

The trick is to zig-zag the 40m dipole up and down the rafters, *but only once you have pulled the first 10ft or so of each leg out horizontally.* It is the current flowing in an antenna that does the radiating and this is concentrated towards the middle of the dipole. In fact 70% of the radiation from a half-wave dipole comes from half of the antenna's total length.

You can staple the dipoles (made out of PVC-coated wire) to the rafters with a staple gun as described earlier. Allow the ends to dangle free for about 6in to prevent end effects and RF leakage to earth via the woodwork.

The second trick is to make sure that each dipole is as far away from the other as possible. This helps bring down the SWR and improves the 10m performance dramatically. When it was originally put up all the dipoles were bundled together and although the 10m SWR was OK it was very 'deaf'. Separating the dipoles made a huge difference.

The third trick is to arrange the dipoles as inverted-Vs where possible - especially the 10m one – this gives good all-round performance and a mixture of horizontal and vertical polarisation. The vertical polarisation can work well on local contacts with amateurs using ex-CB half-wave verticals. Make sure that the included angle between any two halves of a dipole is around 90 - 120°. If it is smaller than this the antenna will start to cancel out its radiation as explained earlier.

If the lengths are calculated correctly you should find the SWR less than 1.5:1 on all bands bar 15m where the dipole acts as three-half waves and the SWR rises to about 2:1. If not, shorten the antenna by folding the ends back and twisting them together – but fold an equal amount at each end so as to maintain balance.

It isn't a beam antenna, but it is very useable and lively. It is an inexpensive antenna that your neighbours will love, as long as you keep the power levels down a bit. I would limit your power to around 50W if possible, preferably lower.

ADDING 80M TO MAKE A SIX-BAND ANTENNA

After using the antenna for a few years my biggest bug-bear was that it didn't cover 80m. Yes, with an ATU you could get the antenna to load on 80m but the performance was down somewhat. I therefore looked at adding traps at the ends of the 40m dipole and then zig-zagging extra wire horizontally across the inside ends of the house walls (**Fig 4.4**).

I had some commercial traps lying around, but you could always make your own. I calculated the amount of wire required using the fact that a W3DZZ trap

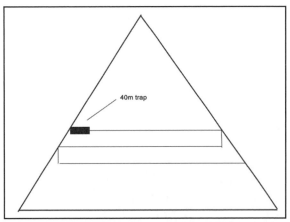

Fig 4.4: Adding a 40m trap and additional wire means that it can work on 80m as well, but the performance is not as good as an external antenna.

dipole is usually 108ft long. Therefore, I added 54 minus 33 = 21ft to each end. A quick SWR test showed that it wasn't enough and I had to add a further three feet to each end to bring it to resonance. The length needed will depend on the inductance of the traps.

If you try this I suggest adding more wire than you need as it is easier to cut wire off once installed in the loft than it is to solder wire on – safer too!

The end result was a minimum SWR of 1.2:1 at the centre of the band, rising to 3:1 at the band ends. An ATU took care of the mismatch.

But how did it perform on 80m? Actually, not bad – at least as good as a 1.7m Capco magnetic loop mounted outdoors and a couple of S-points down on the 85ft W3EDP mentioned earlier. With signal levels around the UK on 80m being the usual S9+10 - 20dB the loss of 10dB or so wasn't a problem. It is not an effective DX antenna on 80m. When east coast US stations were just audible on the outside end-fed they are usually absent on the loft-mounted dipole. Nevertheless, it was very good for high angle NVIS-type radiation such as is required for around UK and near-European contacts.

If you have no other option for 80m then it is worth trying.

CASE STUDY: LOFT-MOUNTED FAN DIPOLE – CHARLIE IVERMEE, M0WYM

Charlie Ivermee, M0WYM, also uses a loft-mounted fan dipole to good effect. This is his story:

"No external antennas are permitted at my QTH, so my antennas were always going to be mounted in the attic. The object of the exercise was to produce an

aerial that would allow me to operate from 40 to 10m, specifically 40, 20, 17, 15 and 10m. The attic allows the antenna to 'beam' roughly northwest / southeast and the house is some 40ft above sea level. Construction could be simplified by the fact that I intended to run a maximum of 10W, which means that the antenna wires could be simply attached to the rafters.

"The attic is just about 10m long, just short of the length needed for a 20m dipole, so for that band around 250mm was bent down the rafter at each end before tuning. Obviously there is no room for a normal 40m dipole and I made full use of a design by GM4JMU that used loading coils on 40m. In my version I have made the 40m loading coils from 29 turns of 24/02 PVC covered wire tightly wound on 40mm diameter PVC pipe. Both coils should be made as identical as possible. The 40m dipole runs along the apex of the roof, below that the 20m dipole is followed by the 17m, 15m and 10m dipoles.

Charlie's, M0WYM, dipole wire pinned to the rafters.

"Rather than make my 1:1 balun I forked out

for a commercial one. In order to terminate five dipoles I used two pieces of single-sided PCB each drilled to accept six M4 bolts and a further one to connect to the balun (the sixth was added for further experimentation). Each wire making up the dipoles was crimped which made attaching to the bolts secure and simple.

"Horizontal spacing between each dipole was approximately 150mm and wires were attached to every other rafter using plastic-headed staples. The ends, fanning out dipoles after tuning, were terminated with old fashioned galvanised staples. Please remember that I am only running a maximum power of 10W and would not suggest that these mounting methods be used at higher powers.

MOWYM's 1:1 balun and PCB distribution point.

"After assembly, the antenna was tuned using an MFJ-259 SWR analyser connected to the balun by approximately 1.5m of coax. Starting from the lowest band each dipole was tuned for resonance. The results for the 40m dipole were not too good with a minimum SWR of 2:1 at resonance.

"My Icom IC-703 is very happy with the antenna and, after tuning, indicates a SWR of 1:1 on 40m, 20m, 17m and 15m. On 10m the SWR varies from 1.3:1 at 28.100MHz to 1.1:1 at 28.800MHz and 1.4:1 at 29.000MHz to 1.1:1 at 29.650MHz. In spite of the fact that the MFJ-259 puts the SWR on 80m in the red zone, the 703's ATU gets it down to 1.4:1. At 50MHz the SWR is 1:1 from 50MHz to 51.6MHz."

Results

"Reception: The antenna is lively on all the HF bands with the exception of topband, which is hardly a surprise! For example, on 17m I have heard Japan, Malta and Brazil. I have heard Costa Rica on 80m and Cyprus on 15m. 20m reception is very good and I got to hear some good DX through some pretty awful pile-ups! Overall, I'm pretty pleased with the level of reception using the fan dipole.

"Transmitting: I seem to be averaging 57 reports into Europe on 40m, 20m and 17m. Countries worked include Slovenia, San Marino, Italy, Moldova, Russia and the Netherlands.

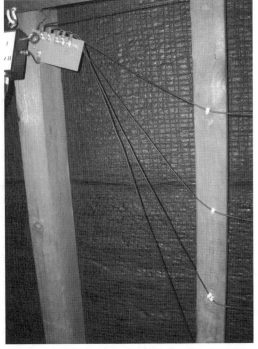

For the best results spread the dipole wires away from each other.

"It does appear that the fan dipole works best on 20m, which ties in with the flat SWR I measured on that band. Given that we are at the bottom of the sunspot cycle I expect great things of this antenna in the next couple of years!

"On 80m the fan dipole works fine on reception and will put out a signal, but it's pretty useless with low signal reports so I will be looking at some other way of working on 80m. Given that my QTH is a first-floor flat I am not too keen on strapping the coax and loading that on 80.

"During a 6m contest in June I discovered that one of the elements of this antenna radiates pretty well on that band! I have been getting reports averaging 57 and have worked stations in Spain, Italy, Croatia (via Sporadic-E) and the UK. It looks to me as if the 17m element third harmonic resonates around 54MHz and that is near enough to put out a reasonable signal.

"I have had good reports on 10m FM from Sweden and Denmark (via Sporadic-E again). The antenna also got me a 58 report on 12m (24MHz) from France, not so far but not bad considering the aerial was never intended to work on 12m!"

USING LOADING COILS TO SHORTEN DIPOLES

So far we have looked at putting up single dipoles in the loft, and a way to parallel feed dipoles to give you multi-band operation. We have also looked at using zig-zag non-inductive loading to fit longer dipoles in the attic.

But there is another way to put dipoles in the loft for lower bands and that is to use loading coils, which is the method used by Charlie, M0WYM. These make the antenna look longer electrically, but do result in some loss of performance and reduced bandwidth.

A good rule of thumb for a shortened dipole is that its length in feet must not be less than 1.25 times the wavelength in metres. So a 40m loaded dipole shouldn't really be less than 50ft long and an 80m antenna shouldn't be less than 100ft long. Incidentally, it is interesting to note that the G5RV antenna is 102ft long and works quite well on 80m where it is only about 1 - 2dB down on a full size 80m dipole.

Other sources say that the antenna will still work reasonably well when it is only 1/3 of a wavelength long, which is 13m (42ft) on 40m or 26.6m (87ft) on 80m. Is your loft or attic 87 - 100ft long? No, I didn't think so. So from the outset we have to say that severely shortening an 80m antenna to make it fit will result in its efficiency going down, perhaps quite dramatically. My experience is that the 85ft W3EDP end-fed configuration over the roof works better on 80m than a shortened, loaded dipole in the loft. But let's look at what you could do for 40m and 80m on a suck-it-and-see basis.

Half-wave loaded dipole for 40m

A full-size half-wave dipole for 40m (7.1MHz) would be 65ft 9in long (20.09m). But let's say that we only have 30ft to play with, which is obviously much shorter than the optimum we require. Let's say that we will have two legs of

15ft each with loading coils in the middle of each leg. So we need four pieces of wire 7ft 6in long. Two of these go to the centre connection and the 50Ω coax, and then we connect our two loading coils at the ends before connecting the remaining pieces of wire.

First we need to work out what sort of loading coils we need. There are several ways of working out the inductance of the two loading coils. The first is to use an on-line calculator – Googling "dipole loading coils" will come up with a number of options. At the time of writing I used Martin Meserve's, K7MEM, site [1] to do the calculations (see **Fig 4.5**), but do bear in mind that URLs do change and websites come and go.

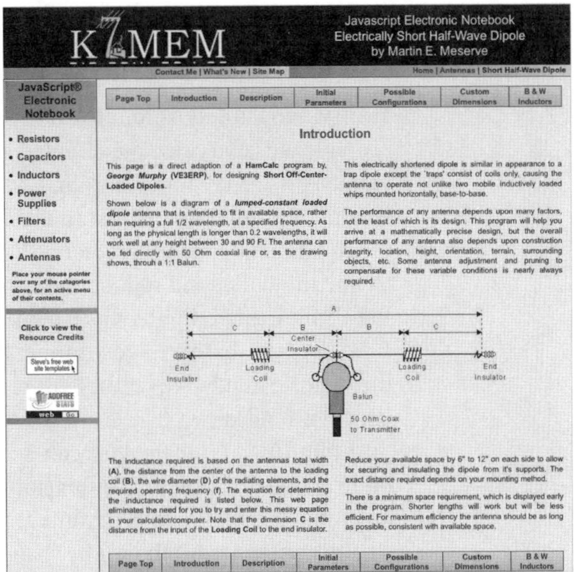

The site says that we need two loading coils of 24µH each. Using 2mm wire, Martin's site says that these can be formed by winding about 14 turns on to a former

Fig 4.5: You can use an on-line calculator, like this one from K7MEM, to build a shortened dipole.

110mm in diameter and 50mm long. Since losses occur in the loading coils a physically large coil allows a larger wire diameter, increases the Q, and improves the antenna's radiating efficiency.

I suggest that you use enamelled copper wire for the coils to reduce losses and plastic for the formers. Large plastic drinks bottles are free once you've emptied them and will support a loading coil for indoor use with no problems. You might be tempted to use white PVC waste pipe from your local hardware superstore but this is only about 40mm in diameter – we want our coils bigger. If you re-run the calculations you will find that with 40mm pipe you need around 40 turns of wire, which increases the resistance and reduces the overall efficiency – that's why you should keep your coils larger.

Any coil will end up with a self-resonant frequency (SRF) and for an optimum design you want this frequency to be well away from the frequency upon which you are trying to get the antenna to work - preferably double the operating frequency. In this worked example the SRF of the 110mm coil is about 13.7MHz which is fine.

The coils don't *have* to be half way along the wire – you can place them anywhere. Ideally, the loading coils should be as far from the centre feed point as possible. But bear in mind that as the distance from the feed point increases, the required coil size increases and the self-resonant frequency decreases until it reaches the operating frequency, at which point the coil Q decays to zero, and the antenna efficiency approaches zero.

By all means play with an online calculator like Martin's, but for a quick and easy solution place the coils half way along the dipole and you won't go wrong.

Half-wave loaded dipole for 80m

Now we have calculated how to get a 40m dipole into a space of just 30ft what happens if we try to do the same with an 80m dipole? Well, if the wavelength is 80m, our optimum lowest figure is 100ft. That is, if we don't want to lose too much efficiency then the antenna shouldn't be any shorter. But if you just have to bite the bullet and reduce the antenna size even more then go ahead. A 30ft-long 80m loaded dipole will need two inductors of 95µH .

It will probably have limited bandwidth and will need an ATU to tune the whole band. Nevertheless it will let you put out a signal, but don't expect miracles.

From this argument you can see that there really isn't an effective way to build a loaded dipole for 160m (topband) that will fit in a loft. By all means try, but I think you'll be disappointed! Remember, you will get better results with stealthy antennas on the higher bands.

THE SLINKY DIPOLE

One of the biggest problems facing amateurs who want to use loft-mounted antennas is how do you put up a decent antenna for 80m (3.5MHz)? The trouble is that a half-wave dipole for 80m is going to be a around 40m or 135ft long – much longer than most attics. You can use the zig-zag loading that I mentioned earlier or you can add loading coils. But another way is to make use of a child's toy – the *Slinky* ('Slinky' is actually a trade mark, but there are other branded varieties available).

If you haven't met a Slinky before it is a coil spring that can be made to 'walk' down stairs and is used in schools to demonstrate the propagation of transverse and longitudinal waves. So its seems appropriate that we can use two Slinkies to make an HF antenna!

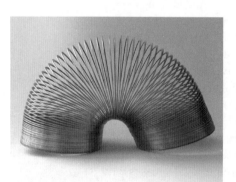

If you pull a Slinky out what you effectively get is a continuously loaded helical antenna. If you then thread two Slinkies onto a piece of cord and feed it in the middle you have a continuously loaded dipole.

Slinkies can be obtained in the UK from Maplin and can also be found in most toy stores around the world. A quick search on eBay showed that you can get them for around £5 each. A quick word of warning – don't buy the plastic version for obvious reasons!

They are usually about 2.75in (70mm) in diameter and consist of about 80 - 90 turns. When a Slinky is compressed it is only 2.25in (60mm) long, but it can be stretched into a helix as long as 15ft (4.5m) in length without deforming. An antenna made from a Slinky is

The Slinky can be used as an HF antenna – just make sure you don't buy one of the plastic versions!

light, simple to suspend and extend, and easy to put out of sight when not in use.

They are usually made of stainless steel, which is not really ideal as an antenna material. You can get brass versions in the US, but they are expensive – more than $100 apiece. Larry Johnston, W4SAT, reports that a standard Slinky coil resonates as a quarter-wave between 7 and 8MHz when it is stretched to lengths between 5 and 15ft. To tune the Slinky within that range you extend the coil to the approximate size, then expand or contract it to reach the desired resonance. At a length close to 7.5ft (2.28m) Larry says that a standard Slinky is quarter-wave resonant on 40m.

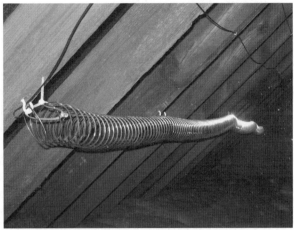

Charlie, M0WYM, used a Slinky dipole in his loft, but found it noisy.

Dipoles resonant at frequencies above the 7 - 8MHz range may be created by removing turns to shorten the helices or by shorting out turns. A 20m dipole, for example, could be made by cutting a Slinky coil in half. It is certainly an area for experimentation.

Charlie, M0WYM, reports that they are easily soldered using a 25W iron. He constructed an 80m Slinky dipole for his loft and takes up the story:

"My antenna uses a total of four Slinkies with two of them soldered together. The Slinkies are supported using nylon cord and cable ties were used at the ends to make it easier to remove. Screw-in hooks spaced at approximately 1m intervals were used to support the Slinkies and the last turn at each end is looped over a hook. I only run a maximum power of 10 watts and would not suggest that these mounting methods be used at higher powers.

"The nylon cord was passed through the Slinkies before putting them into place. The cord and Slinky were attached at one end then stretched tightly and attached at the other end. The Slinkies were carefully extended and attached at the other end. Finally, the cord was hung on the remaining hooks and the wires attached with crimps to the fan dipole terminal boards.

"I had a go at making my own balun using a toroid and eight turns of RG58 coaxial cable. It performs as well as my bought one. My Icom IC-703 seems pretty happy with the 80m Slinky dipole. Signal levels on 80m have risen by about 20dB, compared with my 40m fan dipole - including the noise! The SWR on 80m varies, but is under 1.3:1 for most of the band. Daytime background noise levels have been around S5 - 6 and evening reception has been OK with signals from the UK and Europe getting through the noise," said Charlie.

Charlie has since taken the antenna down, due to the high noise levels, but it would be worth trying at your QTH. If you want to use it as a multi-band antenna I suggest feeding it with open wire or 300Ω balanced feeder.

Larry, W4SAT, says that in a test on a state-wide net, a 30ft 80m Slinky dipole at 20ft received signal reports on average 0.5 – 1.5 S-units lower than a Windom at 35ft. He say that compared with a Hustler mobile whip, its performance and bandwidth were outstanding.

One word of warning - the coils will corrode if left outdoors for more than a few weeks. This means that the Slinky is really best suited to indoor use. If you wish to put your Slinky antenna outside on a more-or-less permanent basis, you could solder all the connections and then spray paint the whole antenna.

Many Slinky users report that this 80m antenna is not the best in the world, but it will get you on the air and should cost less than £20 so is worth a try. There is even a commercial version of the Slinky antenna in the US. Called the CliffDweller II antenna [2] it is said to be the "world's most popular limited space HF antenna - indoors and outdoors" – and is used in 84 countries. It is just 10in wide and fits easily into a suitcase for portable use while traveling, or into a backpack for camping. It packs a full 130ft of pre-coiled wire (a half wavelength on 80m!) into its small footprint and covers all HF bands from 6 to 80m with any standard HF antenna tuner, and handles the full power range of QRP to 100 watts.

HORIZONTAL LOOP (SKYWIRE) ANTENNA

The horizontal loop antenna should not be confused with the magnetic loop. The one I am about to describe is usually at least one full wavelength long at its lowest frequency of operation and can be mounted horizontally by tacking the wire to the loft rafters using a staple gun – just like the dipole. Its current distribution can be seen in **Fig 4.6**.

Unlike a dipole, which is resonant on its fundamental frequency and odd multiples thereof, the loop is resonant on its fundamental and *even* multiple frequencies. Therefore, a 40m (7MHz) full-wave loop would contain about 136ft (40.23m) of wire and would also be resonant on 14MHz and 28MHz.

To make your loop use the formula: Length (in feet) = 1005 divided by frequency (in MHz). Then subtract 5% of the total full wavelength if you are using insulated wire, due to its slightly lower velocity factor. Example: For a 40m loop, 1005 divided by 7 (lowest 40-metre frequency in MHz) x 95% = 136.4 feet.

To calculate the size in metres use the formula: Length (in metres) = 306.4 divided by frequency (in MHz). Also use the 95% factor if using insulated wire.

You may struggle to fit a full-wave loop in for 40m, but the trick is to put up as big a loop as you can and not worry too much about its actual size.

The Horizontal Loop, also known as the Loop Skywire Antenna, works well from the lowest frequency band for which it is designed, all the way through to 10m. It will usually

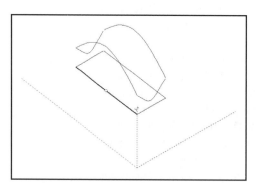

Fig 4.6: In this MMANA-GAL simulation you can see the current distribution of a 40m full-wave horizontal loop.

even work well on 6m if your ATU will handle that band. If mounted at the same height as a dipole, the main radiation lobes of a full-wave loop will be about 4° lower, making it better for DX. Loops are also said to be less affected by nearby buildings and wood, making it ideal for the loft. There are plenty of people who rave about loop antennas and it is easy to see why.

If you wish to feed it with coax it needs to be resonant and you also need to include a quarter-wave length of 75Ω coax at the feed point to lower its nominal impedance from about 100Ω to 50Ω. This will only work at its resonant frequency, so for true multiband operation you will have to forget about coax entirely and use 300 or 450Ω ladder (window) line as the feed line. Because of the wide swings of impedance as you change band a 4:1 balun (balanced to unbalanced transformer) near your tuner may also be needed. Although it is not as pretty as coax, you can feed ladder line through from your loft, but keep it away from metal objects, which will detune it.

Many external tuners have a balanced input that you can use instead. On bands other than its operating frequency there will be a high SWR and therefore losses if you use coax. If you have no choice, fit the balun in the loft and live with the losses on what will really be a short length of coax to the tuner or rig.

Another way of operating a loop like this in the loft is to use a remote battery-operated antenna tuner. Mount the loop in the loft, keeping it off the loft floor as much as possible to keep it away from mains wiring, connect it with a short piece of 300 or 450Ω ribbon to a balun and then with a short piece of coax to the tuner. The tuner is then connected to your main station with coax. An auto-ATU, such as the LDG Z-11 Pro, will run on a set of AA batteries for more than two years. Once it has found a match it will return to those known settings every time you QSY. This is a great way of operating multiple bands with one antenna and without having to worry about tuning it each time you change bands. Note, though, that you should definitely use balanced feeder from the loop to the tuner and you must use a balun – I recommend the 4:1 step-down variety. But once those are installed you can just connect the tuner to the rig via coax and forget it – apart from changing the batteries every couple of years or so.

Although the basic design is a full wave (or longer) at the lowest frequency for which it is intended, the antenna need not be cut to resonant length. It can be cut longer, letting your tuner handle the mismatch.

The loop has a reputation for working well at low installed heights so should work well in a loft. It also has a reputation for being a quiet receiving antenna.

The shape need not be perfectly horizontal, and a rectangle, square or even a multi-sided shape, will work. If you are really clever you can maximise the size by putting the corners as low as possible and the centre of each middle leg higher. The critical factor is that the loop should encompass as large an area as possible.

For best results, don't try to use it at a frequency lower than the lowest resonant frequency as the performance will be poor. However, if your tuner can

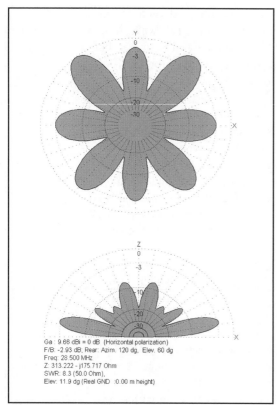

Ga : 9.66 dBi = 0 dB (Horizontal polarization)
F/B: -2.93 dB, Rear: Azim. 120 dg, Elev. 60 dg
Freq: 28.500 MHz
Z: 313.222 - j175.717 Ohm
SWR: 8.3 (50.0 Ohm),
Elev: 11.9 dg (Real GND :0.00 m height)

Fig 4.7: This is the radiation pattern you get when the loop is used on 10m.

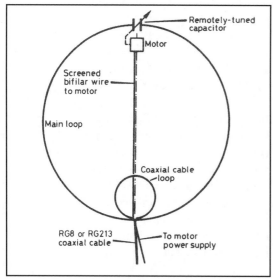

Fig 4.8: A typical magnetic or small tuned loop antenna.

match it, it is a way of getting on a band from a tough location, but don't expect miracles.

I have played with modelling a typical attic-mounted loop in the *MMANA-GAL* antenna simulation program. Assuming a rectangular shape with 15m (49ft) long sides and 6m (20ft) ends, which is about as big as I could get in my loft, this gives a total length of 138ft - about right for a full wavelength on 7MHz (40m). Nevertheless, this would appear to be resonant in the simulation at about 7.1MHz as *MMANA-GAL* assumes non-insulated wire.

If loft-mounted at 12m from the ground it is a bit of a 'cloud warmer' on 40m – great for local contacts when the solar flux rises and the critical frequency rises above 7MHz, but not a great DX antenna. As predicted, on 80m it is very poor with a very high SWR. But on 20m (14MHz) it really starts to excel – outperforming a loft-mounted 20m dipole. 17m (18MHz) and 15m (21MHz) are OK, but not outstanding, but on 10m the antenna has a fantastic six-petal hexagonal radiation pattern with some great lobes every 60° – see **Fig 4.7**. These fill in the gaps left by the dipole's figure-of-eight pattern and could be very useful when the band opens up. But, it also gives you deep nulls, so you had better hope those lobes are just in the right places!

So all in all then, a loft-mounted loop offers you multiband operation above its lowest frequency with some useful gain over a dipole on some bands and in some directions. It is harder to feed properly, but don't let that put you off.

THE MAGNETIC LOOP ANTENNA

The magnetic loop (or, more correctly, small tuned loop - STL) antenna (**Fig 4.8**) has been around for decades, but is one of the most overlooked solutions for a stealthy installation. Peter Dodd, G3LDO, covered a lot of information on STLs in his book *Backyard Antennas* [3]. I don't want to duplicate a lot of what Peter said, but instead give you additional information on a loop's efficiency, how you can calculate the parameters you need to know when building your own loop, such as working voltages and capacitance, plus give you a review of a commercial loop if you don't want to build your own.

I want to emphasise that I think a properly-constructed magnetic loop is probably one of the most efficient antennas for its size, making it an ideal choice for those without the real estate to put up a full-size dipole or other antenna. It is also ideal for loft-mounting, as long as you take care to ensure that it doesn't get detuned by its surroundings and doesn't couple to the house wiring.

Be warned though: you can't just throw one of these together and expect it to work properly. Sure, you will see a low SWR and you will work people, but losses could mean that the antenna isn't that efficient. But build one properly with low-loss construction techniques and a low-loss capacitor and you will reap the benefits.

Background

The STL first saw light of day before WWII and Pat Hawker, G3VA, wrote in the *RSGB Bulletin* about his exploits with the antenna when he was first licensed. In the 1960s the US Army Limited War Laboratory experimented with small loops on HF for use in the jungles of Vietnam. Their report described a 5ft diameter octagonal loop which was meant to be as good as a dipole on 2MHz and 5MHz (but do bear in mind that they were probably talking about a low dipole).

Commercial models of the loop for amateurs were made in the 1970s and 1980s by Tony Johnston, G4OGP / GW4OGP, at Capco (later AAA) and these can still be found on the second-hand market. Tony was a larger-than-life character who attended all the major rallies and introduced many of the UK's ham population to the loop, which was actually designed by Christian (Chris) Kaeferlein, DK5CZ, and Hans Wurtz, DL2FA, in Germany. In fact, the loop is still being manufactured in Germany by AMA Antennen [4].

Fast forward to 1985 and *RadCom* published what became one of the most definitive articles on mag loop design by Roberto Craighero, I1ARZ. This is featured in *Backyard Antennas* [3], so I won't dwell on it here. Over in the USA Ted Hart, W5QJR, also wrote a book and a series of features on magnetic loop antenna design.

Professor Mike Underhill, G3LHZ, is also a strong advocate of magnetic loops and has given many lectures on the subject, even though some people disagree with some of his claims about loop efficiency.

As a result of all this work we are now much better placed to understand how to make the antenna work to our advantage. So what are the pros and cons of a magnetic loop antenna?

Pros

- *Frequency range.* One antenna can typically cover a 2:1 frequency range, such as 20m - 10m. This shouldn't be underestimated as the range just mentioned covers five amateur bands – 20m (14MHz), 17m (18MHz), 15m (21MHz), 12m (24MHz) and 10m (28MHz). At a push you can extend the coverage a little bit more – perhaps adding 30m (10MHz) to the above antenna, albeit at lower efficiency.

- *Filtering effect.* The very sharp tuning of a loop antenna puts a very effective filter on the front end of your radio, thus eliminating out-of-band interference and helping to reduce TVI from you.

- *Noise rejection.* Because the antenna responds to the magnetic portion of the electromagnetic wave it tends to reject locally-generated electrical noise, such as car ignition systems and sparking boiler relays. This is not the big benefit it used to be though, and the loop will still pick up true electromagnetic noise, such as computer hash and noise from switch-mode power supplies.

- *Works at low heights.* The loop, when mounted vertically, will work well even when mounted at low heights. Often there is little advantage to be gained by raising it. The reason for this is quite subtle – a vertically-mounted magnetic loop has its ground reflection predominantly in phase with its main radiation, so adding to it. On the other hand a low horizontal dipole has its reflection out of phase, so partially cancelling it out. Furthermore, the loop doesn't depend on any artificial ground for its efficient operation. While it will probably perform better over a good earth than bad this is a far less critical factor.

- *Nulls for reducing interference.* The loop has two deep nulls in the near field as you look through it, which can be useful for reducing interference. In the far field, which is where your received signals are coming from, this null is less pronounced.

- *High and low-angle radiation.* When mounted vertically the antenna has a fan-like radiation pattern that encompasses both high and low-angle radiation, which is good for DX and more local contacts at the same time.

- *Horizontal null helps reduce electrical noise from house.* When mounted horizontally (at height) the antenna has a null underneath it. This can be useful when mounting the antenna in the loft as the electrical noise in the house is effectively in the null. I have found with my own mag loops that I prefer to mount them horizontally if loft-mounted. The noise level is about two S-points less that way.

Cons

- *Small bandwidth.* The biggest problem with a magnetic loop antenna is the very small bandwidth. On a 1.7m diameter loop used on 80m (3.5MHz) this can be as small as 2 - 3kHz before you have to retune.

However, on a smaller loop, such as an 80cm diameter loop used on 28MHz, you might get 100kHz, which is much more useable.

- *Low-loss construction needed.* The loop has to be built with very low-loss construction techniques. The very small radiation resistance of the loop means that ohmic losses between loop elements or in the capacitor and its connections can add up and reduce the loop's performance substantially. The best mag loops are made of continuous loops of copper or aluminium. While it is relatively easy to bend 10mm copper tubing into loops, doing the same with one inch copper or aluminium is usually a job for an engineering company. The alternative is to make up a rectangular or octagonal copper loop made with 90 or 45° fittings. Mechanical joints are lossy so either soldered or brazed (better) joints are the way to go. In fact, magnetic loop construction usually has more in common with plumbing than radio!

- *Low loss capacitors are needed.* Conventional variable capacitors, which use the bearings and moving parts for their connections, will be found to be lossy. The alternative is to use a so-called butterfly capacitor, which has a connection to both sets of fixed vanes with a movable set of vanes in between. The chances are that you will have to build your own. The alternative is to purchase a vacuum variable capacitor. These do come up on eBay and offer a low-loss alternative to a conventional capacitor. They are capable of handling the very high voltages found in a magnetic loop, but do make sure that the one you are buying covers the capacitance range you need and also the voltage range. There are some ex-Russian military vacuum variables around that are rated at about 3kV, which is OK for QRP, but will not handle 100W where the voltages can exceed 10kV. If you are feeling particularly flush you can buy new Jennings vacuum variable capacitors, but they are expensive.

- *Remote tuning is required.* Unless you want your loop to be fixed on one frequency you are going to need some method of tuning the capacitor. This is usually done by hand, by using a stepper motor or by using a slow-motion gearbox and an electric motor. Keep an eye out for barbecue spit motors which are cheap and usually offer about one RPM. You may even find this too fast for some loops, although it may be fine with vacuum variable capacitors, which work on a multi-turn basis. In that case you will need to work out some way of stopping the motor at the end of the capacitor's travel to avoid damage. You can hand tune a loop if it is next to you, but you will need to fit an insulating shaft to the capacitor. I would also recommend low power only in such a situation for safety reasons.

A magnetic loop antenna – the basic design

In its basic form the antenna is quite simple. Take a large loop of copper or aluminium tubing, around 0.125-wavelength in length and form a circle. If you can't bend the tubing you can make it into a rectangle or octagon, but you will need to create low-loss joints by brazing or welding. The exact size is not critical, but it must not be bigger than 0.25-wavelength, otherwise you won't be able to tune it with a series capacitor. This is why most builders make the loop 0.125 of a wavelength in circumference at the *lower* band limit, giving 0.25 of a wavelength at 2x this – the upper band limit.

Across the open ends of the loop attach a suitable variable capacitor and some means of tuning it, either remotely or by hand.

At the side opposite the capacitor either use a gamma match for tuning (easiest) or create a small single turn (Faraday) coupling loop of about 1/8th of the main loop's diameter. The gamma match is simple – connect the braid outer to the bottom of the loop and taking a piece of copper tubing or heavy wire connect it to the coax inner and then connect it to the loop a few inches away from the feed point. Your actual tapping point will depend on the loop's construction but, once you find the 'sweet spot', braze it to the loop.

With the coupling loop, this can be made from a length of coaxial cable (RG213). You may need to play with the size to get the lowest SWR, but it will be in the range 1/5 to 1/8 of the main loop diameter.

The coil should have the braid open at the top centre. At this point one side of the braid is connected to the opposite inner conductor of the coax cable. At the bottom the inner conductor and braid from one side are connected together and joined to the braid of the other side of the loop.

Let's look at a typical commercial loop antenna.

The MFJ-1786X HF magnetic loop antenna

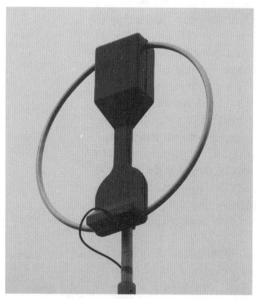

The MFJ-1786X is a 36in diameter aluminium loop that covers 10 - 30MHz. It offers hams six HF amateur bands in one antenna, but the loop will also cover all the short-wave broadcast and utility bands in between. The loop is formed from 1.05in thick aluminium tube, which is welded to the loop's variable capacitor so giving a very low-loss connection – important for maximum efficiency. If you are thinking of mounting the loop in an attic do bear in mind that it can't be stripped down. Make sure that your loft opening can accommodate the 36in required, or you will be taking a hacksaw to your ceiling!

The variable capacitor brings the loop to resonance and is rotated via a motor that receives its current from the coaxial antenna feed. This shouldn't be underestimated as it means you don't have to route an additional control cable when mounting the antenna.

The MFJ-1786X covers 10 - 30m and every frequency in between.

The connection, via an SO239 socket, feeds a Faraday coupling loop, although all the innards are protected by a black ABS casing that effectively hides everything from sight.

The antenna can be mounted vertically or horizontally and gives very different radiation patterns in both configurations. When mounted vertically it gives a fan-shaped pattern in line with the loop. The deep nulls off the sides can be used to notch out local sources of interference and are very effective. You get a mixture of high and low angles of radiation – the

The loop is 'driven' from this small electronic remote control box.

latter may be useful for close-in contacts, although given that the antenna does not cover 3.5MHz and 7MHz (where high-angle radiation is useful for local contacts) this may be wasted RF. If used this way there is a lot to be said for using a rotator, although it isn't strictly necessary.

When mounted horizontally the pattern is effectively omnidirectional, although the minimum radiation angle will depend upon the height above ground – generally the higher the better.

The loop is driven via a small control unit finished in MFJ's characteristic brushed aluminium. The box, which comes with a small plug-in power supply, has buttons for power, SWR meter range (0 - 30W and 0 - 300W) and lamp, which illuminates the meter. On the right are the two sets of tuning buttons for moving up and down in frequency with both fast and slow tune options.

If you have never used a magnetic loop before you may find it disconcerting. When you first plug it in to your transceiver, unless it happens to be tuned to your receive frequency, you will find it incredibly quiet. The loop is very high Q and off-tune signals are highly attenuated. You have two choices for tuning. The first involves applying a little RF to the loop on the frequency of your choice and pushing the latching UP or DOWN fast tune buttons. Unless it is at the end its tuning range the LED will light and the motor in the loop will drive the capacitor in the required direction. When it reaches resonance the control unit will beep and the tuning will stop. You now release the UP or DOWN button and use the fine tune button next to the illuminated LED to tune the loop for lowest SWR according to the cross-needle display. Tuning is very sharp and it may take some to-ing and fro-ing to get it right.

An alternative way of tuning, and one that will no doubt please fellow band users, is to rough tune the loop for maximum receive noise (you will hear the noise of the capacitor motor) before applying RF for the final dip. This is how I choose to tune the loop under test and it works well. Once tuned you can apply up to 150W of RF – more than this and you are likely to get flashover across the capacitor as the high Q nature of the loop means that voltages can easily reach several kilovolts.

Oh, as with all HF antennas don't touch the loop when energised or you will be left with a nasty and painful RF burn! I speak from experience – serves me right for not checking the rig was de-keyed when I was doing the testing.

But does it work? I first mounted the loop vertically in my garage attic space to try and emulate a worst-case scenario. As always 15m (21 MHz), 12m (24MHz) and 10m (28 MHz) were not playing ball at the low point in the solar cycle so most tests were conducted on 30m (10MHz), 20m (14MHz) and 17m (18MHz).

I find that 10MHz (30m) is a very underrated band. Only available to CW and data users it is nevertheless capable of world-wide contacts and is often open in the evening after 20m has closed. The loop is at its most inefficient on 10MHz, but nevertheless I was able to make easy contacts around Europe with the customary 599 signal reports. It compared favourably with an 85ft end-fed W3EDP antenna. I also worked 5A7A (Libya) on 10MHz on the loop. It was a similar story on 20m and 17m, although signal strengths were obviously down on an outdoor dipole due to the loop being in a garage loft, which is quite low.

When mounted in the attic of a two-storey house the MFJ-1786X had better performance, often getting to within 1 or 2 S-points of a dipole on 14MHz and at times equalling it. Some signals were actually louder on the loop. Noise levels were lower when compared with the loft-mounted horizontal dipole.

If someone can find another commercial six-band loft-mounted antenna that will outperform the MFJ-1786X I'd like to hear from them.

Bandwidth is obviously a big issue with the loop – I found my 2:1 SWR bandwidths were about 8kHz on 10MHz, 20kHz on 14MHz, 45kHz on 21MHz and 100kHz on 28MHz. This obviously means a lot of retuning unless you like to stick to one band and one frequency, such as 20m PSK31.

Mounting the antenna outside at about 30ft gave it a better chance to perform. Here I found it to be a much better performer, often equal in performance to resonant half-wave dipoles at a similar height.

A brief hour on 10m during the ARRL 28MHz contest brought many very easy contacts around Europe with the customary 599 reports. At no time did I get a "QRZ?". Some stations were perfectly audible on the loop but in the noise on the dipole due to the loop's low-noise characteristics. Much has been made of the magnetic loop's quiet characteristics, but this has to be qualified. While it is very good at rejecting local electrical noise, such as from motors and thermostats, it doesn't reject broadband hash from computers, TV sets etc quite as well. But you can use the deep nulls off the side to help and this is where a rotator can come in useful.

Overall then, the MFJ-1786X is a useful antenna for those with little or no space. It can be loft-mounted or set on a short pole outside, but to really make the most of it mount it as high and in the clear as possible - advice that could apply to any antenna. Ground losses are not the main issue, but shielding due to houses, trees and other items does come into play. Tuning can be tiresome, especially if you like flicking from band to band as I do. Its performance is obviously better on the higher HF bands, but I was surprised just how well it performed on

10MHz too. Bear in mind that a half-wave dipole on this band is nearly 50ft long so a 3ft antenna may get you on a band that you might otherwise have to ignore.

Do make sure you switch your internal ATU out of line when using the loop as tuning *must* be performed using the control unit. If you don't, you will end up with very poor performance. As the antenna is

```
S.  Shape of loop ...............................    CIRCLE
P.  Perimeter or circumference of main loop, metres .    2.87
D.  Diameter of loop conductor, mm ...............    26.0
H.  Height of lowest part of loop above earth, metres     3.0
F.  Frequency of operation, megahertz ............   14.175
T.  Transmitter output power, watts ..............    100.0

Electrical length of loop ...       0.136    wavelengths at operating freq.
Inductance of main loop .....        2.09    micro-henrys
Coupling loop diameter .....         0.16    metres to match to 50-ohm feeder
Turns ratio on coupling xfmr.        22.1    to 1  ..  ..  ..  ..  ..
Tuning capacitor setting ....          57    pico-farads at resonance
Current in main loop ........        31.3    amperes rms, opposite capacitor
Voltage across capacitor ....        8004    peak volts

Transmitting bandwidth ......         7.8    kilo-hertz between 3dB points
Radiation resistance ........      0.0670    ohms distributed around loop
Conductor RF loss resistance       0.0347    ..          ..    ..    ..
Ground proximity losses .....      0.0002    ..          ..    ..    ..
Transmission efficiency .....       65.76    percent of power input
Loss relative to ideal loop .         1.8    dB = 0.3 "S"-points

Select S,P,D,H,F,T to change input data,  R(e-start) or Q(uit program) ....
```

Fig 4.9: Screen grab of RJE program.

only three feet in diameter it would be easy to discount it as a mere toy. It certainly is not and it is actually very effective for its size.

The MFJ-1788 is very similar, and the same size, but covers 15 – 40m.

Calculating loop efficiency

So how efficient is a well-constructed magnetic loop antenna? That question has been the subject of many arguments in the past, but my benchmark is a computer program written by the late Reg Edwards, G4FGQ.

I have used Reg's PC program for years when designing and evaluating magnetic loop antennas. If you search the Internet for RJELOOP1.exe you will find it. Before we go too far I must admit that I did have an exchange of correspondence with Reg about loop height. This is one of the factors that the program needs to work out the efficiency, but mag loops, when mounted vertically, are supposed to be pretty ground independent. Reg's program does include ground losses, but these are minimal when the antenna is mounted 2 - 3m high.

Let's assume that we have mounted the antenna vertically at 3m and are running 100W. I have chosen the specifications of the MFJ-1786X antenna mentioned earlier for the evaluation as it is a commercial antenna and therefore one that you can buy. These figures also hold for any well-constructed loop with 1in-thick tubing and a diameter of 36in (91cm). So let's plug the figures in to Reg's program and see what we get. A typical screen shot is shown in **Fig 4.9**.

According to the program the loop antenna is 95.69% efficient on 10m (28.5MHz) going down to

The loop was mounted in the loft by just lying it on the rafters – it still worked very well.

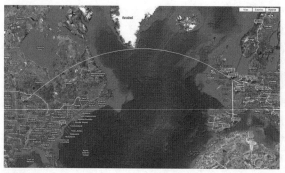

WSPR is a great way of doing back-to-back tests on antennas – this is where I was picked up while transmitting 5W to the MFJ loop.

36.89% efficiency on 30m (10.1MHz). At this frequency it is down 4.33dB compared with a dipole, but that is still less than one S-point [though note that several modern transceivers' S-meters use 3dB per S-unit, rather than the more traditional 6dB – *Ed.*] On 20m (14.175MHz) the antenna is reported to be 65.76% efficient, which is only 1.82dB down or less than half an S-point worse than a dipole.

To test this I later mounted the MFJ-1786 in my loft again (at about 25 - 30ft) and compared it with a 20m dipole (also in the loft). My on-air experience showed that the antenna was about 0 - 2 S-points down on both receive and transmit compared with the dipole, but to get a qualitative comparison I used the *WSPR* (Weak Signal Propagation Reporter) system to get some automated reports from around the world.

I transmitted twice in a 15-minute period using 5W to the indoor half-wave dipole and then switched to the mag loop for 15 minutes. I logged the best result from each transmission, in terms of the received signal / noise ratio in dB. The results were as shown in **Table 4.2**.

Callsign	Half-wave dipole	Magnetic loop	Difference
IV3KID	-23dB	+6dB	+29dB
EA7QV	-1dB	+3dB	+4dB
VK3SMC	-23dB	not heard	-
LB9YE	+8dB	not heard	-
WE0H	-16dB	-23dB	-7dB
G8HYP	-13dB	-18dB	-5dB
WB8HWF	-16dB	-22dB	-6dB
G6JWX	-14dB	-23dB	-9dB
DL6YCU	-12dB	-16dB	-4dB
N3IZN	-24dB	not heard	-
LA6TPA	+5dB	+2dB	-3dB
DF2YB	-17dB	-24dB	-7dB
EB6AOK	0dB	+3dB	+3dB
LA6TPA	not heard	+2dB	-
F5WK	not heard	-17dB	-
DL8BB	not heard	-28dB	-

Table 4.2: Tests using WSPR mode comparing half-wave dipole with magnetic loop antenna.

It is sometimes hard to interpret results from *WSPR*, but the facts are that six stations were either louder on the mag loop or were heard on the loop, but not on the dipole. Ten stations were louder on the dipole or were heard on the dipole, but not on the mag loop.

On DX (USA) one station in Minnesota (WE0H) received me 6dB lower on the loop. N3IZN in California just heard me on the dipole, but didn't hear the loop. It was the same with VK3SMC in Australia. The dipole tends to fire east-west, which might explain why the mag loop heard some European stations north and south of me better than the dipole – being mounted horizontally the loop is omnidirectional. I repeated the test on another occasion and got very similar results. The conclusion, if one can be drawn, seems to support the idea that the loop is at times equal to a dipole, but on average it is down about an S-point or so. As with all these cases there are exceptions to the rule.

Voltages and currents

Reg's program also helps us to understand the voltages and currents that are in play when transmitting on the loop. Using the same 36in-diameter model we see that at 100W and 10.1MHz there will be a voltage of 8.5kV across the capacitor and a current of 46 amps running in the area of the loop opposite the capacitor. The figures are lower on 28MHz (4.4kV), but you start to see some of the design problems associated with building high efficiency small loops and how your choice of materials and capacitor makes a big difference.

This is why larger diameter tubing is better than smaller (or even wire) and why good quality wide-spaced or vacuum capacitors are the way to go.

Efficiency at lower frequencies

The most effective magnetic loop antenna is just under one quarter of a wavelength in circumference at its operating frequency. Bigger than this and you lose its ability to be tuned with a series capacitor. Unfortunately, that results in some pretty massive antennas on the lower bands. For example, at 3.5MHz a circular loop antenna would have to be 21.4m in circumference or 6.82m in diameter.

But you can build smaller antennas that will fit in your loft or garden and just accept the losses. For example, using Reg's program, a 1.7m diameter, 1in-thick loop (which just happens to be the size of a current commercial AMA-83 loop or older Capco AMA-5 loop for 40 - 80m) is just 7% efficient at 3.5MHz, but the losses amount to about 11.9dB, which is around 2 S-points compared with a dipole. In reality it means that your signals will be 59 around the UK and not 59+10dB. That same loop on 40m will be less than half an S-point down on a dipole.

Variable capacitors

I said earlier that the most efficient capacitors for small loops are likely to be either butterfly types or vacuum variables. But how big, in terms of their maximum capacitance, do they need to be? Using G4FGQ's program gives us the answers (**Table 4.3**).

Frequency	Capacitance
10.1MHz	116pF
14.2MHz	57pF
18.1MHz	33pF
21.2MHz	23pF
24.9MHz	16pF
28.5MHz	11pF

Table 4.3: Sizes of capacitor required on various bands for a 36in (91cm) diameter loop.

From **Table 4.3** you can see that the higher in frequency you go the less capacitance is needed. Also, the change needed to move from band to band becomes less. This is borne out in practice as it takes a lot longer to QSY down to 30m on an MFJ1786 loop than it does to move, say, from 18MHz to 24MHz.

You can also see that some of the commercial vacuum capacitors will cover part of this range, but not all. For example, at the time of writing there was a suitable vacuum variable capacitor for sale on eBay that covered 8 - 50pF. You can see that if you were building your own 36in-diameter loop this would give you 18 – 28MHz coverage, but you wouldn't get 14MHz or 10MHz unless you connected further capacitance in parallel. The solution is therefore to make the loop slightly bigger – a 1.0m diameter loop would be tuneable from 14.1MHz to 28.3MHz with a capacitor range of 8 - 50pF, but it is very borderline. To be honest, stray capacitance could mean that you can't tune properly at the higher extreme. This shows that it is important to plan your designs carefully before committing yourself to expensive components – or the blowtorch and your copper tubing.

So what about a loop suitable for 80m? Let's assume that you are going to make an octagonal loop out of brazed copper tuning and you would like to cover 80m, 40m and perhaps 30m. How big should it be?

Let's try an octagonal loop made up of eight pieces of 1in tubing, each piece being 0.85m long. Its overall width would be 1.7m and its circumference would be 6.8m. Here are the required capacitances:

3.5MHz	339pF
3.8MHz	286pF
7.0MHz	79pF
7.2MHz	75pF
10.1MHz	34pF

As you can see you need a very meaty variable capacitor to work 80m, which is why the weapon of choice is normally a 0 - 500pF variable. There are suitable vacuum variables around that will cover up to 500pF, but they are not cheap.

Incidentally, the above loop might just work on part of 14MHz if you can get the capacitance down to below 10pF. To work on topband, though, you would need a capacitance of more than 1600pF, which is why a larger loop is really required. If you are still committed to building your own small loop let's look at a case study to see how you can overcome some of the problems.

CASE STUDY: WILL BEATTIE'S, GM0HKS, MAGNETIC LOOP

Will Beattie, GM0HKS, lives in Motherwell, Scotland, and wanted a fairly stealthy set-up. His magnetic loop, built with a vacuum variable capacitor, fitted the bill nicely as he explains:

"During 2006, I put together a magnetic loop antenna for HF operating," Will said. "As a direct result of life in the Royal Navy, I had to change location regularly and this saw the size of my back garden change too. Some larger, some smaller. My move to the Motherwell area after 26 years of service in the RN was no different and I rapidly

Will Beattie's, GM0HKS, magnetic loop may be unobtrusive but it works well.

discovered that I was going to experience a similar problem at the dwelling I now live in. Out of consideration for my neighbours, I knew that 25ft scaffold poles to the front and rear of the property, supporting a wire antenna was out of the question and 'not in keeping with the surroundings'.

"For many years, I have nurtured a dream to build and, more importantly, use on a regular basis, a transmitting / receiving antenna that would not be the discussion point of my nearest neighbours. To build and use an antenna, that I personally believe could consistently perform at or near to that of a half-wave dipole, but yet is small enough to sit in the corner of one's back garden, even at ground level, was my aim.

"I decided right from the start that instead of using a butterfly, mechanically pressed capacitor, I wanted to try and obtain a vacuum variable device. These are glass encased, capable of withstanding extremely high voltages and, in general,

very, very robust devices. I never really knew an awful lot about them but, during my time in submarines, I sat alongside the tuning cabinet of the Vanderheim power amplifiers wherein these devices lodged. The whirring and clicking was, in actual fact, the vacuum variable capacitors being rotated in and out for loading purposes.

"As luck would have it, I managed to pick up an absolute beauty from eBay, all for the princely sum of £12 plus £5 postage and packaging. The vacuum variable

Vacuum variable capacitors are ideal for magnetic loops, but are not cheap to buy new.

-----8 inches across-----

Will opted for a gamma match feed rather than a shielded loop.

I purchased has a limited capacitance range (16 – 80pF) but it has enabled me (just) to operate on four HF bands. It is rated at approximately 4kV. From what I understand, this voltage rating is based on a 75% safety margin therefore the device will handle much higher RF levels. I have not been in a position to put this to the test as I can only generate 120 watts from the TS-530S. This particular capacitor takes 17 turns to go from having the plates completely meshed to fully open and vice versa. This is good because that, coupled with reduction drive / slow turn rates of the remote tuning DC motor, greatly assists in getting the high Q point spot on.

"Remember, bandwidth is very narrow when using this antenna and requires retuning as you 'cross the band'. This only really applies to the transmitting side of things. I can comfortably tune across 40m without having to rotate the vacuum variable, however, if I wish to transmit, the VSWR does need adjusting. The efficiency on various frequencies is markedly different too so you need to be able to get the 'tuning spot' exact. Taking this in to account sways many amateurs from getting involved with the mag loop. I remotely retune the loop now and do not give it a second thought so far as this feature goes.

"Based on the calculator recommendations and my own figures, the first RG213 coax template was cut to a length of 13.5ft. I then cut another length one fifth this size, i.e. 32.4in. The second smaller length was to be used to form the coupling loop. This particular coax loop worked for me and I managed 21 Stateside contacts during an ARRL CW contest. This was operating both 7 and 14MHz.

"I then decided to make a loop with 15mm copper tubing. I ran it through a set of pipe rollers kindly loaned to me for this project by my mate Tom, MM3TRZ. I used a piece of three by two inch timber approximately 7ft in length on which to mount the 15mm copper loop. I drilled out two 15mm holes at the top of the supporting timber and filled it with mastic sealer, slotted the ends of the loop in on each side and left this to set. If total permanency is required, why not try using 'No More Nails' available from B&Q or any of the standard outlets? That would ensure the loop would not move. I intend to adopt this stance when I have got the loop up in the loft space and mounted on a rotator. I also used a 15mm white plastic clip, specifically designed to hold copper pipe, at the base of the copper loop to increase its rigidity. I left the mastic sealer to set overnight.

"I have a choice of two remote tuning motors. One is a barbecue spit roast motor which has been stored away for over 10 years and the other a beautiful high torque DC motor from Maplins. I visited the local model shop and bought two 24in lengths of 6mm brass rod. I also bought four 6mm universal jointed couplings. They are absolutely ideal for the job of coupling everything together.

"I later changed the inductive loop to a gamma match. I used a length of 15mm gauge copper pipe initially, but settled for a nice workable piece of microbore copper piping. Because it is quite pliable, it is very easy to bend and shape. These have all been very positive improvements to the loop's performance.

"The plain and simple facts are that on all four bands, I am experiencing extremely low VSWR and, running a variety of power levels and modes, I have achieved some very satisfying results, including Lahore (Pakistan) and Crete on 20m SSB using 30W PEP and Los Angeles on 40m CW using 50W. I regularly listen around 2300 and, with the loop pointing towards 220 degrees, hear Venezuela and Brazil. These signals are 599 +20dB. These stations mentioned were worked with the loop at ground level. I did raise the loop on to a 15ft pole but was rather disappointed at the variance in VSWR. I now keep it on the ground. It either gets moved out on to the small lawn at the back of the house or remains in the garage if it's wet and windy.

"The results are consistently the same - very strong reports in both directions inter G and near / middle Europe on 40m and similar with DX on 20m. I'm very pleased," said Will.

THE EH ANTENNA

I had to think twice about including this section in the book. There is an awful lot of controversy surrounding the EH antenna and how it works. Nevertheless, it is worthy of attention and I would rather people built one and tried it for themselves before they start poo-pooing the idea. The basic design is shown in **Fig 4.10**.

I have built two EH antennas – one for 20m (14MHz) and the other for 15m (21MHz). They are very small, not very easy to set up, but they do work. The 20m one is about 4ft long, the 15m version is about 3ft long. I have made contacts on both bands with the antennas and at times

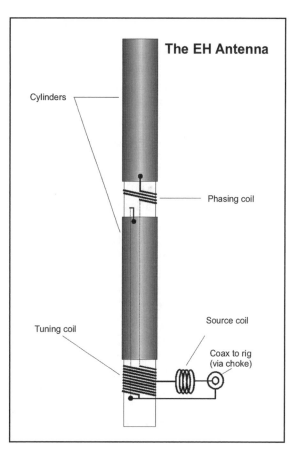

Fig 4.10: Schematic diagram of an EH antenna.

they have been equal to other more conventional antennas and at times they have been 2 - 3 S-points worse.

I am going to steer clear of any discussion as to whether they work by Poynting Vector Synthesis, or whether they are short fat dipoles with a matching network. That is a discussion for others. What I would encourage you to do is build one for yourself and see if they work for you.

The background

The EH antenna is the brainchild of Ted Hart, W5QJR. Ted is well known for his earlier work on magnetic loop antennas and the development work on the EH is based on the work of Maurice Hately, Brian Stewart and Fathi Kabbary. They developed the Crossed Field Antenna (CFA) which allegedly synthesised an electromagnetic wave by phasing an E field and an H field together.

Maurice Hately went on to develop the Crossed Field Loop (CFL) and I had the opportunity to test some of these for a *RadCom* feature in the 1990s with mixed results. What did strike me was that the 40m version, which was a loop of coax about 50cm in diameter, worked very well indeed – far better than its small size suggested it should. Maurice eventually retired and the CFLs are no longer available. Maurice was also reluctant to reveal the secrets of the loops and I was sworn to secrecy on what was in the small matching boxes, a secret that I have kept.

I experimented with my own topband (1.8MHz) version of the CFL, which was about 1m in diameter. I spent many nights trying to get it to work properly and one evening did manage to have a 59 SSB contact with a surprised ham about 200 miles away. I fiddled with the design and ended up making it worse – it ended up in the spare parts box, the capacitors being used for another project.

The W5QJR EH antenna

Fast forward now to the beginning of the 21st century, when Ted Hart, W5QJR, developed his EH antenna which purports to work on a similar principle. Ted says that the EH antenna (and the basic patent) is based on the concept that a -90° phase shift (not a phase delay) network between the two halves of the antenna will cause the electric (E) and magnetic (H) fields to be in phase at the antenna. This allows radiation to occur at the antenna rather than at the far field distance as is the case for conventional Hertzian antennas. Ted says Hertzian antennas produce E and H fields that are 90° out of time phase and the resultant fields do not begin to come into phase until they have propagated away from the antenna about 1/3 of a wavelength. When they become in phase, electromagnetic radiation is created.

The production of an EM wave at the antenna is called Poynting Vector Synthesis and is what gets antenna experts hot under the collar. Many argue that this is impossible.

Defenders also say that as the EH antenna constrains the E and H fields to the local vicinity of the antenna, electromagnetic interference (EMI) is virtually eliminated compared with large E and H fields of Hertz antennas.

As a receiving antenna, even though it is very small, an EH antenna is said to produce the same signal level into the receiver as a full size antenna.

When large diameter cylinders are used for antenna elements on the EH antenna rather than wires, the capacity between the two halves of the dipole antenna can be large, thus causing the bandwidth to be high, even when the cylinders are short. This allows the EH antenna to be very small, typically less than 2% of a wavelength, rather than 50% of a wavelength like a standard dipole or a 1/4 wavelength vertical that must have ground radials.

If building your own EH antenna make sure that you use cylinders that are at least the following diameters:

80m	4in
40m	2in
20m	1.5in
10m	1in

My experimental 15m EH antenna mounted in the loft for testing.

For an EH antenna designed for the low bands (40, 80 and 160m), the recommended length to diameter ratio of each cylinder is 12 or greater. This is said to give high angle radiation for NVIS (local) contacts. To maximize radiation at low angles, a length to diameter ratio of six or less is recommended.

The theory

Let's examine a typical EH antenna, which comprises two non-ferrous tubes stacked one above the other. The gap between them is the same as their diameter. According to Ted's theory, assuming a feedline applies a source current to each cylinder, the source causes a high voltage to be applied, which results in a large E (electrical) field between the two cylinders. The voltage is very high at the feed ends of the cylinders and is reduced to a very low value at the open ends of the cylinders. This creates a large differential voltage across each cylinder. The surface resistance of the cylinders is low, thus the differential voltage across each cylinder causes high current to flow vertically on the cylinders.

In turn, Ted says this current creates a large magnetic field surrounding the cylinders. We now have E and H fields in the proper relative physical orientations to allow them to interact. If the source has the proper time phase relationship between the applied voltage and current, thus causing the

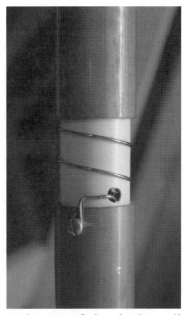

A close up of the phasing coil between the two cylinders.

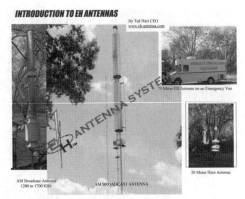

INTRODUCTION TO EH ANTENNAS
By Ted Hart CEO
www.eh-antenna.com

73 Meter EH Antenna on an Emergency Van

20 Meter Ham Antenna

AM Broadcast Antenna
1200 to 1700 KHz

AM BROADCAST ANTENNA

Ted's, W5QJR, free EH antenna book.

E and H fields to be properly phased, radiation will be created. This is why a -90° phase delay is needed in the source.

Please note that many people dispute this theory and say that the antenna works as a short fat dipole with a matching network – I merely offer the design to you so that you can try it yourself.

There are many ways of feeding an EH antenna, but the simplest is called the STAR method – the method we are going to use to build our own version.

Building your own EH antenna

You can build your own EH antenna to examine the theory and also to let you see for yourself whether it works or not. Ted has produced a downloadable booklet that outlines how to build one for 40m (7MHz). You can get the book by joining the EH group at Yahoo Groups [5]. Before you start I urge you to join the group and download the booklet – it will make life a lot easier.

There are two points to note:

- You need either a Field Strength Meter and / or an antenna analyser to build an EH antenna. If you just tune for lowest SWR it won't work properly as you need to find the point where the phasing is correct and reactance is zero. This point of maximum radiation is not necessarily the point of lowest SWR.
- Tuning is very tricky and needs a lot of patience!

You will need a former on which to construct the antenna. Ted recommends the use of 3in diameter plastic pipe from a hardware store. You need a piece about 28in long. Only use white or clear plastic. If the pipe is coloured, the colour is usually as a result of included carbon particles and they get very active in the presence of RF, causing heat and losses. You will need some aluminium foil and some nuts and bolts to secure your wires to the foil.

You will also need some 14 gauge (2mm) copper wire with enamel (varnish) insulation. If your pipe is not three inches in diameter the tuning and phasing coils will be a slightly different size, so you should download the *Excel* spreadsheet that is also available on the EH Yahoo group in the 'Files' section.

Start by gluing two pieces of aluminium foil to the plastic pipe to give you two cylinders, each about 9.85in in length and spaced apart by the same distance as the diameter of the tube.

Connect a wire to the bottom of the top cylinder with a screw and washer and then create a phasing coil around the gap between the cylinders of 2.9 turns. Then make a hole in the cylinder near the bottom of this coil, push the wire through and feed it out the bottom of the pipe. Now connect a second wire to the top of the bottom cylinder with a screw and washer. Make a hole in the pipe and push it through so that it also goes down the middle.

Take the wire that is connected to the top cylinder and, making a small hole about 3in down from the lower edge of the bottom cylinder, push it back through so that it is now on the outside of the pipe. Solder another piece of wire to this and make a coil that has 21 turns on it – make sure that the direction of the coil is the same as the phasing coil you made earlier.

After about 16 turns make small tapping points at turns 17, 18, 19 and 21 by twisting the wire around a small screwdriver. You will need to scrape or burn the enamel wire off at these points and it is worth tinning them with solder as well.

Now make another small hole near the bottom of this coil, pull the other wire through from the centre of the pipe and solder that wire to the bottom of the coil.

Connect your coax braid to this bottom point (turn 21) and connect an alligator clip to the inner of your coax. Now the fun starts!

Tuning the EH

Make sure you have fitted a choke balun about 3ft down from the base of your EH antenna – about 10 turns of RG58 coax on a plastic former about 4in in diameter should do. This is to stop feedline radiation - which *will* occur without the choke. Now hang the completed antenna up in your doorway near to your radio – I push a small plastic-headed pin into the wooden frame above the door and hang mine from there with a piece of string threaded through two small holes in the top of the pipe.

Ground your antenna analyser before starting, otherwise you will get odd results. Now connect the inner of your coax to tap 20 and sweep with the analyser to see if you get an SWR dip somewhere near 7MHz. If you don't, try connecting the crocodile clip to tap 19 and try again. Again, if you don't, try tap 18 – one of these will give you some form of a dip near 7MHz.

If you find that you get a dip *below* 7MHz you need to remove a turn from the top of the coil and start again. If you get a dip above 7.2MHz you need to add extra coils to the top of the coil.

Sooner or later you will get very close to 7.1MHz. When you are close you will find that separating the coil at the top will move the frequency up a little. Pushing the coil together will move it down.

Pushing or moving the *bottom* of the coil will alter the SWR. Once you have the antenna pretty much where you want it stop – we now need to work on the phasing.

If you have an antenna analyser look for where the impedance reads 50Ω and also where the reactance is zero. If you are really lucky these will be at one and the same point, that is 50+j0. If they are not, try moving the tapping point and / or coil spacing to see if you can get the two to coincide.

If you can't we need to add inductance or capacitance in series between the coil and the centre of the coax. This is called a *source coil*. Unfortunately, with some analysers we don't know whether this reactance is inductive or capacitative so we will need to use some trial and error.

Using your analyser see what the value of x is when r = 50Ω. Now using an online calculator – I use the one at www.electronics2000.co.uk/calc/reactance-calculator.php, but Google 'Reactance Calculator' to find one if that doesn't work – work out the value of an inductor at 7.1MHz that has the reactance you saw on your meter. Using this figure use another online calculator, such as www.crystalradio.net/cal/indcal2.shtml, to work out how to make a coil of this value and add it in series between the coax centre and the tuning coil.

Once you have added the coil if the value of x when r = 50Ω is now zero, or as near as damn it, you have made the right choice. If it got *worse* you needed a capacitor and not an inductor to get to $x = 0$.

Do bear in mind that you will need a capacitor capable of handling the current you intend putting through it when using the antenna. If you don't have any high voltage capacitors available you can substitute a low voltage one just to check that you were right. Before using the antenna on transmit you will have to fabricate a replacement, possibly using printed circuit board (PCB) or coax (28pF per foot for RG58).

If you don't have an antenna analyser you can do this process with an SWR meter and a Field Strength Meter (FSM). In this case look to see where the lowest SWR is. Then look with the FSM to see if the maximum radiation is in the same place. If it isn't you have some reactance and you can make up a coil in the first instance to see if that improves things. If it makes it worse you need a capacitor in series.

Once you have the EH antenna set up I recommend taping the coil and tapping points in place so that they can't move. Then hang the antenna somewhere high, like the loft, and see what you think of its performance. I have found that moving the antenna to a different location can alter the tuning. This may involve changing the length of the coax, which suggests that this is actually part of the radiating / tuning system – see what you find. Other people say that it is very sensitive to the capacity of its surroundings. If you can set up the EH antenna and tune it in its final resting place it is preferable.

I have found that once set up properly my EH antennas were either equal to or up to 2 S-points down on a dipole or equivalent antenna. I also found mine were susceptible to noise when used indoors, but others have reported that theirs are quiet.

On 15m tests using WSPR I found that I could be heard by Ben, NB3N, in Maryland USA using 5W to the EH, but signals were down 7 - 13dB compared with my Hustler 5BTV vertical. Late in the afternoon in February I could also be decoded (just - he received me at -23dB SN) by Richard, KE7A, in Dallas, Texas when transmitting

Even a simple field strength meter like this will work when setting up your EH antenna.

on my Hustler, but he couldn't decode me when using the EH.

On the 20m versions I had easy CW contacts with the USA and Libya and it worked well on PSK31 too.

Commercial EH antennas are available from Japan, but it is fun building your own. They do work, but the jury is out on how well and the actual mode of operation.

If you want to build one for 80m or 160m you need to scale up both the diameter and length of the cylinders accordingly. There are a lot of data on the net - just Google "EH antennas". I have had fun

Conny Winrot SM6DCO and the new experimental PVA antenna.

with mine and at times they have matched my other antennas. They work well on CW and PSK31 where absolute signal strength is not a priority, but I'm not convinced that they are equal to reference antennas such as dipoles.

If you have limited space or only a balcony to play with, an EH antenna is pretty inconspicuous and will get you on the air, which is what this book is all about.

Other questions that still need to be answered are:

- What part does feed line radiation play in the operation of the EH antenna? Try fitting a better choke balun or even a trap in the coax (less than 1/4 wavelength away from the antenna) and see if it makes any difference. Should we really think of the EH antenna and the feedline together as a system? There is nothing wrong with feedline radiation if that is what you are aiming for and you manage to work stations with your antenna.
- Does the antenna work by Poynting Vector Synthesis or is it a short fat dipole with a matching network? I'll leave that one for debate!

Latest Developments

As the book was going to press news of a new development in EH antennas came to light. The new Poynting Vector Antenna (PVA) is being developed by Ted Hart, W5QJR; Paul Birke, VE3PVB, and Conny Winrot, SM6DCO. It promises efficient operation with no common mode currents that have plagued earlier EH designs. It too is said to produce its RF energy from the capacitance between two conductors, plus the currents flowing along them. A new book detailing how to build the antenna should be available soon. If you are a keen fan of small antennas and like to experiment keep an eye on the Internet as details emerge.

CASE STUDY: BOB CLAYTON'S, G8SDU, 80M EH ANTENNA

Bob Clayton's, G8SDU, experimental EH antenna for 80m is made from a long piece of plastic waste pipe about 3in in diameter and about 8ft long. It has two aluminium cylinders made by wrapping the sheet metal around the pipe and

Bob Clayton's, G8SDU, stealthy 80m EH antenna.

A close-up of the 80m EH antenna feedpoint and choke.

securing it with self-tapping screws. To be honest these cylinders should be a bit bigger – at least 4in diameter for an 80m EH.

As is usual the coils are mounted underneath the two cylinders and the whole antenna sits on a cast-iron base normally used to support a garden parasol. Bob connected an earth lead to the bottom of the matching coil, which connects to a ground stake next to the antenna. He also added a choke balun formed by winding about 10 turns of RG58 coax.

The whole assembly was sealed with mastic and painted green to help camouflage it. The net result is an 80m EH antenna that is barely noticeable if sited in some shrubbery or trees.

Like me Bob found that tuning wasn't easy and required a lot of iterations. He also found that the antenna is very sensitive to its surroundings and moving it around can affect the SWR quite significantly.

"The antenna does work, with limited bandwidth. When I tested it I found that it resonated at about 3.5MHz, although the SWR wasn't as low as I would have liked. Signals from around the UK were down about three S-points compared with my 135ft OCF dipole, but noise levels were much lower too.

"It was quite capable of PSK31 and CW contacts around the UK, but was not a match for a longer antenna on SSB signals. Nevertheless, it was an interesting attempt at an 80m stealth antenna and could get someone on the band if they didn't have room for anything else," said Bob.

GM3HAT's Crossed Field Loop (CFL) Antenna

My interest in the late Maurice Hately's, GM3HAT, work on Crossed Field Antennas stems from my enthusiasm for small and stealthy HF designs.

As one of the pioneers of the very controversial Crossed Field Antenna (CFA) theory, Maurice used to make and sell small loops for everything from topband to 6m. The loops were tiny – about 40cm in diameter for 40m and less than a metre in diameter for 80m.

His adverts regularly appeared in *RadCom* and I was lucky enough back in 2002 to review some of them for the RSGB.

But! This was on the strict understanding that I didn't reveal how he had configured the matching circuitry. I even had to promise not to break the seals on the boxes. This I duly promised and the review was written and published.

Here is how Maurice said it worked: "This antenna is the latest form of Crossed Field Antenna. The electromagnetic waves are created within the small 'Field Interaction Zone' around the two conductors of the loop. The new process of Poynting Vector Synthesis we have recently invented is the electrical dual of the system we used with success in the voltage stimulated forms of CFA Ref GB Patent 2 215 524 etc and papers in *Electronics World* March '89 and Dec '90 plus *IBC Amsterdam '97 IEE Conf Publn 447* pp421-6.

"The CFL 7 is tuned internally to transmit 100W anywhere within the 40 metre amateur band. There are no user adjustments. The SWR when fed by 50-ohm coax is less than 1.5:1 over the UK 7MHz band.

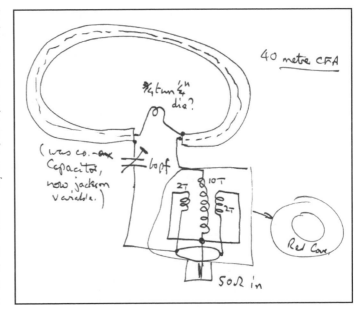

This is how the Hately CFL loops were wired

If it is necessary to operate in the USA band an ATU will correct any small error."

He also recommended 14m of coax or any multiple of 14m. I found that the 40m loop worked very well and it is certainly worth further investigation if you have no space.

I promised Maurice that I would keep his secrets, and so I have for more than 10 years. But now that he is no longer with us I feel that the information on how the antennas were built should pass into the public domain so that antenna enthusiasts can try the design for themselves, debunk it or perhaps even improve on it.

So here it is – the design for the GM3HAT Hately 40m Crossed Field Loop antenna.

I have included a schematic that was sent to me by another ham (now deceased) who *did* 'open the box', and here are a few words of explanation.

The original review appeared in Radcom in 2002.

1. The matching unit / power splitter is wound on a Red (mix 2) toroid. A suitable version might be a T200-2.
2. The wiring is self explanatory.
3. The variable capacitor brings the whole thing to resonance and in the production models it was replaced by a length of RG58 coax. This has a capacitance of around 28.8pF per foot. I would suggest using a variable capacitor when building the antenna and replacing it with coax once you have the correct values. From the diagram the suggestion is that it is less than 60pF for the 40m version and probably lower still for the 20m version.
4. The loop was actually made from copper brake pipe, but could just as

easily be made from RG213 coax. The loop for the 40m version was 40cm in diameter. For the 20m version it was 30cm in diameter. The 20m version used RG58 coax for the loop.

5. As you can see there was a small coil consisting of ¾ of a turn of copper wire about ¼ inch diameter between the inner and outer of the loop.

There should be enough information here for experimenters to build a working model of the 40m CFL and perhaps even the 20m antenna.

The whole Poynting Vector Synthesis debate goes on, with the focus now switched to the EH antenna (also included in the book), which is a distant cousin of the original CFL design. I don't wish to get into a debate as to how the antennas work. But I feel there is room for some experimentation for people who wish to find a small HF antenna, especially if they would otherwise be off the air.

HF WIRE BEAMS

There is no reason why you cannot fit wire beams for HF in your loft. The obvious problem is that they will be fixed in terms of where they are pointing. The other problem is that it may be difficult to fit them in at all.

Probably the easiest antenna to fit would be a beam based on triangular delta elements. The natural triangular shape of the roof area lends itself quite well to this shape and it would be quite easy to fit a two or three-element beam in the roof space.

I would suggest, however, that you think carefully about this. You wouldn't really be able to have any other antennas in the loft space as you would get interaction. Also the antenna would tend to be monoband, which you may find limiting. But if you did decide to go ahead, what could expect to be able to fit?

This is quite an easy one as a delta loop is roughly one wavelength long at its frequency of operation. So a delta loop element for 20m (14MHz) would have to be about 21m long in total. If made from insulating wire this would be reduced to around 20m – but that still means that each side would have to be 6.72m long, which is too big for most lofts.

But what about the 10m band? A full-wave would be about 10.1m long if made from insulated wire. That might just fit. Turning to the *MMANA* antenna modelling program it didn't take long to design a two element delta loop for 10m (**Fig 4.11**). This would need a driven element with three sides each of 3.68m. If using insulated wire start with 3.50m and adjust for length once installed. The reflector would need sides of 3.95m (insulated wire: 3.75m) and be fixed 1.5m behind the driven element.

In the modelling I found that feeding the antenna at the apex or the centre of any one of the legs both gave good results. If fed at the centre of the bottom leg or the apex you

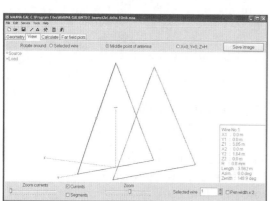

Fig 4.11: You could just about fit a 10m delta loop beam into an average loft.

get horizontal polarisation. If fed at the centre of one of the sloping legs you get a mixture of vertical and horizontal, which could help prevent fading.

The end result (**Fig 4.12**) is a two-element beam that gives you 9.3dBi gain in one direction, which is more than one S-point gain over a dipole. The maximum radiation is also at an elevation of around 9 - 13° assuming a typical two-storey house loft height of 10m, which is ideal for DX. The front to back ratio is about 17dB, which should help reduce QRM from stations on the back of the beam.

In terms of SWR it was modelled at less than 1.25:1 at around 28.6MHz and less than 3:1 across most of the band. You could always adjust the lengths to bring the lowest point to the area of the band you choose – make the antenna longer to bring it to the CW end of the band, shorter to move it to the FM portion of 10m.

Looking at the numbers the only proviso is to keep the total length of the reflector about 7.3% bigger than the driven element.

Obviously, you can scale the antenna for 50MHz if you want a beam for 6m.

The only obvious question is which

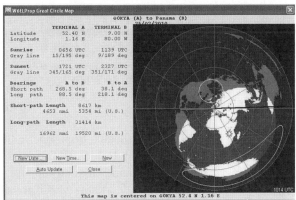

Fig 4.12: This is the radiation pattern on 10m – nice gain in one direction.

Fig 4.13: You need to play with a great circle map, like this one from the W6ELProp program, to work out if your beam would point in a decent direction.

way does your house point and is there anything of interest in that direction? My loft runs east-west, so using the great circle map from *W6ELProp* (**Fig 4.13**) I can see that I could get good coverage to the Caribbean, central America and the eastern seaboard of the USA to the west, and India, the Philippines and north-west Australia to the east.

There are lots of different designs for compact delta loop antennas, some of which are multiband. It is a case of finding one that suits your particular circumstances. The usual rules about maximum power and EMC effects apply.

So what could you do with your loft?

VHF / UHF ANTENNAS

Much of what I have said about HF antennas in the loft can apply equally to VHF and UHF antennas. You have to take into account the extra feeder losses

This 2m delta quad from Sandpiper is very lightweight and would easily fit in a loft.

associated with using VHF and UHF instead of HF, but good quality RG213 / RG8 normally takes care of that.

You must check to see if your maximum power levels are likely to cause problems for people living in the house. I recommend a maximum of 10 - 25W anyway. Losses due to the tiles and other building materials will also have an effect, but these are often not as bad as you think.

Back in the early 1980s when I was first licensed I had a class B, or VHF / UHF only, licence. I lived with my parents and large ungainly antennas were not the order of the day. Like most amateurs of that period the ubiquitous Yaesu FT-290R for 2m was the first rig of choice and I soon made a Slim Jim antenna and bought a 4-element quad from Jaybeam. The quad sat on a cardboard box in the loft and I generally sat next to it with the FT-290R's massive 2.5W output. So you wouldn't think that it was possible to work any decent DX with such a set up, would you? Not so.

With a reasonable tropospheric lift I was able to work most of the UK and into Scotland and Wales. With a good lift I managed to work the south of France, Norway, Denmark, Germany and further afield from Norfolk. This was all done on SSB as I didn't know Morse at that point.

A wise old owl at the local club said that it was a waste of time trying to operate on 2m with a loft-mounted antenna – "You won't work anything," he said. I had the advantage of being very green and not knowing any better (luckily!).

Looking back through the logs I see that signal reports around Europe were generally of the order of 54 or 55, with the occasional 57 – 59.

A loft-mounted halo antenna would give you omnidirectional horizontal polarization, suitable for SSB on 2m, 4m or 6m.

By flicking the antenna through 90° (to give vertical polarisation) I was also able to work quite a few of the UK's repeaters, including as far south as London and Kent and across the UK into the Midlands and the North. This was the heyday of 2m operation in the UK and there were plenty of operators to talk to.

In a later house I had the same quad on a small rotator. I bolted the rotator to the rafters, but put a big piece of rubber matting between the rotator and wood to stop noise as it had a tendency to hum quite a bit when moving. Again, this set up worked very well, although it helps if your house is on a hill - or at least not in a dip. My last house was down a hollow (hard to find in flat Norfolk) and I gave up 2m DXing – it was a waste of time.

If you have been put off trying 2m DX operation because you can't fit a large outside antenna, don't be. You can still have fun, but it helps a lot if there is a lift.

A small quad antenna for 2m doesn't take up much space. It is effectively a square of about 20in per side. Lengthwise, it depends on how many elements, but a 4-element quad for 2m is about 42in (1.07m) long. In terms of gain, a 4-element quad has about the same gain as an 8-element Yagi, so they are worth thinking about.

If you don't want to make one (and there are lots of plans available on the net) you can buy something similar. Sandpiper makes a 3-element delta 'quad' for 2m, which has a boom length of just 75cm. It offers 11.1dBi (nearly 9dBd) and is light enough to fit on a small rotator in the loft.

If you don't want to use a rotator, how about a halo loop for 2m or 6m? These offer horizontal omnidirectional radiation and will easily fit into a loft space, or even on a balcony. Moonraker offers halos for 2m, 4m and 6m – the largest is only 800mm square (6m) and the 2m one is only 300mm square.

In terms of local FM contacts you should also be able to work a good 15 - 20 miles using a loft-mounted omnidirectional antenna like a Slim Jim or collinear. You can either make your own or buy a commercial one. A dual or even tri-band collinear would get you going on 6m, 2m and 70cm with just one feeder.

It is a similar story on 70cm (432MHz) where antennas are smaller, but roof losses tend to be larger. You could actually get away with a small 70cm Yagi outside if you told everyone that it was for TV. Most people wouldn't know the difference.

So don't let the lack of a garden or mast put you off VHF and UHF – you can work DX on these bands, you just need the right antenna.

MOXON BEAM FOR 2M (144MHZ)

I used to own a 2m 4-element quad by Jaybeam which was brilliant, but sold it as I thought I would never use it again – *duh!* With a 2m QRP contest looming I decided to see if I could make my own beam. I wasn't interested in outright gain, but wanted something which was a) small and light, b) cheap and c) offered a little gain and some front-to-back.

The answer turned out to be

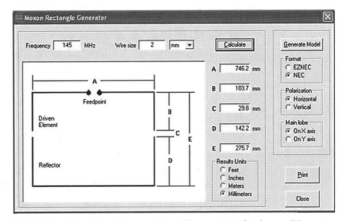

A PC-based calculator makes it easy to design a Moxon – but watch out when using PVC-coated wire!

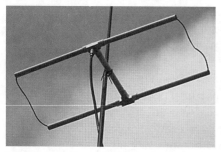

The finished result for two metres.

a Moxon rectangle beam. This is a 2-element beam offering about 3dBd gain and a massive 30dB front-to-back. If you head over to www.moxonantennaproject.com/wb5cxc/wb5cxc.htm you can find out all about it. There is even a PC-based calculator that you can download.

So I headed off to the local DIY store and came back with 2m of white PVC trunking, two connector unions, and some PVC glue. I added some 2m PVC coated copper wire that I had, an SO239 socket and some 3.5mm heatshrink tubing – that's it. About £10 all in.

I modelled the beam for 145MHz and came up with the required dimensions. I then cut the PVC pipe accordingly and soldered / glued it all together. I used the heat-shrink tubing to connect the ends of the elements. If I were making another one I would use a drinking straw first to strengthen them, although they seem OK with the tubing on its own.

Using my MFJ antenna analyser I found that it resonated at about 136MHz. I think this is because the velocity factor of PVC coated wire is about 94 - 95% and the computer simulation assumes bare wire. So out came the junior hacksaw and I cut everything down to 94% of the original size. This gave me a beam with an SWR of about 1.2:1 – 1.5:1 across the 2m band.

I fitted the beam to a 10m fishing pole (about 2m down from the top) using a couple of cable ties and hauled it up. I used 20m of Mini8 coax, but later that day found that it had a measured loss of about 2.4dB on 144MHz. Switching to RG213 reduced this to about 1dB.

So does it work? Yes, and quite well. I was able to hear the GB3VHF beacon at about S1 - S2 from 148km (92 miles) away.

Swinging the beam around made the signal vanish into the noise. I could also hear the PI7CIS beacon in the Netherlands (JO22DC) at a distance of 221km (137 miles).

Swinging the beam vertically brought in repeaters from up to 60 miles away too. This was under flat conditions and I was unable to raise anyone on 144.300MHz SSB, more's the pity.

So for a total cost of about £10 here is a great little lightweight beam that is well worth making.

REFERENCES

[1] Martin Meserve, K7MEM, Electronic Notebook (calculations): www.k7mem.com

[2] CliffDweller II antenna: http://eham.net/reviews/detail/1077

[3] *Backyard Antennas,* Peter Dodd, G3LDO (RSGB).

[4] AMA Antennen (magnetic loop antenna): www.funktechnik-beese.de

[5] Yahoo Groups EH antenna group: http://groups.yahoo.com/group/eh-antenna

External antennas

THERE IS NO DOUBT about it, external antennas work better than indoor ones. Sometimes the difference in received signal strength isn't that huge, but you don't have the added problem of electrical noise to contend with and you are also less likely to cause interference.

Electromagnetic 'fog' is getting to be a real problem nowadays. On my own system I get a noise level of S1 on 20m using my externally-mounted Hustler 5BTV vertical. But on the loft-mounted dipoles this climbs to S2 - 3. It is the same with the Windom mounted over the roof and also the W3EDP end-fed wire – the close proximity to the house means higher noise. So if you can locate your antennas away from the house I would definitely recommend it.

But are there any downsides to external antennas? Well, yes.

Your antennas outside are exposed to the full wrath of a typical winter, which means that you need to take more care with waterproofing all your connections. They are also subjected to high winds, so make sure that they are mounted securely. If outside they are also easier to spot, which is hardly a stealthy option is it? And they may not be totally compatible with your station manager's garden arrangements! A load of aluminium poles may be antenna heaven to you, but can be a complete eyesore to everyone else.

So if we are going to mount antennas outside we need to look at stealthy ways of doing it.

TREES AND FISHING LINE

Trees can be very useful, both in terms of supporting antennas and hiding them. I have used a lot of fishing line in the past to haul end-fed and dipole antennas up into tree branches. At one QTH I had a 100ft oak tree, which blotted out the sun, but was brilliant as an end-fed support.

I used a catapult to get a line into the tree and tried various methods over the years in an effort to find the best one. The catapult I chose wasn't terribly expensive and was bought from my local fishing equipment stall in the market. While I was there I also bought a reel of 10.4lb breaking strain line plus some lead weights. I know nothing

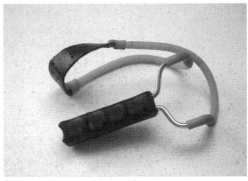

This simple catapult, bought from a local market, has launched many an antenna over houses and trees.

Fishing line and fishing weights are very useful, not only for launching antennas over roofs and trees, but for supporting them as well. It is almost invisible and very strong.

about fishing, but the anglers' shop always seems to have everything I need.

Now, before you use this technique make sure that if anything goes wrong you are not going to hit anyone or anything. Don't do it if there are greenhouses around or kids playing in the garden.

The technique for putting a line over a tree branch is quite easy, but you are bound to need quite a few attempts to get it right. Tie one of the lead weights on to the line and stand away from the tree a little bit. This stops you from being whacked on the head should (when) the weight comes back down. Now hold the weight in the catapult, but hold the catapult upside down so that nothing can get in the line and snag it. Keep the spool of line on the floor at your feet, but make sure nothing can get tangled with it. Pull the catapult back and aim slightly high of where you want the line to go – don't pull it all the way back as you need to judge how much force you need by letting go and seeing how far you get with a test shot. Then the next time give it a little more and build up.

If you get this right the lead weight and line should sail over the branch you picked. If it didn't then either the lead weight whacked you on the hand or the line became caught up and it stopped short of its target. If so, reel it in and try again. Patience is a virtue with this exercise and you will eventually get it right. If the line snags in the tree a tug will usually free it. If it doesn't then a *very* sharp tug will normally break the line and you can start again. Doing this can break the little loop on the end of the lead weight so make sure you have plenty of spares.

If a lead weight breaks free do try to find it – you don't want to leave lead weights lying around the garden. If you are worried about this, paint them bright yellow before you start. If you don't want to use lead weights you can substitute a yellow tennis ball. These are easy to spot in trees and are less likely to do any damage, although they are more prone to getting snagged in branches. I find that I can't catapult a tennis ball as far as a lead weight, but it is fine up to about 30 - 50ft. Just use a bradawl to force the fishing line through the ball and out again. Tie a knot and there you have it.

Once you have a line over a branch you can either use it to pull a thicker cord up into the tree or stay with the fishing line (which will be virtually invisible). You can also use this technique to support vertical wire antennas in trees.

LOSSES DUE TO TREES

You may be wondering if having your antenna close to a tree causes losses. The easy answer is 'yes', although they can be quite difficult to quantify. Trees are obviously made of sap and wood and so should absorb RF energy. There are even tales of people using trees as antennas, albeit very poor ones.

If you have no choice but to hide your antennas in trees do so and don't worry about the losses. Better to be stealthy and lose an S-point than not operate at all. In tests I have placed a half-wave vertical right next to a tree and found that it behaved pretty much the way it did when 10 metres away.

KF4IX and K0QK described some tests with trees in the November 1991 issue of *QST* magazine. They put up two 160m vertical top-loaded cage antennas in a grove of oak trees. Modelling showed that the resistive component of the verticals should have been about 25Ω. One of the antennas showed 37Ω, but the other showed 75Ω, indicating big loss resistance in the second antenna. They experimented and found that having the high voltage point of the antenna closest to the tree made the biggest difference. On a vertical this would be the tip. On a dipole it would be the ends. They concluded: "The implications are that trees can introduce significant losses to a vertical antenna, particularly when the top (or voltage maximum) is close to large trunks or limbs. This problem may even extend to horizontal antennas where the end is close to a large tree or to other antennas that have voltage maximums very close to large trees. Small limbs (less than two or three inches in diameter) did not seem to add loss."

Trees do cause losses, but smaller branches and trunks are not too bad. Keep high voltage ends of verticals and dipoles away from branches if possible.

If you have a small tree (like I do) the effects are probably minimal. With an oak tree with a three-foot diameter trunk it might be a different story.

If possible, erect your antenna away from the tree first of all and test it, keeping a careful note of the precise SWR readings as well. Then move it into its working position and test again. A substantial change to the SWR and / or poor performance will tell you that the tree is affecting your antenna's efficiency. You then have to decide if you can live with it.

FISHING / FIBREGLASS POLES

These are my next favourite antenna support, being cheap, light, collapsible and easy to hide in trees. You can buy them in different sizes from 4m up to 10m or longer. Avoid the short ones as they aren't much use to us. Avoid the carbon fibre rods, though – they are way too expensive and probably conductive as well. We want the cheap fibreglass ones.

You can buy these at your local angling supplies shop, although they may have to order the larger ones specially. Our local

Fibreglass fishing poles are light, cheap, easy to put up, but work best with vertical antennas – they don't like lateral forces.

club got together and put in a bulk order, which reduced the unit price to under £10. Failing that, keep an eye on eBay where you will find them advertised under 'fibreglass pole'.

The size you order will depend on what you want to do. An 8m or 9m pole will be a great support for a Rybakov antenna (described in Chapter 7), or a quarter-wave HF vertical antenna, whereas a 10m pole will make a good support for an end-fed half-wave (EFHW) vertical for 20m.

I had a very effective 20m (14MHz) EFHW, which was mounted on a 10m pole that had been pushed up through the branches of a tree and was secured to the trunk with bungees. It was virtually invisible, even in the winter, yet gave great DX performance. A similar 10m (28MHz) EFHW could hear stations up to 50 miles away on ground wave and would work brilliantly at sunspot maximum.

You will need some way of fixing the pole to whatever you have in the garden, e.g. you can make a ground stake out of sharpened angle iron and some Jubilee clips. Failing that, cheap bungee cords can be used to fix telescopic poles to garden seats or trees.

Before you start to use your pole there are a few things you need to know. While they are fantastic for supporting verticals they do not have much lateral strength so are not very good at supporting horizontal antennas. Also, they use friction to hold each segment in place, but these can easily be dislodged in the wind. If you want a more permanent fixture you must either use rubber O rings just above each joint or insulation tape around the joint itself to stop it working free. What usually happens is that one of the bottom pieces works loose and telescopes into the base. This then sets up a chain reaction and the whole lot comes down, usually knocking out the plastic base cap in the process.

If you break a section you can either leave it out completely (if it is a top one), repair it with tape or even glue it into place permanently. I normally look at replacing one of my poles every two to three years and at less than £20 each it is very inexpensive.

OTHER SUPPORTS
Aluminium poles

You can buy ready-made mast sets made out of telescoping aluminium. I had one of these for about 20 years and it was used to support everything from 2m collinears to a Cushcraft R5 HF vertical. The wind eventually got the better of it and the top section buckled, but the rest was put to good use and I still have parts of it in the shed.

Aluminium poles are not terrible stealthy, but why not mount one behind the shed and just push it up when you need it? An inverted-V over the house then becomes a flat top at 10m height just when you need it.

Or you can get hold of an old scaffold pole. This can lie flat in the back garden until you need it, when it can be put into service as an antenna support.

Tripods

The first time I got this idea was when I had the DMV Pro antenna to review. It used a really sturdy tripod base which extended to about 12ft. It was only later that I found out that a similar tripod base is used by DJs to hold loudspeakers. These make great antenna bases. You could couple one with a fibreglass pole and have a fantastic elevated vertical antenna. You would need to put three or four guys on it, which need be nothing more complicated than four pieces of cord with a large skewer on one end to drive into the ground.

The result is a brilliant, but lightweight, antenna system that could be set up in minutes just when you want it.

Wooden poles / stakes

A friend has a couple of pressure-treated wooden stakes in his garden. When he wants to operate in a contest they slot into two loops made out of gutter fixing rings that are attached to his garden fence. The ends of his dipole are then lifted about 10 - 12ft in the air, making it more efficient.

Chimney / TV antenna

Chimneys are very useful as they are normally the highest point of a house. If your planning regulations allow it, why not use your chimney as the centre support for your HF antenna? You could easily fit a TV lashing kit to your chimney and put a 6ft wooden pole in place to lift the antenna clear of the roof.

Or if you want a really stealthy approach, use a fake TV antenna and attach a long wire to it. The long wire then snakes down the roof and the front of the house into your shack.

If you don't want a long wire, an end-fed half wave up to the chimney top would work well on 20m or 40m.

If your interests are VHF / UHF you can disguise a collinear antenna as the support for a dummy TV antenna made out of plastic parts.

Flagpoles

Flagpoles are more common in the US where they appear to be more patriotic than us! Running a Union flag up a mast in this country would probably have caught the attention of the local busybody in days past, but flags do now seem to be gaining in popularity.

But we don't really want a flagpole – we want an antenna! So what can you do? The obvious answer is to use an aluminium flagpole, mount it in an insulated sleeve and feed it against earth as a quarter-wave vertical. One that caught my eye on eBay was a five-section aluminium pole that was 20ft tall. Reaching for the calculator tells me that it is 6.096m tall – a quarter wave at 24m. Hmm! Not much good. But if you shortened it to 5.3m you would have a neat quarter-wave vertical for 20m. Or if

How about a stealthy vertical made out of a flagpole? This one is from Flags and Flagpoles (www.flagsandflagpoles.co.uk).

you could extend it to 7.6m with another aluminium pole and fit a 4:1 unun at the base, you could have a multiband Rybakov antenna, which would work from 40m - 10m.

To be honest, a 10m fibreglass flagpole, complete with a hinged base plate, still costs less than a commercial vertical antenna.

Buy a fibreglass pole and you could sneakily install a three-band trapped vertical antenna for 14, 21 and 28MHz. Build the traps yourself, lay down a decent earth radial system and no-one would be the wiser. Or build a 20m EFHW which needs no radials at all. Running a 65ft wire up the pole and then out to your shed gives you a quarter-wave inverted-L for 80m, which will get you on the band.

Guttering

As we have shown elsewhere, you can hide wires behind plastic guttering, giving you an inverted-L or dipole depending on your house layout. If you have a plastic down pipe coming down the centre of your house you could even fit a doublet, complete with 300 / 450Ω open-wire feeder hidden in or behind the guttering.

And if you don't have a down pipe in the right place why not fit one? No-one would even blink!

Hide a wire behind your guttering for a stealthy vertical or inverted-L – this is the ferrite choke for my 80m Off Centre Fed Dipole.

Barge boards

Either white uPVC or wooden barge boards are just crying out to have an inverted-V fitted behind them. Extend the legs of the inverted-V back along the gutters and you have quite a potent doublet or dipole antenna too.

Garage roof space

If you don't like the idea of fitting HF antennas in your house roof, what about the garage? These are usually away from the main house and therefore less likely to cause interference or be affected by electrical noise. In my last house I had a pair of magnetic loops mounted in the garage roof space, one for 80 - 30m and the other for 30 - 10m. That's the whole of the HF spectrum in just two antennas.

The 80m loop was usually about 10dB down on an 85ft end-fed, but that only meant that stations were 59 and not 59+10dB. I often had QSOs with stations in Canada and the USA on 28MHz using the smaller one as the low-noise characteristics of a magnetic loop often means you can hear a lot more.

You just have to use your imagination in the garden – you don't need a shiny steel tower to play radio.

Over-the-roof stealth antennas

THE TRADITIONAL WAY of mounting a central support for wire antennas over your roof is to fit a short pole, either to your chimney or to a bracket on the end of your house. This is fine and works well – you can either do it yourself or get a TV aerial contractor to do it for you. If you also fit a small pulley and cord you can haul different antennas up any time you wish, although it does start to look a little like a flagpole at that point.

But what if you want to remain stealthy - can you lie the antenna wires directly on to the roof? The answer is yes you can, and although it isn't ideal it does work. You will lose a decibel or two but, as you will have gathered, this book is about getting you on the air at all costs and that is a small price to pay.

I have a W3EDP 85ft end-fed wire over one side of my roof and an off-centre fed dipole (OCFD) on the other. Sometimes one works better than the other. As I am writing this I am talking to George, W4UWC, in Tennessee on 15m (21MHz) – he is actually louder on the W3EDP, which is not bad for a £5 antenna.

Having whetted your appetite what can you do?

The first message has to be, if you have *any* electrical cables anywhere near your house forget this right away – it is just too dangerous. Either go for an internal antenna or fit a vertical in the garden.

If you are going to use this method make sure you use insulated wire. This is easier to pull over and offers a degree of insulation from the wet roof. How stealthy you want your antennas will determine the wire thickness. Most black or blue covered wire is pretty invisible at a distance, but you will need ultra thin wire if you really don't want people to see it. But then it has a habit of breaking, so it is a compromise really.

Assuming that you don't have any cabling we can go ahead. The easiest way to get a dipole or similar antenna over your roof is with a catapult. I use the same one that I described in the section on getting wires over tree branches. The yellow ball is much safer than using lead weights and will preserve your tiles and windows should your aim be off. It is also easy to find if and when it comes down in the back garden.

This 80m OCFD antenna works well, even though the antenna wire lies on the roof tiles.

Hold the catapult upside down to stop the fishing line getting tangled up. Note the tennis ball, which is a lot safer than using lead weights.

The good point about using a tennis ball is that if it goes over the house but hits the roof it will usually bounce back off and end up in the back garden. You may need to have a couple of attempts at getting this right, but it usually works quite well.

I was able to get a line over my latest house on the first attempt. In fact, I was a little overzealous and managed to fire the tennis ball into the neighbour's garden, from where it was quickly recovered!

Once you have the line over the house go to the back and move it away from the house – this is so that a) you can see what you are doing and b) the line doesn't snag in the guttering.

Now attach your antenna wire. I find it best not to have insulators on at this point as they can snag in the tiles. Go back to the front of the house and pull the wire over the house.

If it snags, stop and find out why. This is a lot easier with two people but you can do it on your own if you take your time. What you don't want to do is get the line caught under a tile. This isn't fatal and can usually be recovered by pulling backwards on the antenna wire. But keep on tugging on the line over the roof and you could displace a tile.

Once you have the antenna wire over the roof you can attach the coax or whatever you have and haul the whole thing into position. If you have a typical pitched roof you can usually work out which side you want your feed point to fall. It is always better *not* to pull your feedpoint over the roof, as that is more to snag.

The important thing to remember is that if anything pulls tight just stop and find out what is wrong.

Fit insulators to the end of your antenna and tie it off to the nearest item. It is best if these are high, so as to get the antennas as far in the air as you can. If you only have a back garden and no front garden an end-fed like the W3EDP design will work well. If you have both a front and back garden a design like the G5RV, a doublet or the off centre fed dipole will work better.

If you tie the antenna off to a tree do bear in mind that these move in the wind – either leave some slack or make a movable connection, such as a weight sliding up and down a PVC tube. I use 10.4lb fishing line to tie off my antennas – it is pretty invisible under most conditions, although sunlight at some angles can make it shine.

Now let's look at the pros and cons of each antenna design.

THE G5RV REVISITED

I use a G5RV every year during the Jamboree on the Air event and it works pretty well. The only problem I have found is it is hard to tune on 10m – I burned out a switch on my ATU as I forgot to lower the power while trying to get a match.

It was only when I moved to my present house that I started to think about whether a G5RV antenna could work here. After all, the length of 102ft would

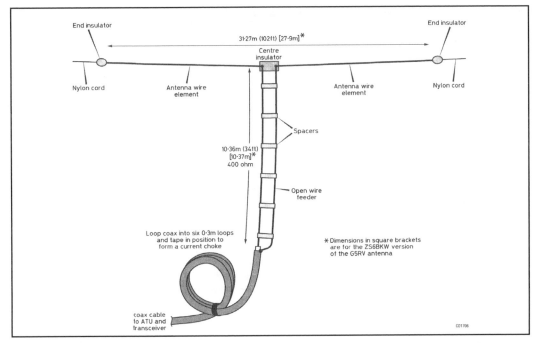

Fig 6.1: The classic G5RV may not be quite as good a multiband antenna as you think.

fit nicely between the garage at the front and the shed at the rear. Using insulated wire it could happily sit on the roof as well. It was at this point that I started modelling it with *MMANA* to see how it would play. The G5RV (**Fig 6.1**) would appear to be a good, cheap 'over the roof' stealthy antenna, but is it?

The G5RV has had plenty of coverage in other books so in this piece I want to concentrate on some of its characteristics that don't get mentioned very often. For those not familiar with the antenna it was designed by Louis Varney, G5RV, and consists of a 102ft (31.1m) dipole top with a 28.5ft (8.5m) centre section made out of open wire feeder or 300Ω windowed ribbon cable. You then connect your 50Ω coax to the bottom. I say 28.5ft, but in reality this depends on the velocity factor (VF) of the ribbon cable. Some designs say 34.5ft (10.36m) for the matching section, while others say that ribbon cable with 'windows' has a velocity factor that will almost be that of open-wire feeder, so its mechanical length should be 30.6ft (9.3m). The reality is that you should really select this on test or calculate the VF of the cable you intend to use and act accordingly.

You should really fit a choke or 'ugly' balun at the base of the matching section too – about 8 - 10 turns of coax in a 6in coil should do it.

The antenna was originally designed to be one and a half wavelengths long at 14MHz. I don't think Louis Varney ever really envisaged it as a multiband antenna as such, and he certainly didn't have access to the WARC bands that we now have. So let's look at just how good a G5RV is across the bands.

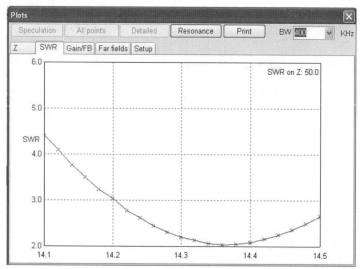

Fig 6.2: This computer simulation of a G5RV using MMANA-GAL shows that the antenna does have a SWR dip on 20m, but only to about 2:1.

The G5RV – a multiband antenna?

I started with *MMANA* and modelled the G5RV in a flat-top configuration. This is unlikely to be the way most people configure theirs as a stealthy antenna but I wanted to prove a point.

If you model the antenna with a matching section of 10.36m you find that, yes, the G5RV does have an SWR dip at around 14.350MHz so it looks like the antenna was designed for this band. Having said that, the lowest SWR is only about 2:1 (**Fig 6.2**) so you will still need an ATU.

So what about the other bands? On 80m (3.5MHz) it dips at about 2.4:1 at 3.8MHz. At the lower end of the band it is a more horrendous 7.5:1. On 40m there is no dip and the SWR is stubbornly above 7:1. It is also a terrible match on 30m (10MHz) with an SWR greater than 30:1. On 17m (18MHz), once again it offers a poor SWR – in excess of 30:1. On 15m (21MHz) it redeems itself a little bit with an SWR of under 2:1 at the low end of the band, rising to about 5:1 at the top end. On 12m (24MHz) it dips at around 2:1 near 24.950MHz and on 10m the antenna disappoints again with a very high SWR.

So the conclusions reached from this are:

1. The length of the matching section should be calculated as 10.6m x the velocity factor of the cable – don't just assume that it is any particular length.
2. If you use insulated wire I am sure that the 102ft top should be shortened accordingly – perhaps down to 97 - 98ft.
3. The antenna only offers a reasonable match on parts of the 12m, 15m, 20m and 80m bands. On others it is pretty horrendous. This means that you are going to have to use an ATU and you will get mismatched line losses on your coax due to the high SWR. If you feed it with a long enough length of coax the losses on the line will mask the high SWR (it will look better than the raw calculations).

I can't really recommend the G5RV as a multiband antenna – I think there are better alternatives. Having said that, it will work reasonably well on 80m (3.5MHz) and get you on the band with an antenna length of only 102ft instead of the full 132ft normally found with a half-wave dipole on that band. My experience at home was that it was easily beaten on HF by a dedicated dipole and the figures show why.

But what happens when you erect a G5RV as an inverted V, which is probably the way you would use one in a stealthy 'over the roof' configuration?

The G5RV as an inverted-V

I tried the G5RV as an inverted-V at this QTH and while it fitted the space quite well I was very disappointed. It performed about as well as any other antenna on 80m, but on HF DX it was pretty awful.

I have recordings of a contact with VQ9JC on the Chagos Islands. He is about S3 - S4 on my indoor dipoles and just vanishes when you switch to the G5RV. Some might say that this was not a fair test and that the station might have been in a null. But the experience was repeated over and over with other stations – so what was going wrong?

The SWR readings I obtained in real life with the inverted-V at the end of 30ft of RG213 coax are shown in **Table 6.1**.

Given that the antenna does not offer a 50Ω impedance at the matching point, adding a length of 50Ω coax merely changes the overall impedance you see at the rig.

I don't think G5RV ever meant for his antenna to be used as an inverted-V. What you find if you model it is that on 20m those nice lobes that you get with a flat-mounted G5RV pretty much vanish when it is configured as an inverted-V – see **Fig 6.3**. Also, the low angle characteristics also vanish, so the DX capabilities of the antenna change dramatically.

It is a similar story on the other HF bands as well – the antenna's radiation pattern squashes and it becomes more omnidirectional, at the expense of the gain that the flat-top G5RV displays on bands such as 10m.

On 80m (3.5MHz) there is little difference as the antenna is very low to the ground. If anything, it is slightly better as an inverted-V as it loses some of the directional characteristics it has as a flat-top.

Freq	SWR
3.5MHz:	1.7:1
3.6MHz:	2.3:1
3.8MHz:	5:1
7.0MHz:	2.1:1
7.1MHz:	2.0:1
10.1MHz:	10.2:1
14.150MHz:	5.6:1
18.150MHz:	3.3:1
21MHz:	5.4:1
21.450MHz:	5.4:1
24.9MHz:	6.7:1
28MHz:	5.6:1
29MHz:	3.6:1

Table 6.1: 'Real life' SWR readings obtained with inverted-V G5RV fed by 30ft of RG213 coax.

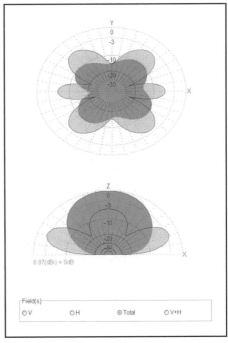

Fig 6.3: Erecting a G5RV as an inverted-V (dark grey plot) tends to kill its DX performance as this simulation shows.

To summarise:

1. Putting up a G5RV as an inverted-V flattens the radiation pattern and reduces the lobes that you get with the flat-top version. You may therefore find that it loses some of its DX capabilities. On 10m it is easily beaten by a half-wave dipole at the same height in terms of its low-angle radiation and on 20m a dipole will probably be at least 2 S-points better broadside to its run.
2. The upside is that the G5RV becomes more omnidirectional when set up as an inverted-V.
3. The actual SWR you see at the end of the feeder will depend on your individual configuration.

In conclusion then, I think the G5RV has won a lot of followers who use it for a general natter antenna on 80m and as a general do-it-all antenna everywhere else. It doesn't really like being put up as an inverted-V and isn't a good match on any band.

THE ZS6BKW VARIANT

Brian Austin, ZS6BKW / G0GSF, spent some time trying to optimise the G5RV. He found that by reducing the overall length to 93ft and extending the matching section to 39.8ft (12.13m) of 400Ω ladder-line (VF = 0.9) it would provide a reasonable match on five bands. The antenna would be usable on all of 40m, 17m and 12m without any tuner, and much of 20m and 10m. It still needs a tuner to cover the popular 80m and 15m bands, though.

Modelling this with *MMANA* confirms Brian's results. As an inverted-V it offers a much better match on 20m (14MHz), probably less than 2.5:1 across the whole band by the time coax losses are factored in. It is a similar story on 40m (7MHz), 17m (18MHz), 12m (24MHz) and 10m (28MHz).

Unfortunately, 80m actually gets worse, and 15m (21MHz) and 30m (10MHz), would also need an ATU. But you end up with an antenna that will work reasonably well on five bands, and will be a compromise on three others. The overall performance on 80m is only down about 1 - 1.5dB on 80m compared with the full-size G5RV in an inverted-V configuration.

So if you are limited with space, the ZS6BKW could be made from scratch, or from a cannibalised G5RV, and give you a reasonable all-round antenna for very little money.

If you have a house in the middle of a plot the legs can extend down from the roof on either side and would really be quite inconspicuous.

When antenna guru L B Cebik, W4RNL (SK), analysed the G5RV and variants, he concluded: "Of all the G5RV antenna system cousins, the ZS6BKW/ G0GSF antenna system has come closest to achieving the goal that is part of the G5RV mythology: a multi-band HF antenna consisting of a single wire and simple matching system to cover as many of the amateur HF bands as possible. From

80 to 10m, Austin's system provides an acceptable match on five out of the eight bands under most conditions without an antenna tuner. This is the best result that has been achieved of any of the systems that has come to my attention."

But can we do better still? Oh yes!

W5GI 'MYSTERY ANTENNA'

Here's another dipole antenna that can be thrown over a roof and seems to perform quite well on 80m and 40m. The W5GI 'Mystery Antenna' gets a lot of attention, possibly because of its daft name!

It looks like a G5RV, but John Basilotto, W5GI (now SK), used coax stubs to give what he called "a coaxial collinear array on 20m". It consists of a half wavelength (at 20m) of 300-ohm ribbon that feeds a dipole centre. Either side of the dipole centre are two pieces of wire 16ft 6in long. These are then each connected to the inner of a 16ft 6in piece of RG58 coax. The outer is left unconnected. The far end of this coax is then shorted and connected to a further 16ft 6in of wire, giving an antenna with a total span of about 100ft.

The only constructional difficulties are making sure that the joints are strong enough to support the weight (there are many reports of breakages – mine broke too!) and it is best to use shrink wrap tubing on the joints to waterproof them.

Cutting the ribbon feeder to an exact half wavelength (taking into account the velocity factor of the cable) is a little problematic. One solution relies on the fact that a true half wavelength of feeder will always replicate the impedance at its far end. So, put a 50-ohm resistor on the far end of your 300-ohm ribbon feeder. String it up in clear space and trim the length until you see a 1:1 SWR at 14.175MHz when using an antenna analyser.

I used 300-ohm ribbon from Moonraker in the UK and the half wavelength came out at 8.3m (27ft 3in). It is likely to end up between 8.2 and 10.7m (27 - 35ft) long depending upon your feeder.

Now, the 'mystery' part of the name refers to the fact that it is supposed to be almost impossible to model as it uses coax stubs. What we can say is that W5GI said that the stubs caused the antenna to feed the three radiating elements in phase. But all the evidence points to the fact that the antenna does *not* have three in-phase elements on 20m. The modelling and real-life results show a six-lobed pattern – just what you would expect with three half-waves fed *out* of phase.

But the question is, does the antenna 'work'? Is it worth making?

I built a W5GI dipole (I refuse to call it a 'mystery antenna') to see how it would compare with other antennas. Mine is fixed over the roof where I used to have a full-size 80m OCF dipole and I have been able to

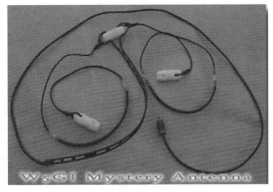

The W5GI looks a little like a G5RV and is roughly the same length.

SWR results (brackets after trimming – see text)

1.8MHz – SWR >31:1 (>31:1)
3.5MHz – SWR 2.8:1 (2.6:1)
3.8MHz – SWR 8.1:1 (4.2:1)
7MHz – SWR 2.8:1 (3.3:1)
7.1MHz – SWR 3.0:1 (3.0:1)
7.2MHz – SWR 3.6:1 (3.0:1)
10.1MHz – SWR 5.7:1 (5.0:1)
14MHz – SWR 4.1:1 (3.0:1)
14.2MHz – SWR 5.3:1 (3.2:1)
18.1MHz – SWR 5.2:1 (8:1)
18.168MHz – SWR 4.7:1 (8.0:1)
21.2MHz – SWR 6.7:1 (5.7:1)
24.9MHz – SWR 6:1 (3.0:1)
28MHz – SWR 5.7:1 (5.4:1)
28.5MHz – SWR 6.4:1 (5.7:1)
29.7MHz – SWR 3.9:1 (6.2:1)
51MHz – SWR 4.0:1 (4.5:1)

Lowest SWR point on 80m was 3.434 (2.9:1) after trimming it was 3.6MHz (2.4:1).

A table of the SWR results.

compare it with an 85ft W3EDP end-fed, a 65ft inverted-L, a multitude of dipoles and a Western HF10 among others.

In the original write-up W5GI quoted SWR figures for the antenna that were mostly below 3:1. Unfortunately he didn't say how much or what type of feeder he used: put a long enough piece of lossy feeder on and you will end up with a low SWR on *any* antenna. My own figures, taken when the bottom of the ladder line is fed with 15ft of RG58, showed that it isn't such a good match on all bands.

What I did decide to do was to see if I could optimise it for 80m as this is the band I really wanted to use it on for the RSGB 80m Club Championship. As the lowest SWR point was below 80m I decided to shorten the 300-ohm feeder by about 12 inches and then fold back the ends of the antenna. I ended up with the lowest SWR point at 3.6MHz (2.4:1). This also improved the match on 20m and 40m, but made it worse on other bands.

But how did it perform? The antenna is quite useful on 80m if you can't fit in a full size half-wave dipole. It works well around the UK and lots of DX has also been heard in the middle of the night. In essence it shouldn't be much better than a G5RV though.

The antenna is quite useful on 40m as well. If you are looking for a 100ft antenna just for 40 / 80m it is worth considering, along with the G5RV / ZS6BKW or W3DZZ. It is not a brilliant match on 30m, but it will get you going. I did work T32C (East Kiribati) on 10MHz with it, so it can't be too bad!

Tests showed the antenna's multi-lobe pattern on 20m. This can work in your favour or work against you. There have been many times that I've switched to the W5GI and weak signals have just vanished. At other times signals have occasionally become stronger or are equal to a dipole. This is frustrating as whether you class this as a 'good' antenna on 20m depends on whether the station you wish to work is in a lobe or not.

I have seen a similar performance on a G5RV and, despite claims from reviews on eham.net, I'm not convinced that the W5GI is the stellar performer on 20m that some people think it is. On the bands above 20m I didn't find it too impressive.

Overall, I liked the antenna's performance on 80m. It seemed to outperform the 132ft OCF dipole that it replaced.

I have been using the W5GI in the RSGB 80m Club Championship and people often remark how loud I am, despite the antenna lying on the apex of the roof. It also seems useful for 40m, giving a relatively easy match and good performance. I have broken pile-ups into Europe with it on 40m. Once you climb past 40m it become a little more unpredictable. This can be a characteristic of 'long' antennas, where their multi-lobe pattern either works for or against you.

In conclusion, I'm not sure that the antenna works any better than a G5RV. In fact, if you are looking for an antenna of roughly the same length, with similar performance but with a better match, check out the ZS6BKW variant.

Is it a bad antenna? No, I've tested worse – and some that cost a lot more money. Is it a multiband antenna? Well, yes, but it doesn't offer a 1:1 match on all bands. In fact, mine doesn't offer a 1:1 match on *any* band. But then neither did the original designer's!

For the sake of an afternoon's work, some coax and a piece of ribbon feeder you can build one and try it for yourself. Or you might like to consider a doublet.

THE DOUBLET

The problem with coax is that it offers relatively low loss if the SWR is low, but is pretty poor if you have a high SWR. There is a chapter later in the book that looks at this in more detail. You don't get the same problem with open wire feeder – its losses are much less than coax if you have a high SWR on the feedline.

So the solution to many problems is to put up a doublet – string up as much wire as you can possibly fit, split it in the middle and feed it with open wire or windowed ribbon cable all the way back to the ATU.

You will need a balanced ATU or a balun at the ATU end of the feeder, but the end result will be a multiband antenna with minimal losses.

If you find that you can't get a good match on one particular band just try extending the length of open wire feeder by a few feet and that should solve the problem.

The only issue with open wire feeder is that you have to keep it away from metal objects, but with most houses now using plastic guttering and down pipes that really isn't a big problem.

The doublet has been the mainstay of many DXers' antennas over the years and is showing signs of resurgence. It is very simple, but the fact that you can't just plug it in to the back of your rig seems to put many people off.

THE OFF-CENTRE FED DIPOLE (OCFD)

Technically, what I am about to describe is an Off-Centre Fed Dipole (OCFD), but you sometimes hear these described as Windoms, although the original Windom had a single line feed to the main antenna wire. The Windom was first designed in 1923 by William Litell Everitt, but Loren G Windom, W8GZ, wrote about it in the September 1929 issue of *QST* magazine and the name stuck.

In the form I am about to describe, the OCFD is a dipole with one leg 90ft long and the other 45ft long (total length 135ft), as shown in **Fig 6.4**. It is fed at the junction

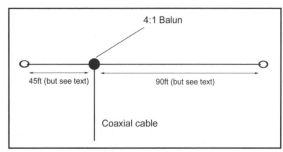

4:1 Balun

45ft (but see text)　　90ft (but see text)

Coaxial cable

Fig 6.4: The OCFD with a balun is a relatively efficient way to get multiband performance out of a single horizontal wire.

A commercial 4:1 balun suitable for use with an off centre fed dipole.

of the two wires with a 4:1 or 6:1 balun and the coax feed falls away vertically from the antenna.

In other designs, notably the 'Carolina Windom', you will see the overall length described as 133ft (50ft + 83ft). So why the difference in length? The 'raw' length of a half-wave for 80m in free space made out of thin wire is 129.5ft at 3.8MHz and 140.6ft at 3.5MHz. But don't forget that end effects will reduce this to 124ft / 135ft. Using PVC-coated wire will reduce this yet further. So the total length of your antenna will ultimately depend on what part of the band you wish to operate and whether you are using PVC coated wire. I would therefore suggest that you cut your antenna long (say 136ft in total) and twist the wire back on itself to tune it.

Now, what about the difference in feed points? It is hard to say for certain exactly where the best point to feed an OCFD dipole actually is, as the precise impedance at that point will depend on local factors. If using a 4:1 balun ideally you want it to be 200Ω. In the Carolina Windom design they found that splitting the antenna in a ratio of 37.8% / 62.1% instead of 33.3% / 66.6% gave a better match.

But if you cut your antenna too long (136ft) as I suggest you can adjust it to find the sweet spot for you. As you make one leg slight longer and the other slightly shorter you will soon find which one gives you the lowest SWR. Once you find that point you can then move it up or down the band by lengthening / shortening the antenna, as long as you keep the ratio roughly 2:1.

In the Carolina Windom a choke balun is also fitted 22ft down the 50Ω coax feed. Because of the offset nature of the feed point you do get currents on the feedline and the choke is supposed to both a) block these at that point and b) actually use the vertical section of the feedline as a radiator, so giving better DX performance. I have a choke balun in my feedline at that point, but it is an area for experimentation.

It is a lot easier to build a 4:1 balun than a 6:1, so that is what we'll concentrate on. A 4:1 balun also seems to work better at the 35 - 40ft height mark, which is about the height I'll presume you are going to install your antenna if you have a two-storey house. In fact, US antenna manufacturer Buxcomm recommends a 6:1 balun only if you intend to install your antenna at 55 - 70ft.

I have a soft spot for the OCFD as it is my main antenna at my home and works well. I have tried all sorts of other multiband antennas, but this is the one that has stayed up the longest – that must tell you something.

You can buy these antennas commercially or you can build your own. I built my own and it lies on the house roof with the ends going down to the garage at one end and a shed at the other. In fact, it is too long for the garden and the last 6ft or so goes around the side of the shed before being tied off. This is not ideal but needs must.

At a height of about 30 - 35ft and with an included angle of approximately 110 to 120° at the feedpoint it makes an ideal inverted-V and it seems to beat a G5RV hands down. It also beats a ground-mounted multi-band vertical most of the time and gives my loft-mounted dipoles a run for their money.

So how does it work? The feedpoint is one third along the length of what is effectively a half-wave length of wire on 80m (3.5MHz). The feed point is chosen as the impedance here is roughly 200 - 300Ω. So at this point a 4:1 balun will present a match to your radio of between 50 - 75Ω, or an SWR of 1:1 or 1:1.5 at its lowest. So far so good.

But the antenna will also be resonant on even multiples of 3.5 MHz, so you will find low SWR points at or near 7MHz, 14MHz and 28MHz. By a quirk of physics the OCFD can also offer a low SWR on 18MHz (17m).

You'll notice that I say "at or near". I have found that when installed in a real-life situation, especially when close to other conductors, the actual SWR dips that you get may not always be where you expect them.

Another point that is often overlooked is that if you are setting up an OCFD with an antenna analyser it pays to ground the analyser. If you don't you may get incorrect readings. I think this is because the coax feedline becomes part of the radiating system and I have seen this effect on other similar antennas. With my antenna I have the minimum SWR set at 3.6MHz, and I get 1.6:1. To do this I have folded back the antenna wires and twisted them together, but bear in mind that any shortening should be done in the ratio of 2:1. That is, if you fold back the long length by 1ft you should fold back the short length by 6in to maintain the 2:1 length ratio.

As you move up the bands the next minimum on my antenna comes out at just under the 40m band, at 6.8MHz. Nevertheless, the SWR across the whole of the 40m band is less than 3:1 and my rig's internal ATU can find a match. Again, the next dip is at 14.8MHz, although the SWR across the whole of 20m is below 2:1. The next dip is at 18.6MHz, although most of the 17m band is below about 4:1, as are 21MHz (15m), 24MHz (12m) and 28MHz (10m).

The antenna even offers a reasonable SWR on 6m (50MHz) and 2m (145MHz)! I have used the antenna for some Sporadic-E contacts on 6m and it does work.

By adjusting the relative feedpoint ratios you will find that you can move the resonant points up and down the bands slightly. You can therefore fine tune an OFCD to suit your needs.

Incidentally, although the antenna should not work very well on 10MHz (30m) I have found that it does, although you need an ATU. A friend has found the same so it is worth trying.

What is worth pointing out is that the OCFD needs an ATU on most, if not all, bands. Unless you are incredibly lucky, you will find that the SWR minima are not quite where you want them. Even an internal ATU will usually find a match though.

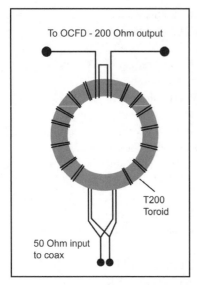

To OCFD - 200 Ohm output

T200
Toroid

50 Ohm input
to coax

Fig 6.5: The 4:1 Guanella balun is quite easy to make – just make sure you get the wiring correct.

As you can see, the antenna does not behave the way you would expect and I think this is due to interactions. I mention this because if you put an OFCD up at your location your results may also differ from the textbook cases, although few books ever seem to mention this.

40m OCFD

If you don't have space for a full-size 136ft OCFD you can always put up one for 40m. The 66ft OCFD has to be cut according to the 2:1 rule so the lengths are 22ft and 44ft. If you find this resonates below the 7MHz band just fold the ends back in the same 2:1 ratio until it does. The antenna should then work on 7MHz, 14MHz and 28MHz. It uses the same 4:1 balun, which leads me nicely on to the next section.

Building a 4:1 balun

You might think that a balun is a weird magical device and if you read the late Jerry Sevick's, W2FMI, book *Understanding, Building and Using Baluns and Ununs* you may be forgiven for thinking you are right! There are basically two types of balun – a voltage (Ruthroff) balun and a current (Guanella) balun. I am not going into detail as to the difference, but for our needs a current (Guanella) balun (**Fig 6.5**) is the best option. You can either buy one or build one – the latter is more fun and you can then say that you built your own antenna.

If you decide to make your own what I am going to describe here is a 4:1 balanced to unbalanced impedance transformer (to give it its full title) that is easy to make. Its method of operation is quite easy to understand as well – it works on the basis that the nominal impedance of two closely-spaced wires is around 100Ω. We are going to put two windings around a toroid core and connect them in parallel at one end and in series at the other.

So we get an impedance of 200Ω at the series end and 50Ω where we have connected the end of the turns in parallel. In other words, a ratio of 200:50 or 4:1.

To make one you will need:
1. A small plastic box to which you have fitted an SO239 socket and connectors on each end to connect the antenna wires;
2. A T200-2 or T106-2 toroid;
3. Two lengths of enamel-coated copper wire each about 60in long – the actual size of the wire isn't critical, but about 0.3 - 0.7mm diameter will work well (24 - 30SWG). I have seen them built with PVC-coated wire as well.

If you don't have a T200-2 toroid you can use another, such as the Amidon FT-140-61. Both are good enough for 100W or more.

First take each piece of wire and fold it in half. Now, taking one of the pieces wind it around one half of the toroid keeping the pair of wires neatly together. You need about nine turns, a turn counting each time you thread the wire through the toroid.

Now take the other length of wire and do the same on the other half of the toroid. You should end up with a toroid with four ends of wire at each side of the toroid.

Taking one end, connect two of the wires together – the other two ends at that side of the balun now become your antenna connections to the OCFD wires.

At the other side of the balun take a wire from one side of the toroid and connect it to one of the wires on the other side of the toroid. Now connect the remaining two wires.

These two wires are now connected to your coax inner and outer connections on the SO239 – which way around you connect them is not critical.

If you wish to test the balun note there will be a DC short between the inner and outer of the coax - this is normal. If it is working correctly you can now use hot melt glue to hold the toroid in place and also weatherproof the box.

In my design the box is held in mid air between the two antenna wires and doesn't appear to have taken any damage after two years. I take it down every spring just to check. I also smear lots of grease over the connections to prevent rusting.

The antenna is a good performer and will even match on topband (1.8MHz) through an ATU, admittedly with reduced performance.

TRAP DIPOLES

So far we have looked at using parallel-fed dipoles to give us multiband capability. But there is an alternative that can give us two, three, or more bands from a single antenna span and that is to use antenna *traps*.

A trap is just the right combination of L (inductance) and C (capacitance) to give a specific resonant frequency. Traditionally this was done using high-voltage capacitors and coils of wire, although the use of double-sided PCB as the capacitor makes the assembly cheap and easy. At this resonant frequency it offers a high impedance - it is like cutting the wire - while on frequencies higher and lower it is just like adding additional inductance or capacitance. To all intents and purposes the trap is electrically 'invisible' at anything other than its resonant frequency. We can use this technique to make an antenna look electrically shorter at some frequencies and not at others.

More recently there have been designs that use coax to create the traps and these work well too.

I am not a great fan of trap dipoles as stealth antennas – if fitting something in the loft the multi-dipole approach is usually easier to set up. But if you are looking at putting up a multi-band external antenna traps can be useful, if fiddly.

Before we go any further, if you plan to make your own traps you had better invest in either an antenna analyser or a Grid Dip Oscillator (GDO). To be honest,

Grid dip oscillators (GDOs) can often be found at reasonable prices at hamfests or rallies. You really need a GDO, or an analyser, to set up traps properly.

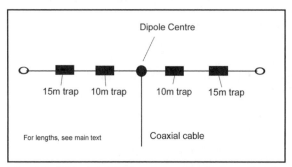

Fig 6.6: This 10-15-20m trap dipole is a simple way of getting an antenna to work efficiently on three bands.

Diagram labels: Dipole Centre; 15m trap; 10m trap; 10m trap; 15m trap; For lengths, see main text; Coaxial cable

The finished trap using PCB as the capacitor.

I favour the analyser approach as you can be far more accurate, but given that GDOs turn up on the second-hand market for £10 - £20 this is a good way to go about it. Either way, you can't build traps without one or the other.

Anyway, let's look at the two common methods of making traps.

Trap dipole using PCB / coil traps

To build a three-band trap dipole (**Fig 6.6**) we need to build two sets of traps – i.e. four in total. In this example we are going to build a three-band trap dipole for 10m (28MHz), 15m (21MHz) and 20m (14MHz), although you can build any combination that you like.

To do this we need to build two pairs of traps that are resonant at about 28.5MHz and 21.2MHz.

Start off with visiting your local hardware store and buying some white PVC waste pipe of about 40mm diameter. You will also need some wire – this isn't critical and just about any insulated wire will do. You will also need some unused double-sided copper PCB and a set of plastic groundsheet grommets from a local camping shop. The reason for these will become clear later.

Now, cut off four pieces of the white PVC tube about 60mm in length. You also need to cut four pieces of PCB so that they are a snug fit inside the tubing and extend about 10mm either end. Before you fit the boards chamfer the sides a little bit to help prevent high-voltage breakdown. These traps will be fine for up to 100W, but I don't suggest you run much more than that. Drill a 10mm hole in each end of the board – this is where the plastic grommets will be fitted. Now use a hot-melt glue gun or an adhesive like UHU to glue the boards centrally in the pipes.

Ideally we need to know the capacitance

of the boards you have just made so that we can work out the amount of wire needed to make them resonate on our desired frequency. But to be honest it doesn't really matter too much as we can adjust the number of turns later to suit our needs.

Now, with a bradawl make a hole in the PVC pipe towards one end and push a length of wire through and solder it to one side of the board. Now closely wind two turns of wire around the tubing and push it back through another hole *on the opposite side to the one you created earlier* and solder it to the opposite side of the board. Believe it or not you have just created a trap – we just need to find out where it is resonant!

Using your GDO or analyser place the instrument's coil inside the trap and look for a dip, adjusting the meter's sensitivity as you go. This should be fairly obvious, although there is always some hysteresis in the cheap GDOs that can make it hard to work out exactly where the dip is. Once you have found it we can now work out what we need to do.

If the resonant frequency is too low we either have to take away some L or C. It is much easier to take away L – try spacing the coils out a bit and see what difference that makes. If you are close it might do the trick. If you are still a long way away you might have to remove half a turn or so – if you have to make a new hole in the PVC tube go ahead, but make sure you solder the wire back on to the correct side of the board.

If it is too high you need to add more L – try another turn on the coil.

You are aiming to get the resonant frequency just *low* of where you want it. Once you have achieved that - and it can take quite a few attempts - you can carefully tape the coils in place using PVC insulation tape.

Now, in order to make the final adjustment I recommend filing or grinding away the corners of the PCB. Don't go mad – file away a little and test again. Once you are close be careful that you don't overdo it.

Once you have one trap made put it to one side and work on the others. You are aiming to make two perfectly-matched pairs. Once you have them finished, push the plastic grommets into place. Don't paint them at this point as we need to solder the antenna to them – and we might need to adjust this length many times before we get it right.

The dipole itself

Now we have the traps made we can make the whole dipole, although be warned this can be a tricky and finicky job to set up. Firstly, either use a dipole centre piece or if you are feeling hard up make your own using a plastic 35mm film canister and an electrical chocolate block connector. If you can't get hold of a film canister (my local photo processing lab will normally give me a bag full) try a plastic pill canister or vitamin container. Use a bradawl to make two holes in the sides, which is where the wires will come out, and a hole in the bottom for the RG58 coax.

The dipole centre made from an old 35mm film canister.

Now, as we are making a trap dipole for 10m, 15m

and 20m, the first leg of the dipole will be for the 10m section. So we need two pieces of wire that are 2.5m long. To be safe, and to allow us a little extra to tie knots at the trap, make it a little longer. If you are using plastic-coated wire you may find that this is too long anyway. It doesn't matter: we can adjust it later, but it is easier to cut wire than add it.

Push the wire through the hole in the plastic container and tie a knot in it so that it can't pull through. Now connect it to the electrical connector. The other end goes through the plastic grommet on the 10m trap, is tied in a knot and is then soldered to the PCB – it doesn't really matter which side, as long as you make sure that the wire you connect to the other end of the trap gets soldered to the opposite side of the PCB.

Now we need to add the wire between the 10m trap and the 15m trap, which can get tricky. If we were making a straightforward dipole a 15m version would be about 6.72m long, or 3.36m each leg. So you would think that we would only need to add a further 0.86m (3.36m – 2.5m) after the 10m trap to the 15m trap to make it work. Unfortunately, the trap adds some inductance which means the actual length required will be less than this. Nevertheless, to get us going and to prove the point add a piece of wire about 85cm long to the end of each of the 10m traps and solder it to the 15m trap, after tying a knot around the plastic grommet first.

Now we need to add a length of wire to the end of the 15m trap to make the whole antenna resonant on 20m (14MHz). Again, a 20m dipole on its own would need to be 10.06m long, so you would expect the addition we need to make to each leg after the 15m trap to be 1.67m (5.03m – 2.5m – 0.86m). In reality, the combined inductance in the traps will mean that the overall length is significantly shorter, but we can always adjust the antenna once finished – it will just take a little time.

Once you have added the final piece of wire you need to add end insulators. Now, we are ready for testing.

I found that setting the antenna up in my back garden on a fibreglass fishing pole meant that I was able to quickly put it up and own – and you'll be doing a lot of this! Once you have attached the coax to the antenna you are ready to go. An antenna analyser will make this a whole lot easier, but it is possible with an external SWR meter or your rig's built-in meter. We will be adjusting the antenna from the highest frequency to the lowest.

Firstly, check the antenna's SWR in the middle of 10m (28.5MHz). You will probably find that it is high and that the lowest SWR point is much lower, say around 28MHz. To fix this, remove some of the wire from the centre of the antenna at the feed point and test again. Don't go mad: just a couple of inches can make a big difference.

Once you have the antenna working on 10m we then need to adjust the length of wire between the 10m trap and the 15m trap, so see what the SWR is in the middle of the 15m band, say at 21.225MHz. Again, you may find that the antenna is too long and that the resonant point is more like 21MHz or even lower. If it is, take it down and shorten the wire between the two traps. Once you have it right put it back up and finally check the SWR in the middle of the 14MHz band, say on 14.175MHz.

Now if it is lower at the bottom end of the band you can shorten the antenna by twisting the ends of the antenna wire over each other - using simple knots at the antenna insulators makes life a lot easier.

This tuning process may take some time, but the end result will be a trap dipole for three bands – 10, 15 and 20m – that is actually much shorter than a dipole cut just for 20m.

The likelihood is that you will find that the antenna has its lowest SWR on 20m – the SWR will be higher on 15m and 10m, but should be in the range of a simple ATU. Once you have finished give the traps a coat of paint to waterproof them.

Results

I built this three-band trap dipole for 10, 15 and 20m and used a 10m fishing pole hidden in a tree to support it at about 9m as an inverted-V. The ends were supported by fishing line and it was really quite stealthy. In terms of performance it worked really well. The lowest SWR on 14MHz was about 1:1, rising to about 1.4:1 at the band edges.

On 21MHz, the lowest SWR was 1.3:1, rising to 1.8:1 at 21.000MHz and 21.450MHz. It was a similar story on 28MHz – mid-band was 1:1, rising to 2.2:1 at 28MHz and 29.7MHz.

The antenna worked well and on the first afternoon it was put up I worked many stateside stations on 14 and 21MHz, right out to California and Vancouver. I also worked Laura, 3A2MD, in Monaco for a new entity – not a big distance, but it was a good omen for a new antenna. The total cost for the antenna was less than £5 – I can thoroughly recommend it.

Improving on the design

The above method is a cheap and cheerful way of building traps, but if you start to analyse the design with a program like *MMANA* you find that the best way to build traps for the higher bands is to use smaller capacitors and more inductance.

The PCBs we used for the antenna had a capacitance of around 200 - 250pF. If you model an antenna built with traps of around 50pF you will find that it has lower SWR and greater bandwidth. But PCB capacitors that are just 50pF are very small and the antenna doesn't become self-supporting – it is better to mount the small capacitors in the tubing and put plastic end caps on.

If you model the antenna with capacitors of just 10pF you find that the inductance gets very large and you have to shorten it dramatically after the 10m trap to get it to resonate on 15m, if you can get it to resonate at all. So, as a compromise if you aim to use capacitors in the range 50pF - 100pF you will probably get the best results.

There is plenty of room for experimentation here and you are not restricted to antennas for just three bands only – I have seen one design that covered eight bands with seven pairs of traps. Setting one of those up is not a five-minute job!

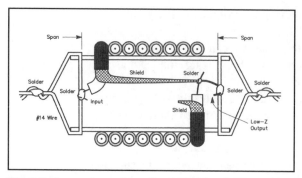

Fig 6.7: A coax trap, from the ARRL book *More Wire Antenna Classics*.

Coaxial Trap Design

Design Parameters

Frequency:	28.4	mHz	
Form Diameter:	4	cm	Units
Coax Diameter:	0.490	cm	⦿ Metirc
Capacitance:	93.504	pF/m	○ British
Select coax cable type	Belden 9201 RG58/U		

Calculated: Turns:	3.49		L:	0.648	uH
Coil Length:	1.71	cm	C:	48.43	pF
Coax Length:	51.80	cm	X:	115.71	ohms
End Sensitivity:	264.46	kHz/cm			
Turn Sensitivity:	725.71	kHz/cm			
Length/Diameter:	0.38		Help	Quit	

Fig 6.8: Use a PC-based program to calculate the number of turns needed for coax traps.

Using coax traps

There is another way of building traps that is in some ways simpler, but in others more complex. This involves using RG58 coaxial cable. The cable, when wired correctly, not only gives you the required inductance as it is coiled around a former, but also gives you the parallel capacitance.

You can build your coax traps using the same 40mm white PVC water pipe as the PCB traps. You have to wire the coax cable in parallel. That is, connect the outer of one end to the inner of the other. You then use the remaining outer and inner as the end connections for your traps. This makes far more sense with a diagram – see **Fig 6.7**.

All you need to know is how many turns you need to resonate the trap at the frequency of your choice. This will obviously depend upon the type of coax you are using and the diameter of the waste pipe. If you Google "coax trap calculator" you will find quite a few sites that will help you work out what you need. The one I use is PC-based and is by Tony Field, VE6YP [1] - see **Fig 6.8**.

As a guide, **Table 6.2** gives the suggested number of turns for RG58/U coax based on standard 40mm diameter pipe. Allow some extra coax to form the pigtails for soldering.

You'll notice that the difference between a 21MHz trap and a 28MHz trap is tiny – you really do have to take your time to make sure that they resonate properly. You don't even have to use 50Ω coax – TV coax will do, although the number of required turns will change.

Once you have the trap correct you must make sure that the coax can't move and ruin your new creation. Lots of glue and PVC are called for. When you have finished make sure the whole thing is waterproof if you intend to use it outside. Coaxial-cable traps are inexpensive, quite stable and will take quite high power

Frequency	Number of turns
7.1MHz	11.25
10.15MHz	8.22
14.2MHz	6.17
18.1MHz	5.04
21.2MHz	4.43
24.93MHz	3.88
28.4MHz	3.49

Table 6.2: Recommended numbers of turns for traps made of RG58/U coax, based on standard 40mm diameter pipe.

levels before breaking down. A trap made from RG58 coax should take the UK legal limit of 400W quite easily. The biggest problem is getting them to resonate just where you need them as you can't adjust the capacitor by grinding it away like you did with the PCB.

One trick, which comes from Ted Rule, G3FEW, of the Radio Amateur Old Timers' Association [2], is to make the trap resonate just *lower* than the frequency you need and then put a shorted link or wire loop near the end of the coax coil. Moving this towards or away from the coax coil will bring it to the required frequency.

Charles Rauch, W8JI [3], has done extensive work on traps and has come up with some interesting results. For example, he found that a typical coaxial trap introduces less than 1dB loss a piece – a typical pair introduces about 1.6dB loss. He also found that a trap is most lossy at its resonant frequency, so it doesn't necessarily make sense to set that at your planned operating frequency. He suggests setting it slightly LF – say at 6.9MHz if building a 7MHz trap.

Traps can be useful when used with dipoles, but they can also be used with verticals as we will show later.

THE W3DZZ TRAP DIPOLE

This famous antenna was often touted as a multiband solution. It is a trap dipole consisting of two 7MHz traps and a total length of 108ft. It is made to operate on 80m (3.6MHz) and 40m (7MHz) and the apparent shortening on 80m is due to the added inductance of the 40m traps. So far, so good. But how does the antenna perform as a *multiband* antenna?

The problem with this question is that it rather depends on the characteristics of the traps and the bands in question. The original design came about in 1955 when amateurs had access to 80m, 40m, 20m and 10m, when open-wire feeder was all the rage, and rigs didn't have delicate solid-state PAs.

By design, C L Buchanan's, W3DZZ, antenna has a low SWR on 80m and 40m. But modelling shows that the results you get elsewhere are rather dependent on the LC combination chosen for the 7MHz trap. Get this wrong and you find SWRs of more than 20:1 on 10m and 9:1 on 20m. The SWR on 15m (21MHz) can also be variable. Yet many people report great results on the other bands, so can you optimise the LC characteristics of the antenna to give the best results?

Playing with the antenna design using *MMANA* showed first that if you set this up as an inverted-V you are likely to get different results than if you had it as a straight dipole. But it is easier to model a straight antenna, so that became the starting point. We know that the W3DZZ is 108ft long and is designed to work on 40m and 80m, so these became the base parameters.

As the 40m band in the UK now goes from 7 - 7.2MHz I set the optimum frequency at 7.1MHz, which gave me a design length of 9.9m either side of the dipole feedpoint. Do bear in mind that if you use insulated wire this will be shorter, perhaps by 4 – 6%. I fixed the overall length at 21.92m (108ft) which then meant that I could play with the LC ratio of the traps.

I set the traps at 7.05MHz using an LC combination of 9.266µH and 55pF. This gave me a minimum SWR at 3.75MHz, but lousy SWRs on 14, 21 and 28MHz – back to the drawing board!

Setting the traps resonant at 7.1MHz and choosing 9.13µH / 55pF and changing the overall length to 35.1m (115.1ft) improved the SWR on 20m to just over 5:1 (better than 9:1 previously). The SWR on 15m (21MHz) also came down dramatically too, to under 3:1. But it was now much worse on 28MHz!

Going back to W3DZZ's original design showed that he used a total length of 33.56m, which is just over 110ft, so I don't know where the 108ft came from.

The distance from the centre to the trap is 1.07m. Plugging in those lengths and the original designs for the traps of 8.3µH / 60pF shows that he wanted the traps resonant at 7.132MHz. This put the SWR minimum on 80m at 3.775MHz and spot on in the middle of the 40m band at 7.1MHz. So what of the other bands? Well it comes out like this:

Band	Lowest SWR point	Actual SWR
20m	14.450MHz	4.65:1
15m	21.450MHz	11.5:1
10m	None	>40:1

Incidentally, the SWR figures for 30, 17 and 12m were also off the scale.

The ARRL Antenna Handbook [4] also has a slightly different design: total length = 32.9m (108ft), length to 40m trap = 9.75 m (32ft), length from trap to end = 6.7 m (22ft), L = 8.2µH and C = 60pF for a trap resonance of 7.175MHz. Again, good SWR results on 80m and 40m, but not very good anywhere else.

From this, the conclusion has to be that in its original form the antenna is not really suited to our modern day needs, unless you just want to stick to 40m and 80m. You can get the antenna to work better on 20m and 15m, but then 10m is worse. There are better multiband antennas around.

REFERENCES

[1] Tony Field, VE6YP: www.qsl.net/ve6yp/index.html
[2] Radio Amateur Old Timers' Association: www.raota.org
[3] W8JI.com (Charles Rauch):   www.w8ji.com
[4] *The ARRL Antenna Handbook*, 21st edition (ARRL): www.arrl.org/shop/Antennas

Examples of external stealth antennas

AS ANTENNAS GO, the monoband quarter-wave vertical is one of the simplest and perhaps one of the easiest to erect in a stealthy fashion. However, don't be fooled. If you don't install one of these correctly it won't be a good performer. This is probably where the old saying "a vertical radiates equally poorly in all directions" comes from. This is actually very unfair. There are plenty of people using verticals on the low bands that are working DX that horizontal antennas just can't hear. But then they have set theirs up properly.

THE MONOBAND QUARTER-WAVE VERTICAL

A quarter-wave vertical can be a good DX antenna as it has a relatively low angle of radiation (**Fig 7.1**). I'll assume that you don't have room for a quarter-wave vertical on 80m (66ft high) so will concentrate on verticals for 40 - 10m.

A quarter-wave vertical for 40m (7MHz) can be stealthy if you hide it near or in a tree. A 10m fishing pole makes a great support and you could end up with a stealthy, but potent, DX antenna for 40m for less than £25. By the way, that same antenna *won't* be very good for local contacts, as verticals have a null in their radiation pattern overhead, just where you need it for local NVIS (Near Vertical Incidence Skywave) communications.

Fibreglass fishing poles make good supports for verticals, but you can also string them up in trees. Just make yourself a small plastic box to connect your PL259 and coax and run a wire out of the top of the box. Connect that to an insulated piece of cord and then run that up into the tree, over a pulley if need be. That becomes your vertical element. The braid is connected via an electrical connector to your earth stake and radials.

If your tree is near the garden fence you could even rig just two elevated radials along the garden fence which negates the need for an earth stake and

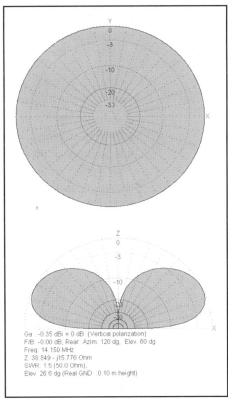

Ga: -0.35 dBi = 0 dB (Vertical polarization)
F/B: -0.00 dB; Rear: Azim. 120 dg, Elev. 60 dg
Freq: 14.150 MHz
Z: 38.849 - j15.776 Ohm
SWR: 1.5 (50.0 Ohm),
Elev. 26.6 dg (Real GND 0.10 m height)

Fig 7.1: The polar plot for a quarter wave vertical. If installed properly it will offer good DX performance with low-angle radiation.

Frequency (MHz)	Total length (feet & inches)	(metres)
7.100	32ft 11in	10.04m
10.100	23ft 2in	7.06m
14.175	16ft 6in	5.03m
18.100	12ft 11in	3.94m
21.225	22ft 0.5in	3.36m
24.940	9ft 5in	2.87m
28.500	8ft 2.5in	2.5m
29.500	7ft 11in	2.42m
50.200	4ft 8in	1.43m

Table 7.1: Lengths of quarter-wave vertical radiating element and radials.

comprehensive radial system. This is a very stealthy antenna if you use black insulated wire and fishing line to support the vertical element.

In its simplest form the quarter-wave vertical is just that – a single vertical radiator connected to the inner of your coax, while the outer of your coax is connected to earth. The lengths of the radiating element and each radial are given in **Table 7.1**:

You can feed a quarter-wave vertical from your shack with the wire going out of the window and a single earth stake outside. But I suggest that you don't. If you do this the current maximum will be at the feed point – right next to you. This, coupled with the fact that you won't be using a very good earth, means that the antenna won't be very effective and you are likely to cause all sorts of interference. If you want to use an end-fed antenna from your shack I suggest that you look at the W3EDP configuration, described later.

If you mount your quarter-wave vertical *above* the earth (as opposed to *on* the ground) you have to provide it with some tuned radials, also cut to a quarter-wave long. In this configuration you can get away with just two, on opposite sides of the antenna, although four in a cross pattern is more usual. The trouble is, it isn't very stealthy.

Unfortunately, if you are looking for a loft-mounted solution you can only really do this with a 10m quarter-wave as that's probably the only one that will fit. By all means try it, but a half-wave dipole in the loft will be probably be better.

Getting an effective RF earth

If you don't have a loft the solution therefore is to mount your vertical on the ground and use the earth itself as the 'missing' half of your antenna. But this is where people come unstuck with the quarter-wave – your earth must be good enough to replace the missing element that was there when the antenna was a half-wave dipole. A single earth stake will be OK as a safety earth, but it takes far more than that to get an efficient ground plane.

What you need are *radials* - and lots of them. There has been extensive research over the years on what makes a good ground plane and you probably won't like what you are about to read. The ideal 'golden' ground plane consists of around 120 radials, spread out in a circular fan shape, radiating out from the antenna. Ideally they should be at least an eighth of a wavelength long at your operating frequency, with some longer. But for a given amount of wire, more shorter radials are better than fewer longer ones. The radials help to improve the RF ground conductivity for the ground current return path. Earth is not a very good conductor at all really – more of a lossy dielectric. A salt-water swamp would be much better, but if you are like the rest of us you need to work hard to get those ground currents back to the antenna.

Eight to 12 0.1-wavelength ground-mounted radials will give you about 60 - 65% efficiency, according to SteppIR [1]. But it takes 120 ground-mounted radials to equal an elevated vertical with just two resonant radials (90% efficiency). You probably won't see much difference once you exceed about 36 - 60 radials.

If you want your quarter-wave vertical antenna to work properly you are going to have to do some work. The reality is that its overall efficiency is going to depend upon just how much you are prepared to do.

So let's start with the worst case scenario and work our way up.

Stage 1 – a single earth stake or mounting post

You've just installed your vertical antenna on a mounting post driven 4ft into the ground and measured the SWR as being near enough 1:1. Time to celebrate? Well, no!

The free space impedance of a half-wave antenna at height is about 70 - 75Ω, so a quarter-wave vertical should be about half that – say 35 - 37Ω. Your meter tells you that yours measures 50Ω. So why? That's easy, what you are seeing is the poor efficiency of your antenna – its natural impedance, which is 35Ω, plus the 15Ω of losses incurred because it doesn't have a decent ground plane.

You'll find that the antenna works, but it is a little deaf and it is hard to work stations. Incidentally, this is one of the reasons why people buy commercial trapped verticals and give up on them – they don't work well without a decent ground plane.

Stage 2 – a single earth stake plus four to six radials

This is getting better. The antenna will start to let you work stations. How long should the radials be? We'll find out later.

Stage 3 – a single earth stake and eight – 24 radials

As you approach 24 radials you will find that the SWR on your antenna starts to head towards 1.5:1. This is normal as the feed impedance is now heading more towards the 35 - 36Ω that it is supposed to be. You will find that the antenna is now starting to work reasonably well.

Stage 4 – a single earth stake and 24 - 64 radials and / or a wire mesh earth mat

You are now getting towards the optimum. As you add additional radials you may find that the SWR doesn't change. This is a good sign and shows you are getting towards the point of diminishing returns. If you can, add a wire mesh mat too – just solder it in with the radials.

You can bury the radials and the mat in two ways – either use a slitting tool and push the radials into the slit or cut the grass short at the beginning of the season, and stake out the radials or earth mat. They will disappear quite quickly as the grass grows and will vanish in due course.

So how long should the radials be?

The golden rule with radials is that more shorter radials are better than fewer longer ones and as you can see it is a lot of hard work. Another golden rule is that a single earth stake with no radials is pretty useless!

Conventional wisdom has it that the radials should be a quarter-wave long. But as you lie them on the ground (or bury them) they will be detuned anyway. The best rule of thumb is to have them each at least an eighth of a wavelength long, lay out as many as you can, and put them out in a star (complete radial) pattern if possible. More shorter radials are better than fewer longer ones. The first few radials you put down will make the biggest difference. It then becomes a law of diminishing returns.

But if you want to try to get the best out of your radials you can try to tune them. In an article in *QST* [2] the author found that the earth seriously detuned radials. So much so, that they needed to be a heck of a lot shorter to resonate properly. If you are putting up a monoband vertical with radials lying on the grass or buried just underneath it might be worth checking their electrical length with an antenna analyser and cutting them so that electrically they are a quarter wave long (not the same as physically being a quarter wave long). Just plug a radial into the analyser and see where the SWR dip occurs and cut the radial until it is where it needs to be.

Ventenna [3] also found that radials cut to an exact electrical quarter-wave on a 20m antenna didn't work too well – they were being detuned by the earth, so making them too long. Their impedance at the base of the antenna was so bad that they were actually not working as radials should. In the end their 5.29m (17.35ft) radials had to be trimmed back – they found that 8.5 - 14ft worked best.

If you want to experiment try reducing your radial length to about 50 - 75% of the calculated quarter-wave length and see if it improves the antenna.

If you have a *multiband* vertical this approach won't work, unless you have eight or so tuned radials for each band. You could try trimming at least four ground-mounted radials to resonance on each band, so giving you a mixture of lengths on a five-band vertical. But if you can't be bothered, or don't have an analyser, just put down as many radials as you can, making them at least an eighth of a wavelength long.

My experience shows that you have to work hard with a quarter-wave vertical to get the same performance as you do from a horizontal half-wave dipole at a reasonable height. They have inherently less gain than a dipole and are also quite noisy electrically. And if you are not prepared to put the work in on the radials you may be disappointed.

I think a vertical is the way to go for a 30m (10MHz) or 40m (7MHz) DX antenna, but there are better antennas for the higher bands.

And so far all this effort has been for a monoband vertical. Hmm – perhaps we need to think again!

THE TRAP QUARTER-WAVE VERTICAL

There is a relatively easy way to turn our quarter-wave vertical into a multiband antenna, and that is to use traps. Just like the trap dipole we talked about in the last chapter we can turn our wire vertical into a three (or more) band trap vertical (**Fig 7.2**).

The good news is that we only need to make one trap per band (the bad news is that we still have to make them). For the constructional details see the last chapter on making traps.

What we need to do is make half of a trap dipole. In this example, we will look at a quarter-wave trap vertical for 10m, 15m and 20m using traps made to resonate on about 28.5MHz and 21.2MHz.

Firstly, we need to have a decent earth system. In the last section we said put as many radials down as you can. Now that we have a three-band antenna the same rule applies and we need our radials to be roughly an eighth of a wavelength long at the lowest operating frequency - 16 one-eighth wavelength radials will work better than eight quarter-wave radials. So for a 10-15-20 metre vertical you might want to put 12 radials of about 5ft long, 12 of about 7ft and 12 of about 10ft. If the latest theory holds, this should work better than 36 radials that are all 17.5ft long.

But is this enough? Once again, the more the merrier, although you will start to see diminishing returns. Once you get to 36 tuned radials it might be worth adding some longer ones too – say 17 - 25ft long. Use an earth stake as well for good measure to ensure you actually have a DC connection to earth.

The first leg of the trap vertical will be for the 10m section. So we need a piece of wire that is 2.5m long. To be safe, and to allow us a little extra in order to tie knots at the trap, make it a little longer. If you are using plastic-coated wire you may find that this is too long anyway. It doesn't matter – we can adjust it later, but it is easier to cut wire than add to it. Push the wire through the hole in the plastic container you are going to use at the base and tie a knot in it so that it can't pull through. Now connect it to an electrical 'chocolate block' connector. The other end goes through the plastic grommet

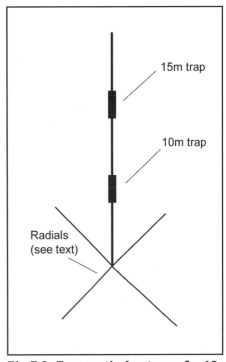

Fig 7.2: Trap vertical antenna for 10, 15 and 20m.

on the 10m trap and is tied in a knot before being soldered to the PCB – it doesn't really matter which side, as long as you make sure that the wire you connect to the other end of the trap gets soldered to the opposite side of the PCB.

Now we need to add the wire between the 10m trap and the 15m trap, which can get tricky. If we were making a straightforward vertical a 15m version would be 3.36m long. So you would think that we would only need to add a further 0.86m (3.36m – 2.5m) after the 10m trap to the 15m trap to make it work. Unfortunately, once again, the trap adds some inductance which means the actual length required will be shorter than this. Nevertheless, to get us going and to prove the point add a piece of wire about 85cm long to the end of each of the 10m taps and solder it to the 15m trap, after tying a knot around the plastic grommet first.

Now we need to add a length of wire to the end of the 15m trap to make the whole antenna resonant on 20m (14MHz). Again, a 20m vertical on its own would need to be about 5.03m long, so you would expect the addition we need to make to be 1.67m (5.03m – 2.5m – 0.86m). In reality, the combined inductance in the traps will mean that the overall length is significantly shorter, but we can always adjust the antenna once finished – it will just take a little more time.

Once you have added the final piece of wire you need to add an end insulator. Now, we are ready for testing.

Set the antenna up vertically using a fibreglass pole and attach the radials and earth stake. Firstly, check the antenna's SWR in the middle of 10m (28.500MHz). You will probably find that it is high and that the lowest SWR point is much lower, say around 27.5 - 28MHz. To fix this, remove some of the wire from the bottom section and test again. Don't go mad, just an inch or so can make a big difference.

Once you have the antenna working on 10m we then need to adjust the length of wire between the 10m trap and the 15m trap, so see what the SWR is in the middle of the 15m band, say at 21.225MHz. Again, you may find that the antenna is too long and that the resonant point is more like 21MHz or even lower. If it is, take it down and shorten the wire between the two traps. Once you have it right, put it back up and finally check the SWR in the middle of the 14MHz band, say at 14.175MHz.

Now if it is lower at the bottom end of the band you can shorten the antenna's overall length by adjusting the last (top) section. This tuning process may take some time, but the end result will be a trap vertical for three bands – 20m, 15 and 10m - that is actually much shorter than a vertical cut just for 20m.

You can make a trap vertical for any combination of bands depending on your needs. Either suspend it from a cord over a tree branch or use a fibreglass fishing pole. If you want to be *really* stealthy, push the pole up against the tree and secure it with bungee cords.

You can also help to hide a commercial trap vertical, like the Hustler 6-BTV, by mounting it close to a tree (the 5-BTV has a capacity hat towards the top, which makes it hard to push near a tree, but the 6-BTV doesn't).

Do you lose any performance by having it that close to a tree? The answer is probably yes, but it is likely to be less than 1 - 2 S-points, depending on how much moisture is in the tree trunk. If you want to remain stealthy it is a small price to pay. My own Hustler 5BTV is mounted about 2ft away from a tree and is virtually invisible in the summer when the leaves are out. You will lose more efficiency from having a poor radial system so attend to that first.

THE W3EDP END-FED

This is one of my favourite cheap antennas. I have been using one for years and they don't get much simpler. It consists of an 85ft wire fed against a 17ft counterpoise. Some books say that you don't use the counterpoise at all on 10m. Others say that you use a 6.5ft counterpoise on 20m. It seems to work with or without the change in counterpoise length, though you do need an ATU.

An internal ATU probably won't manage the impedance range, although if you don't have an external ATU build a 4:1 balun and fed it via that. Most internal ATUs will then be able to match the W3EDP on at least five bands.

The W3EDP makes a good stealth antenna. Mine was catapulted over the roof at my house. It goes out of the ground-floor shack window, straight up, over the roof and then down to the end of the garden where it is tied off with fishing line, leaving the end about 10ft high. The counterpoise goes off at 90° (see **Fig 7.3**).

At my previous house it went 50ft up into an oak tree. It is very stealthy and a firm favourite of the QRP fraternity.

So why does it work? You will recall that I said earlier that a quarter-wave long antenna fed direct from the operating position was not a good idea. This is because the current maximum (and therefore point of maximum radiation) on an antenna is always at a quarter wave (or odd multiple) from its end. This means that if you end feed a quarter-wave you are sitting right next to the point of maximum radiation – it will get in everywhere, causing EMC problems and even RF burns if you don't have a good earth.

So what if we could move the current maximum away from the operating position and further up the wire? Well – that's just what the W3EDP does.

The design characteristics are that it:

1. Must be longer than a quarter-wave at the lowest operating frequency (80m);
2. Must *not* be a half-wave long at any of our desired frequencies as that would be hard to match.
3. Must *not* be a quarter-wave (or multiple) either, as we still want to keep the current maximum away from the shack.

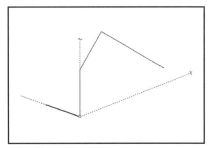

Fig 7.3: The W3EDP as fitted to my house and modelled in MMANA-GAL. For what it is, it works well and is very stealthy as it is virtually hidden, especially when you get more than 30ft away.

The length W3EDP came up with to solve this problem was 85ft (25.9m). The wire just plugs into the back of an external ATU and the 17ft counterpoise connects to the earth connection.

Some say that you should feed it as a balanced antenna or that you need a choke balun between the ATU and the radio. I have tried both ways and there wasn't much difference, although the tuning is slightly 'twitchier' using it as a balanced antenna.

The antenna works well on 80m and 40m. In a straight A and B comparison between the W3EDP and a 132ft OCF Windom on 80m there is very little in it. It even gives a dipole a run for its money on 20m (see **Fig 7.4**). I am writing this as I listen to US stations on 20m and Californian and Michigan stations are actually slightly louder on the W3EDP rather than the 20m dipole.

DX worked on this £5 wonder include 6W/DL4JS (Senegal), YK9G (Syria), VQ5XF (Turks and Caicos), VP6DX (Ducie Island) and VQ9JC (Diego Garcia).

I have noticed that the antenna is directional towards its end on the higher HF bands. In other words I find it very good for working stations to the south of me. This was confirmed by an analysis with *MMANA* which clearly shows that it is bidirectional on those bands. This might be worth considering if you are putting yours up in a similar configuration.

The downside of the W3EDP is that it can be noisier than a dipole - and watch out for RF in the shack. An earth wire to a stake and the counterpoise helps to keep this to a minimum.

Counterpoises and solving RF problems in the shack

By now you should have learned that if you elevate a quarter-wave vertical off the ground you need tuned resonant radials – at least two on either side of the antenna.

If the antenna is mounted at ground level and the radials are either lying on the ground or buried just underneath they will be detuned and will likely need to be shorter to actually resonate.

So that's radials, but what is a *counterpoise*? Technically a counterpoise is any radial that is lifted away from the earth. In radio engineering terms it used to mean a network of radials wires at the base of an antenna, just off the ground and physically not connected to it. If that sounds like elevated radials to you then you are right! In modern amateur radio parlance, though, the term counterpoise has come to mean something else – usually a single elevated radial, one quarter-wave long, used to aid transmitting efficiency or to reduce RF radiation back into the radio shack.

And it's that second use that I want to take a closer look at - especially as we are stealthy operators.

Often when using end-fed antennas you will find significant RF near to your operating system. This can manifest itself in a number of ways, one being feedback into your microphone, causing distorted audio. But I have also seen a 12V power supply that would shut down as soon as you started to transmit and all manner of USB devices, such as mice and keyboards that would cease to work. In a worst-case scenario you can

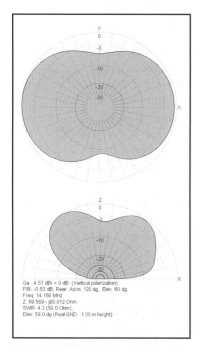

Ga: 4.57 dBi = 0 dB (Vertical polarization)
F/B: -0.53 dB, Rear: Azim. 120 dg, Elev: 60 dg
Freq: 14.150 MHz
Z: 89.569 - j95.812 Ohm
SWR: 4.2 (50.0 Ohm),
Elev: 59.0 dg (Real GND :1.00 m height)

Fig 7.4: The polar plot when the W3EDP is used on 20m - fairly omnidirectional, but with slightly stronger lobes north and south. This is noticeable in QSOs with Africa and the Middle East.

get RF burns off your Morse key and even the microphone. Once you have had an RF burn you are unlikely to forget the experience – it is like being stabbed with a red-hot needle and very painful.

All of these 'symptoms' are a sure sign that you have an 'RF hot' shack and it needs attention.

If your shack is on the ground floor the first thing you should do is install an earth stake just outside the window and connect it to your radio or ATU via a PVC-covered copper wire. This is an absolute must if you are using end-fed antennas and a good idea if you are using any other form as well.

But what if your shack is upstairs? I had this problem at one of my first QTHs and being young and green didn't really know what to do about it. The problem is that installing an earth stake and running a long wire to it is not the answer – the wire will act as a kind of antenna and will represent a high impedance at some frequencies. In other words, it won't work! So if you want to use an end-fed antenna and have an upstairs shack (or live in a flat) what can you do?

The easiest way to get rid of unwanted RF in the shack is to use a quarter-wave counterpoise attached to the earth connection of your radio or ATU. The suggested lengths for each band are given in **Table 7.2**. Fitting such a counterpoise will solve all but the most troublesome cases of RFI and is easy and cheap to fit.

If you have problems on more than one band you are going to need multiple counterpoises, each one cut to a quarter-wavelength at the frequency of operation. Do be aware that the end of the counterpoise will be at a high voltage when you transmit, so it may be a good idea to cover the end with PVC insulating tape.

You can install the counterpoise anywhere – running it around the skirting board or under the carpet – but remember, we are meant to be using low power, 100W or preferably less. In my case the counterpoise goes out of the window and around the side of the house before being tied to a plastic drainpipe.

If you don't want multiple counterpoises running around the place there

Frequency (MHz)	Total length (imperial)	(metric)
3.500	66ft 8in	20.38m
7.100	32ft 11in	10.04m
10.100	23ft 2in	7.06m
14.175	16ft 6in	5.03m
18.100	12ft 11in	3.94m
21.225	11ft 0.3in	3.36m
24.940	9ft 5in	2.87m
28.500	8ft 2.5in	2.5m
29.500	7ft 11in	2.42m
50.200	4ft 8in	1.43m

Table 7.2: Quarter-wave counterpoise lengths.

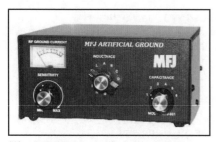

The MFJ-931 artificial earth tuner.

are more technical options. One is to use an 'artificial earth' or counterpoise tuner. This takes a random length of wire and electrically 'tunes' it to represent a low impedance at the operating frequency. You can make your own or buy one. It is rather like an ATU and combines inductance and capacitance to 'tune' the counterpoise.

The MFJ-931 is typical of a commercial artificial earth tuner - it resonates a random length of wire placed along the floor and produces a tuned counterpoise. This ground effectively places your rig near actual earth ground potential even if your rig is on the second floor or higher with no earth ground possible.

MFJ recommends a wire which is a quarter-wavelength or less at the operating frequency. The worst length you can have is one that is about a half-wavelength long – this will present a very high impedance to RF. A quarter-wave counterpoise or artificial earth system should get rid of most RF problems in the shack for good.

ENTER THE UNUN

A half-wave dipole has a nominal impedance of around 70 - 75Ω. The actual impedance will depend on many factors including its height above ground and whether it is straight or set up as an inverted-V. The latter will reduce its impedance, closer to the 50Ω that your radio will expect to see.

Likewise, a quarter-wave vertical over perfect ground should have an impedance of 37.5Ω. But place it over an imperfect, real earth and its impedance is likely to be more than this due to ground losses. This explains why a quarter-wave vertical with no or few earth radials will appear to be a good match with a 1:1 SWR, but will actually be a very poor performer.

Now take a half-wave long piece of wire and you will find that the impedance at its end is something like 3000 - 4000Ω. The impedance of that same piece of wire used at higher frequency will change yet again as the relative wavelength changes.

So, in other words that magical 50Ω (1:1 SWR) impedance that you expect to get from your dedicated antenna is likely to be something else. Now use that same antenna on another frequency and the impedance (and therefore SWR) that you get will be nothing like 50Ω and the SWR will be higher.

So what can you do if you want to use a single wire antenna on a number of different bands? If you are using an end-fed antenna that comes right into the shack the obvious solution is to use an Antenna Tuning Unit (ATU). But if you want to feed a remotely-sited antenna with coax there is another solution.

That solution is to use an *unun*, or unbalanced to unbalanced transformer. You may have heard of a balun, but what is an unun? To understand that we need to go back to basics.

A half-wave dipole is essentially a *balanced* antenna. Just take a look at it and you will see that it has two identical halves. The current flowing in one half is mirrored by the current flowing in the other. But our transceiver is designed with an *unbalanced* output. To resolve this mismatch we can use a balanced to unbalanced transformer or *balun* at the dipole's feedpoint. But what about ground-plane antennas and end-feds? They are obviously not balanced as they are not symmetrical. They are in fact *unbalanced antennas*.

If we are using an unbalanced antenna on something other than its design frequency as we said earlier it will display an impedance other than 50Ω. So what we want is a transformer to transform the impedance the radio would otherwise see to something closer to 50Ω. What we want is a unbalanced to unbalanced transformer – or unun for short. This is the key to feeding a ground-plane or end-fed antenna remotely, while trying to minimise our coax losses due to high SWR on the feedline (see the chapter on coax losses).

Ununs come in a variety of ratios including 2:1, 4:1, 6:1 and even 9:1. Which one you use will depend entirely on the impedance you are trying to transform. Straight away we need to make something clear – ununs and baluns are transmission line transformers and not conventional transformers. They don't work by having different turns ratios to give the step-up or step-down ratios. Instead they work by combining two or more conductors in close proximity in series and parallel modes to give the various ratios.

My own homemade 9:1 unun. Next to it is a T200-2 toroid – inexpensive and the basic building block of medium-power ununs and baluns.

For example, in a 4:1 Guanella-design balun, which is the easiest to visualise, and is described in the section on the OCFD (Windom) antenna, you take two parallel wires with a characteristic impedance of 100Ω. On one side of the toroid you connect them in series, giving 200Ω. On the other they are in parallel, so giving 50 Ω. So the ratio is 200:50 or 4:1.

In Jerry Sevick's, W2FMI, book *Understanding, Building, and Using Baluns and Ununs*, he argues that we shouldn't even call them transformers at all; he prefers the title 'broadband transmission line matching networks'.

Building a 9:1 unun

To understand how to construct an unun, let's build a 9:1 version. You will need a T200-2 (red) toroid and three pieces of wire, each 24in (60cm) long. It will also help if you have a small plastic box with an SO239 socket mounted at one end and with two wing nuts or mounting posts at the other. In the UK you can buy a small plastic box from Maplin which is watertight with a rubber seal, yet inexpensive.

It will help if the wires are different colours, although that isn't critical if you have a multimeter available. It just makes it a lot easier to follow these instructions. For the sake of this explanation I'll assume that you are using green, red and black wires.

Inside view of the unun. Note that the PVC tape is only being used to hold the turns neatly on the toroid. I find a Dremmel-type tool invaluable for making the holes for the SO239 and other connectors in the plastic box.

Put the three pieces of wire together and wind them carefully on to the T200-2 toroid. Place the wires (left to right) green - black - red, and wrap nine turns on to the toroid. Try not to let the wires overlap.

You should end up with a toroid with three wires extending from the left winding and three wires extending from the right.

Now twist and solder the left black wire with the right red wire. This can be covered with PVC tape once complete.

Now twist the left green wire with the right black wire. Strip the ends of the two wires, twist and solder them together leaving a length of about 2in from the toroid.

Finally trim and strip the remaining right green wire and solder another 5in length of green solid wire to it.

Now take the left green wire and right black wires that you twisted together and connect them to the centre pin of the SO239 socket – this is the input side and will connect to your radio via a length of coax.

One of the green wires is now soldered to the ground connection of the SO239 socket. The other end of the wire you soldered on (which is connected to it) becomes the earth connection for the unun and typically goes to a ground stake and ground radials.

This leaves the remaining red wire which connects to the other wing nut and will become the connection for the antenna.

If you are worried about the wires unravelling you can either use PVC tape or plastic cable ties to hold them in place.

So how do we use an unun? Let's look at a typical example.

Using a 9:1 unun and a 65ft end-fed inverted-L

In this test I used the home-made 9:1 unun, wound using PVC covered cable and a T200-2 toroid as described above. I erected a 10m high fishing pole and attached a 65ft quarter wave antenna for 80m in an inverted-L fashion, i.e. 10m up and then 9.8m out to the nearby summerhouse.

This was arranged away from the house and fed with 12m of RG8 coax, a single earth stake and two 20ft radials at the feed point. This is not really enough, but was good enough for the test.

Now a 65ft (19.8m) end-fed (a quarter-wave on 80m) would be expected to give a good match on 80m, a very poor match on 40m (where it is a half-wave long) and various SWRs on the other bands where it ranges in length from around 0.66 of wavelength on 30m (10MHz) to nearly two wavelengths on 10m (28MHz). **Table 7.3** shows the predicted SWRs at the feedpoint of a 65ft inverted-L on the various bands, according to the *MMANA-GAL* antenna modelling program.

If you actually do this as an exercise you will find that the actual measured SWR at the end of, say, 30ft of coax is lower than the calculations due to line

Frequency	SWR
3.75MHz	2.51:1
7.05MHz	75.2:1
10.1MHz	35.5:1
14.2MHz	21.9:1
18.11MHz	21.8:1
21.2MHz	21.2.1
24.9MHz	8.1:1
28.5MHz	409:1

Table 7.3: Predicted SWRs at feedpoint of 65ft inverted-L (MMANA-GAL).

losses. But the exercise shows that the antenna does not exhibit a good match on anything other than 80m (3.5MHz).

So what happens if we put the 9:1 unun in at the bottom of the inverted-L? **Table 7.4** shows the standing wave ratios as actually measured at the end of the coax feed-line in my shack:

From Table 7.4 you can see that the antenna now offers a low-ish SWR on most bands, and most modern rigs will be able quite happily to tune at least seven of these with their internal ATUs. In fact, I found that an Icom IC-7400 and a Yaesu FT-2000 would tune *all* of the above bands using their internal ATUs - even 40m where the SWR was the highest.

Now, the purists would argue that you are obviously incurring losses by feeding an antenna with coax with a 13.6:1 SWR on it. Others may argue that you get losses in the unun itself.

But let's look more closely. Using an online coax loss calculator (I used the one at [4], but searching for "coax loss calculator" on the Internet will bring up a variety), I found that 10m of RG8 (Belden 8237) coax would exhibit losses

Frequency	SWR
3.5MHz	3:1
3.65MHz	4.2:1
3.8MHz	5.9:1
7.10MHz	13.6:1
10.1MHz	2.5:1
14.2MHz	3.3:1
18.14MHz	1.8:1
21.2MHz	2.4:1
24.9MHz	1.9:1
28.5MHz	1.2:1

Table 7.4: Real-life measured SWRs at feedpoint of a 65ft inverted-L using a 9:1 unun.

of 0.152 dB at a 1:1 SWR. If the SWR were 15:1 the total losses would rise to 1.1016 dB – not good, but not terribly significant.

And as for losses in the unun, Jerry Sevick, W2FMI, calculates unun efficiencies to be around 93 - 99.5%, depending on the load being transformed, so losses are minimal.

Agreed, this method of feeding an antenna is not the most efficient, but it does mean that you can remotely feed a single-element antenna (in this case a 65ft inverted-L) and use it on a large number of bands with your rig's internal ATU. The added bonus is that you can locate the antenna away from the house and therefore minimise noise pick-up. If you have a suitable tree, the first 10m or so can go straight up and the remaining 9.8m can go out to a shed or back to the house. I doubt anyone would even notice it - especially in the summer when the leaves are out.

The antenna built and tested turned out to be a good performer and within an S-point of my other reference antennas.

If you don't fancy making your own unun you can buy one or even a whole antenna from a number of suppliers.

THE RYBAKOV VERTICAL ANTENNA

I had no idea why this was called a Rybakov, but subsequently found out that it means 'fisherman' or 'family of the fisherman' in Russian (thanks to Oleg, RV3GM). It is so called because it is made with a fibreglass roach pole or fishing rod.

The story of the Rybakov started on a lazy August day in 2003. Enrico Li Perni, 5Z4ES (then IV3SBE), and Mauro, IV3SCP, were trying to created a multiband antenna that was cheap, but would give results comparable to the dipoles on Enrico's roof. Together they salvaged an old vertical antenna and removed the bottom loading coil. They then started experimenting with RF transformers using some toroids they found in the shack. They ended up with the Rybakov design, which outperformed many commercial antennas that they tried.

It is essentially a 7.6m vertical fed with a 4:1 unun (unbalanced to unbalanced transformer) and an earth stake with radials - the more the merrier. **Fig 7.5** shows a suitable 4:1 unun, while **Fig 7.6** shows how to build it.

It works very well with a fibreglass fishing pole and can be put up in a few minutes. The pattern shown in **Fig 7.7** is what you get on 17m (18MHz) which is very good for DX.

The idea is that the antenna represents a non-50Ω (1:1 SWR) match at all frequencies – 7.6m

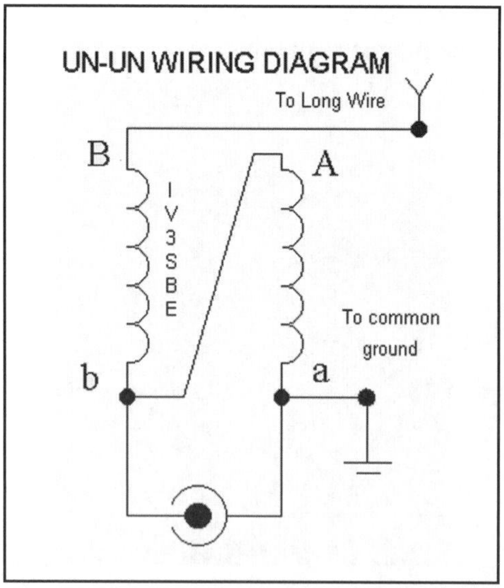

Fig 7.5: 4:1 A schematic of the Rybakov unun wiring (courtesy IV3SBE).

is chosen as it isn't actually a half-wave (high impedance) or quarter-wave (low impedance) on any band. In other words it is designed to be *non*-resonant on any of the amateur bands.

The unun transforms the impedance to something closer to 1:1 and therefore reduces coax losses. But it still needs an ATU to match it.

Does it work? I have tried a 7.6m Rybakov at a few locations and yes it does. Is it as good as a dedicated resonant antenna – no, not quite. You get some losses in the unun and there will always be a residual SWR on the feedline, which adds to the losses. You will also need to use an ATU to get the SWR down to 1:1, although most internal ATUs can usually cope with the mismatch.

As a matter of interest, **Table 7.5** shows the SWRs I found at the feedpoint with the 7.6m vertical (using the 4:1 unun) with a single earth stake and two 20ft radials.

The radiation pattern on 10, 14 and 18MHz is typical of a vertical and good for DX. It is not so good on the higher bands, as the antenna gets progressively longer than a quarter-wave and the pattern gets complex. It is also rotten on 80m (SWR 330:1) as it is *waay* too short – if you extend the wire to 8.6m it will be better on 40m, but possibly worse on 10m. At 7.6m it is a bit short for 40m, but does work.

It was OK on 20m - some

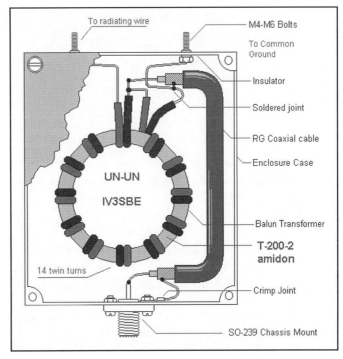

Fig 7.6: How to build the 4:1 unun used to feed the 7.6m Rybakov vertical (courtesy IV3SBE).

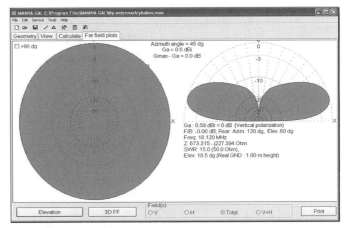

Fig 7.7: The radiation pattern on 18MHz shows that the 7.6m Rybakov should work well on 17m DX.

stations were louder than on a 132ft Windom at 30ft, some worse. The RR9O (Russian) beacon was down about 1 S-point, the 4X6TU (Israel) and 4U1UN

Frequency	SWR
7.050MHz	3.2:1
10.1MHz	3.6:1
14.2MHz	5.6:1
18.1MHz	5.4:1
21.2MHz	2.6:1
24.9MHz	2:1
28.5MHz	2.1:1

Table 7.5: Measured SWRs at feedpoint of 7.6m Rybakov vertical using 4:1 unun.

(New York) beacons were about equal with the dipole. A VY2 station (Prince Edward Island, Canada) was down 2 S-points. KQ2M (in Connecticut) was equal or slightly worse, K1RX (New Hampshire) slightly better.

Performance on 17m was similar, but the higher bands were closed at the time of the test so I don't know its performance on 15m (21MHz) and 12m (24MHz). In tests it could hear local CB stations on 27MHz that were inaudible on my Windom, W3EDP or horizontal dipole. I know most CBers use vertical polarisation, but it shows that it might be good for low-angle DX radiation on 10m too.

For 20 – 10m use I think you are better sticking to 7.6m. The modelling shows that the radials are critical. You may get different SWR readings depending on how many you have. A single earth stake might give you a low SWR, but will be lossy.

If you have little space and like experimenting it might be worth a go. More radials might help – if you are lying them on or under the ground they don't have to be resonant, just make sure they are roughly the same length as the radiating element and aim for as many as possible (32+ is good). If you try this antenna with just a ground stake I think you may be disappointed.

As for stealth - if you push the pole up through the branches of a tree, taping each joint as you go, do you end up with a stealth antenna? The answer is yes. When used in my back garden the pole was practically invisible and the leaves weren't even out as it was winter.

My FT-2000's built-in ATU was able to match it to 1:1 on 40 - 6m. The SWR on 80m was too high and the rig wouldn't match it, which was to be expected.

So there you are - a stealth antenna that works from 40m to 6m for about £10 plus the pole (and if you string the wire up into the branches you don't even need the pole!)

A MONOBAND END-FED HALF-WAVE VERTICAL

If you only have space for a vertical antenna, but don't have much space for radials, there is another home-brew solution – the end-fed half-wave vertical.

While the impedance at the *centre* of a dipole is about 50 - 75Ω, and very easy to match to coax, an *end-fed* half-wave has a very high impedance indeed. If you just connect it to your coax or rig you will be disappointed. So is there a simple way to bring the impedance down and match the end of a half-wave to 50Ω coax?

After a lot of searching on the web I found the answer. Steve Yates, AA5TB, of Fort Worth, Texas, has a great site with lots of information [5]. It was his site that helped me build end-fed half-wave antennas for 10m and 20m, although the design can be modified for any of the HF bands.

First you need a half-wave length of wire. For the 10m version, using the formula 468/frequency, I cut a piece 16ft 5in long (in fact, this is precisely 5.0m). You connect one end to the fibreglass roach pole or to your plastic guttering and the other end to a matching unit at the base, which you are about to build (**Fig 7.8**).

Next you need a T200-2 (red) toroid. These are very cheap and can be picked up at many rallies or online. This is the same type of toroid mentioned earlier for use as a balun and unun. I wound 17 turns of enamelled copper wire on the toroid as the secondary winding – each time the wire passes through the toroid counts as one turn. My wire was some I had lying around and was about 1.25mm (18 SWG) in diameter. Leave a little at the end for connections and then wind two turns *over* this for the primary, again leaving a little spare.

Across the 17-turn winding you need to connect a capacitor. I tried a small variable, but as the minimum capacitance was about 22pF I couldn't get the circuit to work. But never fear, the answer is very simple and very cheap. RG58 coax has a capacitance of about 28.8pF per foot, so cut off about 10in and connect that across the ends of the winding. You'll find that an electrical connector ('chocolate block') makes life easier.

Now, connect your coax across the two-turn primary, connect your antenna to one of the secondary wires *and connect* another *piece of copper wire from the* other *secondary wire back to the* braid *of the coax*.

The half-wave end-fed really needs an earth or short counterpoise to work, but you can try to connect it straight to the braid as the impedance is so high that little current actually flows down the braid. If you try to use the antenna without this connection to braid or earth the SWR will be terrible. I know, I tried.

If you do get any RF problems just form a coax choke by coiling about 8 - 10 loops of coax in a 6in coil about a foot from the antenna. Or you can connect the braid connection to an earth stake – you don't need a full set of radials like you would have on a

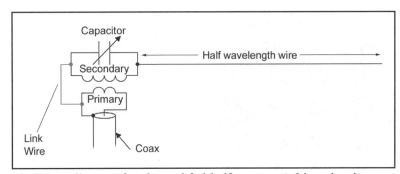

Fig 7.8: A diagram for the end-fed half-wave matching circuit.

A close-up of the matching transformer.

An SWR of 1.2:1 – more than good enough.

quarter-wave vertical, which is what makes this design so much easier to build and work with.

Now the fun starts. If you have an antenna analyser it will make life a lot easier. If not, you can do it with a rig and SWR meter. If using an analyser, connect it to the end of the coax and see where the antenna resonates. It will probably be lower than 10m. Snipping off half-inch lengths of the coax capacitor will reduce the capacitance and move the resonant frequency higher. If you get down to about 4in and are still not there try removing a turn off the secondary coil.

I ended up with 15 turns on the secondary and a piece of coax about 4in long – it is better to remove turns than snip too much off the coax. The end result was an SWR across the entire 10m band of less than 2:1. In fact, at resonance it was about 1.2:1. But did it work?

As always, the 10m band wasn't open as I connected it to my rig to test, but I was able to hear CB stations on 27MHz that were at least 20 miles away from my QTH – we just need an increase in sunspots and the solar flux to really give it a thorough test, but it should work well.

The angle of radiation of a vertical half-wave is quite low so it should be quite a DX performer, and it is very easy to install too. It is very easy to build the matching network into a plastic box to waterproof it.

It was at this point that I had a brainwave – if the antenna could be made to work on 10m, it should be easy to scale for other bands. I worked out that if I doubled the length of the wire radiator to 10.05m (33ft) I would have an effective low-angle half-wave radiator for 20m. As one of my fishing poles was 10m long it was able to support the new wire quite easily, even if it did look a little unwieldy.

A couple of minutes with a pen and paper and I soon realised that the equation for the resonant frequency of an LC network showed that halving the frequency meant that I had to multiply the capacitance value by four to make it resonant.

$$f = \frac{1}{2\,\pi \times \sqrt{LC}}$$

So I cut another piece of coax at four times the length of the original piece, hooked it all up and plugged it into the MFJ analyser. I couldn't believe it - the instant result was an SWR of 1.1:1 on 14.150MHz rising to only 1.5:1 at the ends of the band.

Tests showed that it was at least as good as a half-wave 20m dipole at 30ft and US stations were romping in during the afternoon on SSB. I used it at a Jamboree on the Air (JOTA) station, GB0CAW, in Norfolk, and it outperformed a G5RV at 30ft by about 1 S-point. The matching unit was put into a Maplin's waterproof box and the 10m pole was put up through a tree in the garden. While some signals are weaker by 1 - 2 S-points, invariably it works better on DX – notably the USA and the Caribbean.

For a really stealthy antenna I could take the pole down and put a fishing line over the top branch (using the pole to do it) so that I could haul a wire up into the branches. It would be virtually invisible.

A friend also built one after our experience at the JOTA event and he was very impressed.

You can scale this idea up for any of the HF bands or even 40m or 80m, although the capacitor gets very big and you would struggle to find a 66ft or 132ft vertical roach pole! But what you could do it set it up as an monoband inverted-L for either of those bands using a 10m roach pole. There is plenty of room for experimentation.

You could also set up a horizontal end-fed half-wave from an upstairs window. That is easier than using a centre-fed half-wave as your coax would be right next to the window, along with the matching box. The performance, although monoband, would be very good.

These antennas are very easy to make and only need a few components. If you have little space in your back garden for dipoles, a vertical half-wave could be the way to go. Why not try one?

OTHER DESIGNS FOR SMALL HF ANTENNAS

The next three antennas all claim to work well even though they are very small indeed. Some experts will scream that they *can't* work, that they break the laws of physics or radiate only off the feeder. Rather than tell you that they work or don't I would rather you try them out for yourself. If they work for you, fine. If they don't, well, try something else! Anyone can criticise a design without actually trying it out in the first place: a real radio ham gets their soldering iron out and has a bash. If you build one of these antennas and work other stations then great - better to be on the air with a compromise antenna than no antenna at all. And if you find that any of them outperform a full-size dipole or vertical let me know!

The DL7PE-MicroVert

There is nothing like a small antenna to get people arguing about how well they work. If they do work the usual suggestion is that it must be the coax that is doing the radiating. In this case the inventor of the MicroVert antenna, Juergen Schaefer, DL7PE, has been very honest – the coax forms the counterpoise for the main radiator. I tried to contact Juergen while writing the book, but to no avail. Nevertheless, I think the design has some merit and wanted to reproduce it here.

As described on Antennex, the antenna experimenters' website [6], Juergen says it took him many years to test various designs of short antennas such as magnetic loops, mobile radiators, helically-wound wires on fibreglass tubes, a wire simply hanging on a fishing rod and tuned by a coupler, and the Isotron (described in the chapter on commercially-made stealth antennas). He says that all the antennas managed to radiate, however, they did not deliver great signals at his location. Only the Isotron came close to his expectations. He therefore decided to try to design his own short antenna and the DL7PE-MicroVert was the result.

The DL7PE-MicroVert is extremely short in comparison to its wavelength of operation - around 0.02λ. It is shown in **Fig 7.9**. Its principle is based on an open LC series resonance circuit and consists of four components:

* a capacitive radiator;
* a reactance coil;
* a resonant coaxial cable counterpoise, and
* an RF-choke.

The antenna is not a magnetic loop and the predominant mode of operation in the near field is electrical. DL7PE claims that efficiency of a 1ft long 20m DL7PE-MicroVert is comparable with a 5ft diameter small circular magnetic loop antenna, although you must bear in mind that the counterpoise or coax connection is also part of the radiating system, so a straight size-for-size comparison is unfair.

So what are the components?

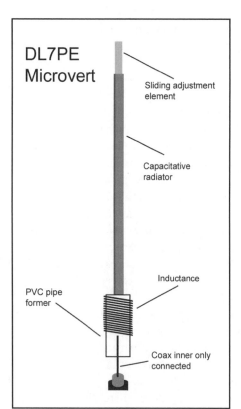

The capacitive radiator

This is a length of aluminium tubing, perhaps curtain or shower rail, approx 1in (25mm) in diameter. The length (in millimetres) is calculated by the equation 4700/f (MHz). So a 20m (14MHz) radiator would be just 331mm (or 13in) long. DL7PE recommends that you have a smaller rod or tube that fits in to the end of the main tubing, which you use for tuning purposes. This doesn't have to be connected electrically as it will couple capacitively.

The reactance coil

Connected to one end of the radiator is a coil wound on a 1in former with wire of around number 18 size (1.2mm). The length of the coil and therefore its inductance will depend on the exact dimensions of your capitative radiator and there is room for experimentation.

Resonant counterpoise

Connected to the coil is the *inner* of a piece of coax. The outer of the coax is not connected and is left free,

Fig 7.9: The DL7PE-MicroVert developed by Juergen Schaefer.

which appears counterintuitive. The coax should be cut according to the formula 58/f (MHz) = length in metres. So, for an antenna operating in the centre of the 20m band (14.175MHz) it would be 4.09 metres. This is obviously shorter than a quarter-wave, which DL7PE says is due to the fact that a further coaxial cable of random length will be connected behind the choke.

RF choke

DL7PE suggests two opposite windings of four to five turns on two ferrite rings should be sufficient. Another source suggests the FT 140-43 toroid can be used with up to 12 turns of RG58.

Tuning is effected by:

a) Adjusting the coil inductance by reducing or increasing turns;

b) Adjusting the radiator rod length; and

c) Shortening or extending the counterpoise.

DL7PE says that a VSWR of 1.3:1 or better should be achieved after tuning and this is a very iterative process. I would start with the coil first and then adjust the radiator rod length as a means of fine tuning. He also says that due to its rather sharp resonance there will be no harmonics or sub-harmonics generated and the risk of interference is minimal, although I think that rather depends on how you route your coax.

Willy Kroll, DM3WSO, reported that he had made 1030 QSOs and worked 116 DXCC entities within seven months with his DL7PE-MicroVerts on the 15 and 20m bands.

Raimund Jakob, DG9MAQ [7], has also used MicroVerts for seven years – one of his models is made up of tin cans soldered together! His 20m version is used on his second floor balcony, mostly with 10W output from a Kenwood TS-50. He sent me an extract from his log and it shows that the antenna certainly works, with plenty of contacts around Europe.

1	14/04/2007 17:30	IA0IPY	Antarctica	13	40m	SSB		59	59
2	31/12/2005 15:22	RA9SAS	Asiatic Russia	15	20m	<FREQ:9>14.000000		599	599
3	01/05/2008 14:04	OE2008PMI	Austria	206	40m	<FREQ:8>7.000000		599	599
4	14/07/2008 13:21	EA6/DJ5GI	Balearic Is.	21	20m	SSB		59	54
5	26/03/2007 08:25	EW1MM	Belarus	27	20m	SSB		59	59
6	01/05/2008 12:45	ON7KTR	Belgium	209	40m	<FREQ:8>7.000000		599	599
7	03/08/2001 13:43	T9/DJ8MS	Bosnia-Herzegovinia	501	20m	<FREQ:9>14.000000		579	599
8	30/10/2004 14:55	PX2A	Brazil	108	10m	SSB		59	59
9	25/11/2004 14:29	LZ2BH	Bulgaria	212	20m	SSB		59	59
10	15/06/2008 09:44	AO9IB	Ceuta & Melilla	32	10m	SSB		59	59
11	04/10/2004 10:46	TK/IK2AQZ	Corsica	214	40m	SSB		59	59
12	08/01/2006 10:51	9A150NT	Croatia	497	40m	<FREQ:8>7.000000		599	599
13	27/08/2006 13:35	5B4AHL	Cyprus	215	20m	SSB		59	57
14	01/04/2007 08:45	OK1DOZ	Czech Republic	503	40m	<FREQ:8>7.000000		599	599
15	22/04/2007 09:58	9Q1D	Dem. Rep. of Congo	414	15m	SSB		59	55
16	19/02/2005 13:25	OZ1BGP	Denmark	221	20m	SSB		58	56
17	04/05/2008 14:29	M0OXO	England	223	40m	SSB		59	59
18	05/03/2006 10:19	ES0IC	Estonia	52	40m	<FREQ:8>7.000000		599	599
19	08/01/2006 16:13	UA6YJT	European Russia	54	40m	<FREQ:8>7.000000		599	599
20	01/05/2008 15:05	DF3ZE/P	Fed. Rep. of Germany	230	40m	<FREQ:8>7.000000		599	599
21	21/01/2006 17:56	F5GPE	France	227	80m	<FREQ:8>3.500000		599	599
22	04/03/2006 17:41	4L1FP	Georgia	75	40m	<FREQ:8>7.000000		599	599
23	25/02/2007 09:25	ZB2/4O3AL	Gibraltar	233	20m	SSB		59	59
24	02/08/2001 20:23	SV2/DL7XK	Greece	236	20m	<FREQ:9>14.000000		599	599

Extract from DG9MAQ's log of contacts made with MicroVert antennas.

Raimund's, DG9MAQ, 40m MicroVert made from tin cans.

My 40m MicroVert was surprisingly easy to make, but the performance was a little disappointing.

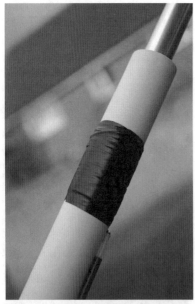

Close up of the GOKYA MicroVert coil – wrapped in PVC insulating tape to ensure that it didn't move and change the SWR.

Tom Sedlack, AC9TS, has also played with MicroVerts and now moderates the Yahoo MicroVert Group. The first one he built was for the PSK section of 40m (7MHz) and did pretty well considering the size. If you want to build one of these antennas, Google "MicroVert", which will come up with a host of pages, including AC9TS's calculator for the coil, or join the Yahoo group.

My own experimental 40m MicroVert was built using a telescopic 22mm diameter aluminium broom handle from a local hardware store. I built it according to the calculator available on the MicroVert Yahoo group site and managed to get an SWR of 1.3:1 in the middle of the 40m band. I could tune it by moving the telescopic section in and out. I built a choke by winding about 10 turns of RG58 in two directions on two ferrite rings superglued together. Tests showed that this worked well.

I mounted the MicroVert outside on a camera tripod and found that it worked best with the coax laying on the floor. If I picked it up and moved it into free space the SWR went high. Compared with my loft-mounted 40m dipole it was down about 2 - 4 S-points, although CW and PSK31 contacts were possible. One or two stations were the same signal strength as the dipole.

It wasn't a huge success, but if you only have a balcony it could get you on the air. MicroVerts for the higher frequencies should be more efficient.

DL7AHW's 'Hairspray Can' antenna

There are two antennas that look to be similar in design to the MicroVert. The first is the 'Hairspray Can' antenna, described by Arthur Wenzel, DL7AHW. For a 40m (7MHz) band antenna he says to use a large empty hairspray can about 50mm in diameter and 200mm long. Into the bottom of this mount a small 30cm telescopic whip for final tuning purposes. Arthur says that this length of whip will allow you to tune about 700kHz on his 40m version.

The top of the can (the nozzle end) is mounted into a PVC pipe about 150 - 250mm long. A coil of wire is connected to the hairspray can at this end and to the inner of an SO239 socket mounted on the pipe at the other.

This wire is coiled around the PVC former and the number of turns will depend upon the type of wire, the diameter of the can and the frequency of operation. Arthur's website [8] has a calculator that can be used to calculate the coil. As an example, a 40m (7MHz) hairspray can antenna with a 50mm diameter by 200mm long can needs seven metres of 1mm wire wound around the PVC pipe.

You then connect your counterpoise to the SO239 mounted on the PVC pipe – note that, once again, the braid is not actually connected to anything. The length of counterpoise behind the antenna is calculated by the formula L = 49.5/f (MHz). For example, the feed cable for the 40m version must be 7.02 metres long. Again you will see that this is less than a full quarter-wave.

At the end of the counterpoise the RF choke is fitted, just like the MicroVert, and then the cable back to your transceiver.

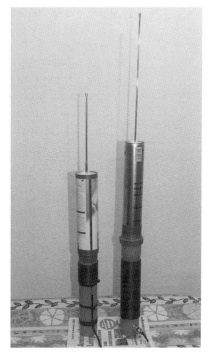

Two 'HairSpray Can' antennas.

The HB9ABX 'RoomCap' antenna

Felix Meyer, HB9ABX [9], has also designed an antenna that appears to look similar to the previous two, although he says that it doesn't use the coax to radiate. You will have to buy his plans to get the exact constructional details. RoomCap stands for 'Room Capacity' and the antenna is designed for use on bands from 10 – 80m.

The HF versions of the antenna feature a 2in (50mm) tube of a length between 50 and 170cm. The 40m version is only 1.5m long and there are also versions for 80m and 160m that are not much bigger: Felix's 160m design has a radiating tube 75mm in diameter and is 3m long. The antenna can be built as a monoband antenna, or as a two- or three-band antenna. He says that his antenna is designed for 200W PEP and can be built for 1kW PEP.

How does it perform? The antenna has not been subjected to independent tests, but users seem to be happy. Felix says that the antenna matches and even beats full-size commercial verticals in many cases.

Noriaki Fujiyama, JA8CNF, in Hokkaido, Japan, built a version for 80m (3.5MHz), which was only 1.8m long, and installed it on the roof of his house. In a CQWW contest he worked 54 DXCC entities while running 200W. Now admittedly it is actually quite easy to work stations in CQWW as there are usually some mega stations around – I worked W7WA in Seattle with 3W to a long wire on 20m (14MHz) one year, gaining my 1000 miles per watt award in the process.

Milton Riutort, NP4KT (ex-WP4DQK), and his father Alberto, WP4L, in Puerto Rico, built a 160m version of the RoomCap antenna. It is only 3m long and is mounted on a mast about 5m above the ground. With 100W they

The RoomCap antenna always attracts attention at hamfests and mobile rallies.

125

have made contacts with the USA and Europe, including G3PQA (distance 7500km). They say that they also have a 40m (7MHz) version only 2m long that outperforms a 10m high vertical at times.

As always the proof of the pudding is in the eating, but anyone who wants to build a RoomCap has to buy the construction guide and sign a Non-Disclosure Agreement. The cost of the guide, which Felix says offsets his expenses on this project, was 100 Swiss francs, 65 euros, or 100 US dollars at the time of writing. For more information see [9].

REFERENCES

[1] SteppIR: www.steppir.com

[2] 'An Experimental Look at Ground Systems for HF Verticals', Rudy Severns, N6LF, *QST* March 2010.

[3] Ventenna: www.ventenna.com

[4] Coax calculator: www.arrg.us/pages/Loss-Calc.htm

[5] Steve Yates, AA5TB: www.aa5tb.com

[6] Antenna experimenters' website: www.antennex.com

[7] DG9MAQ website: www.mydarc.de/dg9maq

[8] Arthur Wenzel, DL7AHW, website:
http://dl7ahw.bplaced.net/start01E.htm

[9] HB9ABX 'RoomCap' antenna:
http://hb9abx.no-ip.biz/ant--abx-e.htm

Let's get *really* stealthy

SOMETIMES YOU JUST have to admire people's imagination and perseverance – these are the people who will get a signal out against all the odds. These antenna ideas might not be the best in terms of coupling our RF to the air, but they work.

THE LOOP TUNER AND WINDOW LOOP

I'm not taking any credit for this design. It is based on the US Army loop tuner design and was inspired by an article in the G-QRP magazine *Sprat*. Jim Stirling, GM3UWX, wrote about his experience of using mini loops made out of PVC tubing and a small loop tuner that uses a couple of capacitors. I built my own just to try the design and was amazed at the results.

My loop consisted of two turns of thick insulated copper wire inserted into a diamond shape made out of 22mm white PVC tubing from the local DIY superstore. The diamond had 21in sides. The loop tuner was made from another defunct project and consisted of two variable capacitors of about 300pF each – see **Fig 8.1**. I also had a small meter in the box so I inserted a small diode and a variable resistor in series with the meter and wound the leads around one of the connections to the loop to pick up some RF. This allowed me to tune the antenna for maximum current.

The whole thing was put together in about an hour and I taped the loop to my curtain rail just to try it. I could easily run 10W without the capacitors flashing over and found that it would tune on 40m (7MHz) easily, down to an SWR of 1.5:1. If I removed one of the turns in the loop I found that I could tune 30m (10MHz) instead.

I connected the antenna up to my radio, tuned the loop for 7.030MHz and dropped the power to 5W. I listened around and found that signals on the loop were generally down about 1 - 3 S-points compared with my 40m loft-mounted dipole and external 80m OCFD. I tentatively put

This tiny 21in square antenna made out of PVC tubing and wire made an easy contact into the Netherlands with just 5W.

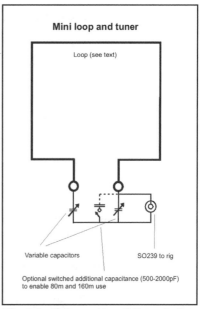

Fig 8.1: Schematic of the window loop and tuner. You can add additional switchable capacitance for 80m and 160m.

The tuner consists of just two variable capacitors. The meter is optional.

out a CQ call on CW and PA1MAX from the Netherlands came back to me. Max gave me a 579 report and we had a quick chat – all of it solid copy. He was using 100W to a dipole. Amazing! The thing actually worked.

Jim, GM3UWX, says that you can play with the size of the loop to get it to work on other bands. This will depend on having big enough capacitors or adding extra capacitance in parallel. **Table 8.1** shows Jim's suggestions.

Tuning is not as sharp as it is on a conventional magnetic loop and the antenna is quite broadband. Using a field strength meter I also found that you don't get the nulls off the sides of the loop that you would expect to find.

Band(s)	Loop size	Number of turns
1.8MHz	26in sides	5
3.5MHz	24in sides	3
7 / 10MHz	26in sides	1
7 / 10 / 14MHz	21in sides	1
7 / 10MHz	12in sides	1

Table 8.1: GM3UWX's suggestions for 'Window Loop' size and number of turns.

So there you are – an antenna for the lower bands that takes up no space at all and can be hung from a curtain rail when you want to play radio. Its performance is down on a dipole (not surprisingly), but it will make contacts, especially using CW or PSK31. Now tell me you don't have space for antennas!

K3MT'S GRASSWIRE ANTENNA

When I first read Mike Toia's, K3MT, piece on the Grasswire antenna I checked the calendar to see if it was an April fool joke – it wasn't! I'll let him take up the story. Mike says: "This antenna will not out-perform a Yagi, or a decent dipole up a half wavelength. Not in gain or signal strength, at least. But it will survive an ice storm, wind storm, and is practically immune to lightning. And it doesn't need a large tower or tall support. I deploy one from my hip pocket at times - the balun to match it is larger than the antenna!

"Put simply, it is an end-fed, long-wire antenna that is laid right on the grass, hence the name. The original Grasswire used by me in the summer of 1988 was just 204ft of #18 AWG magnet wire laid along the property line, anywhere from 1in to 6in above the ground. Either a ground rod or optional counterpoise wires are also needed - use one or the other as both are not needed." See **Fig 8.2**.

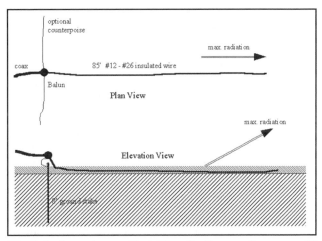

Fig 8.2: An antenna that literally lies on the ground? Mike, K3MT, says that it does radiate.

These antennas are largely resistive, with values ranging from 150 to 500Ω or so on average ground. They have been used successfully on all sorts of soil. One was used with great success by K3MT/VP9 in Southampton, Bermuda - the object of nightly pile-ups on 30m CW for four nights.

Mike says that the sceptic in you will doubt that such low antennas can work. After all, its image in the ground radiates and cancels out all radiation. True - if the ground is perfect. But nothing is perfect! The Grasswire radiates vertically-polarised signals off the end of the wire. Extensive monitoring tests have demonstrated the end-fire nature of the antenna. Mike says that launching a ray at, say, 15 - 20° take-off angle can be useful and that's what his Grasswire does. It is lossy in all directions, but least lossy when exciting the ionosphere for a long-haul DX contact. He says that signal reports are not fantastic, but contacts are made and ham radio is enjoyed! And the best part of this set-up is that his neighbours never knew that a ham station was on the air.

Mike feeds the antenna through a simple trifilar unun (an unbalanced to unbalanced impedance transformer), choosing the connections he wants for 2.5:1, 4:1 or 9:1 ratios (see **Fig 8.3**). It is basically a wide-band, three-winding autotransformer. Impedance ratios are as shown on the drawing. Generally it is necessary to connect the coax to either A2/B1 or B2/C1, and the antenna to B2/C1 or to C2. This may change from one band to another, and usually does.

Mike has also experimented with laying a Windom antenna on the ground. He says that it also becomes directional in the direction of the longest end. In both of these examples you will need to use an ATU.

Mike has written a book, *K3MT's HF Antenna Topics* [1], with a number of different antenna designs, including the Grasswire.

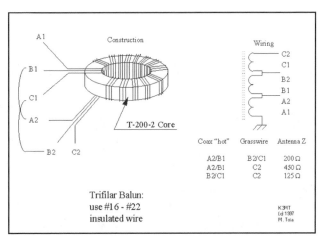

Fig 8.3: The wiring for the Grasswire matching unit.

METAL FOIL ANTENNAS

You can make HF antennas out of cooking foil, but you will need quite a lot. Aluminium foil isn't very strong so this is a strictly indoor solution. It is also impossible to solder, so you are going to have to use crocodile clips or bolts and washers to get a good connection. It is relatively easy to make a foil antenna for 2m (145MHz) or 70cm (430MHz) – a half-wave dipole using foil will only take a few minutes.

You can also buy self-adhesive *copper* foil which is used to screen enclosures, such as guitar amplifiers. This is more rugged than aluminium and would work well if you wanted to create a window antenna.

Larger antennas will need more foil and more time, but you should be able to make a decent half-wave dipole for 10m with little effort.

Now, if you are really clever and handy with the kitchen scissors you can make a multi-band dipole that would work from, say, 10 - 20m: five bands in total. The secret is to cut the foil at an angle so that the lowest edge measures a half wave at 10m and the top measures a half wave at 20m, as shown in **Fig 8.4**. The RF will see a high impedance along the foil strip at anything other than its operating frequency, and will so effectively ignore the parts of the strip that it 'doesn't like'.

Will it work? Yes, but to be honest it might be easier to create a series of five parallel-fed dipoles!

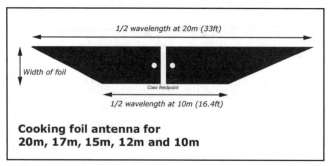

1/2 wavelength at 20m (33ft)

Width of foil

Coax feedpoint

1/2 wavelength at 10m (16.4ft)

Cooking foil antenna for 20m, 17m, 15m, 12m and 10m

Fig 8.4: A multiband dipole made out of simple aluminium cooking foil.

N5ESE'S NOTEBOOK ANTENNA

Monty Northrup, N5ESE, came up with a portable indoor antenna solution that is ideal for people on the move or who have no room for a permanent installation. And when it is not in use it just packs away into its own little 1in thick three-ring binder. Neat, eh?

Monty takes up the story: "In the Autumn 1990 edition of *Sprat* (Issue 64), the journal of the G-QRP Club, Gus Taylor, G8PG, expanding on material presented by G2MQ, described a 12ft, seven-band wire doublet. In the article, he suggested that one could raise the efficiency of a short antenna by using the entire (1/4-wave) length

two end-loading assemblies

twinlead feeder

doublet wire (in pocket behind end-loading sheets

N5FC 2000

N5ESE's Notebook antenna uses zig-zag loading.

of wire on each leg, but forming the ends into a 'non-inductive' end-loaded assembly. [Editor's note: This is the same technique used for the zig-zag loft-mounted dipole, which was inspired by the same article!] He claimed that such a winding had been found to increase the radiation resistance of a short antenna. And that implies higher antenna efficiency. Using these thoughts as the foundation for an antenna design, I endeavoured to come up with something both practical and usable for operating QRP from a hotel room.

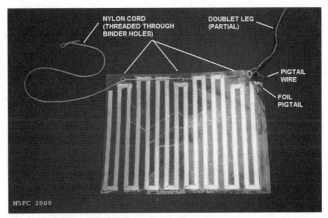

The zig-zag loading elements are made from self-adhesive copper tape.

"Whips have been used, but are notoriously inefficient, and certainly won't fit in my suitcase. Wire loops have also been tried, and are either hard to tune or very inefficient when less than a full-wave long. Magnetic loops are very, very efficient, but are hard to fabricate, expensive commercially, and cumbersome to transport. I wanted an antenna that was very portable (i.e. fit in my briefcase), easy to set up and take down, and reasonably efficient (or at least, relatively so, compared to other equally portable antennas). The Notebook Antenna is the result of my efforts.

"Some time ago, I found that hobby stores carry adhesive-backed copper-tape. The 1/4 inch wide tape is approximately equivalent to AWG 25 wire (in cross-section), and two in parallel equal about AWG 22. This would be quite useable (and believe it or not, quite possible to solder).

"My idea was to use an 8.5in x 11in (US letter-sized) transparency, and lay the tape down, zig-zagging on both sides in parallel (**Fig 8.5**). I made two, of course (one for each leg of the doublet) and punched holes for a three-ring binder. The transparency would easily tear if excess force was applied, so I placed an eyelet on the top inside corner (the kind found in cloth stores) and threaded support rope and antenna wire into this eyelet.

"The support 'rope', a small diameter nylon string, passed through the transparency's three-ring binder holes, to keep it in place,

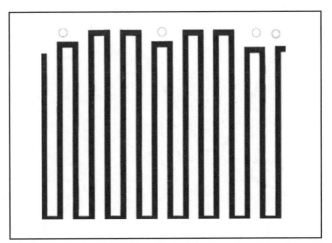

Fig 8.5: Detail of the Notebook antenna zig-zag construction.

but the eyelet takes all the strain. I fed the antenna with 15ft of low-loss twin lead, as suggested by the author," said Monty.

The binder antenna works like this:

1. Near or on the ceiling, screw in place two cup hooks about 12ft apart. Think about and avoid proximity to AC power / noise sources and appliances.
2. Using the free ends of the nylon cords, hang the antenna on the cup hooks.
3. Attach the twin lead feeder to your antenna tuner (and your centre insulator, if using mechanical connections). For maximum effectiveness, your antenna tuner should be a balanced-output design.
4. Tune for minimum SWR on the transmitter to antenna tuner transmission line. Note: For 10 – 20m no counterpoise should be needed. For 30 and 40m improved efficiency may be obtained by using a quarter-wave counterpoise, attached to the ground or chassis of the antenna tuner or transmitter. If you don't have enough room to lay the counterpoise straight, lay it on the floor in gentle S-curves.

If your tuner has difficulty tuning on 30 or 40m using the balanced feedline, tie the feedline together and feed it like an end-fed wire (in this case, you'll definitely need the counterpoise).

Monty said that his first QSO from central Texas, with the antenna hanging from coffee hooks placed in the ceiling of his first floor bedroom, and using five watts on 15m, was with VE3ADX in Ontario, who gave him a 549 report. He says the antenna is a little more susceptible to power-line radiated noise than an outside dipole and this can be problematic in some locations. While received signals were down about 1.5 to 2 S-units compared with the full-sized outdoor dipole, the power line hash was not similarly reduced.

Sverre Holm, LA3ZA, also built the antenna and said that it worked well, giving him contacts on 40, 30, 20, 17 and 15m.

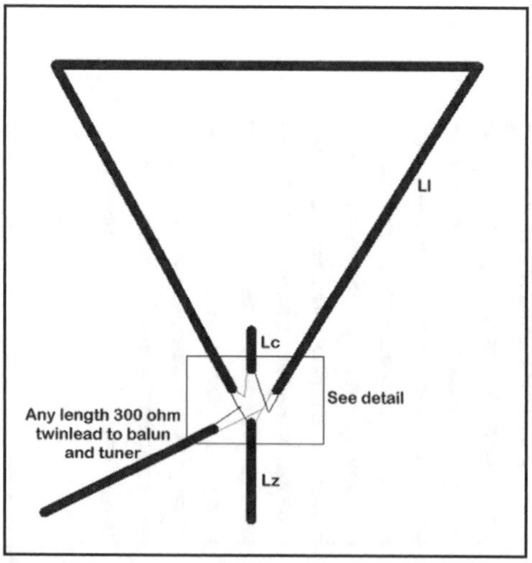

Fig 8.6: The Distributed Capacitance Twisted Loop antenna is monoband, but very simple to build.

THE DCTL PORTABLE ANTENNA

The Distributed Capacitance Twisted Loop (DCTL) antenna is an inexpensive, effective, resonant antenna that can fit in a space some 8ft high by 12ft wide, such as a wall or balcony. It will even work on 80 and 160m. The DCTL was developed by Jim McLelland, WA6QBU, and was published in *CQ* and *73* magazines in mid and late 1994. The construction material couldn't be simpler - it uses 300Ω twin lead (Fig 8.6). It is a monoband antenna, but it is so simple that you could make multiple versions for different bands.

For the 80m version, use a 28ft length (L1) of 300Ω twin lead. The opposite wires are connected to a shorted 4ft 6in stub of 300Ω twin lead. The remaining two ends of the 28ft twin lead connects to an open capacitive stub, 30in in length, also made of 300Ω twin lead. This makes more sense when you look at **Fig 8.7**.

Lz has a shorted end, while Lc is left open on the non-connected end. The critical part is in the connections. Each 'side' of twin lead is in a different colour, and the connections are shown below. The Ll (large loop) connection, properly made, puts a twist in the twin lead of half a turn. These diagrams assume that *no* twisting is made in the twin lead, and what the resulting connections look like. Use an ohmmeter to ensure you are *not* connecting the same wires! Use heat shrink or other *good* insulating material - the voltages and heat can get very high at the

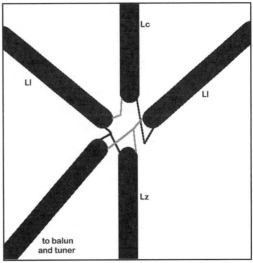

Fig 8.7: A close-up of the wiring detail.

junction points. Good soldered connections are also critical.

The antenna's usable bandwidth (2:1 SWR points) is pretty narrow, so using a tuner helps a lot. If your tuner requires a 50Ω coaxial input (like most do) you can use a 6:1 or 4:1 balun in line.

Trimming the open capacitive stub by 6in will raise the resonance point approximately 100kHz on 80m. The formulas are:

The total length (Ll and Lz, or Lt) = 130 / F(MHz)
The shorted stub (Lz) = 27 / [(2xF(MHz))-2]
Loop length (Ll) = Lt-Lz
Capacitive tuning stub (Lc) = 24 x (1 / [F(MHz)/2]**2)

Remember, *adding* the capacitive stub *lowers* the resonant frequency.

Some pre-calculated dimensions are given in **Table 8.2**. Remember that the total loop length can be divided by three (in a delta configuration) or four (in a square configuration) to give you an idea of the space required.

Band	Lt	Lz	Ll	Lc (to lower resonant freq by 100kHz)
160	65ft 0in	13ft 6in	51ft 6in	24in
80	32ft 6in	4ft 6in	28ft 0in	6in
40	17ft 10in	2ft 2in	15ft 8in	1 3/8in
30	12ft 10in	1ft 6in	11ft 4in	1in
20	9ft 0in	1ft 0in	8ft	1/2in

Table 8.2: Calculated dimensions for Distributed Capacitance Twisted Loop antenna.

Monty, N5ESE, built two versions of this antenna, both cut for 40m CW. One version used cheap 300Ω twin lead, and the other used premium 300Ω ladder line in order to reduce IR losses. The day he built it, the 40m band was in terrible shape, almost dead. While looking for a contact, however, he briefly heard a ZL (New Zealand) station calling CQ. His 599 signal was there and gone in 15 seconds, but that convinced Monty of the antenna's receiving abilities. Since Monty lives in a house with a very small back garden he built a weatherproof version of the DCTL for 80m. He says that as a receiving antenna, signal strength was about 1 to 1.5 S-units down compared with a full-size outdoor dipole. Power line noise susceptibility was about 2 S-units down, meaning that this antenna had better noise performance than an outdoor dipole, even given gain differences and the fact that the DCTL antenna was indoors.

When dismantled and coiled, the antenna fits nicely into a large zip-lock sandwich bag which can be tossed into a briefcase.

There are very few small antenna designs for 80m so this one might be worth a try.

W5ALT INDOOR VERTICAL ANTENNA

Walt Fair, W5ALT, has built a small, compact antenna that will operate from 6 to 40m. Walt says: "I operated from an apartment in Maracaibo, Venezuela, for over a year and during that time worked well over 100 countries, all 50 states on HF, and well over 100 grid squares on 6m using CW, SSB and PSK31. Although my design is fairly typical and I claim nothing new, my indoor vertical was custom

designed for my location. The constraints are that it must fit into the corner of the room where I operate, be unobtrusive to my wife and visitors, work well, and be easily constructed.

"After playing with various designs and ideas, I decided to build a base-loaded vertical antenna with two radials for use on all the bands from 6 to 40m. The size of the vertical element is 2m, so it will comfortably fit under the ceiling in the room.

"The diameter was determined by the available aluminium tubing. The loading coil needed to be as large diameter as possible to provide enough inductance for loading. The dimensions were tweaked a little using *MultiNEC* antenna modelling and then I started looking for parts. The vertical element consists of two 1m lengths of aluminium tubing used for hanging curtains. One piece is 1/2in diameter and the other is 5/8in diameter, so they could be telescoped. There's

Walt's small vertical fits into the corner of his apartment.

nothing critical about the dimensions. I paid about $1.50 for them at a hardware store. The wire for the radials and coil was also bought at the hardware store for about $2.25 and consisted of 10m of three conductor #14 gauge solid copper house wire.

"I was in a quandary about what to do for a coil former and how to make a stand for the antenna. My wife found a small plastic trash container that was very slightly tapered and about 5.5in in diameter and 1ft long. Then, with her typical flash of brilliance, she found a plastic toilet brush with a stand and said, 'Why don't you put those pipes on this?' In fact, it worked out quite well!

"The cost of the trash can and toilet brush stand was less than $2.00. Besides an alligator clip and a coax chassis mount socket, the total cost of materials was around $5.00.

A close-up of the loading and matching coil.

"Construction was quite simple. The ends of the tubing sections were scraped shiny, slipped together and joined with a small bolt. The loading coil was wound on the plastic trash container. I cut a hole in the bottom of the trash container to fit over the toilet brush and mounted it upside down on the brush stand. The vertical element slipped over the toilet brush and a hole drilled through the tubing and handle holds the whole thing in place.

"The ends of the radials were attached with small hardware to an SO239 coax chassis socket and then run along the baseboards from the corner where the antenna sits. A short wire with an alligator clip is attached to the centre conductor of the coax socket and used to tap the loading coil. The whole thing is fed with standard 50Ω coax from an MFJ antenna tuner. The whole thing took about one afternoon to build and test.

"Tuning the vertical was accomplished by adjusting the tap on the coil for lowest SWR on each band without the tuner. On most bands the lowest SWR is around 2:1, which is marginally OK. After finding the tap point, the tuner is used to tweak the match so the transceiver is happy. I made some paper labels to stick on the coil to indicate the tap points," Walt says.

So how does it work? Walt says it tunes on all the bands from 6 to 40m and he has worked the world. He says that he is usually able to get through DX pile-ups, although he knows his signal is not the best or strongest. The best indication of its performance is probably the QSL cards that he's received. In the first three months using the vertical, Walt made more than 300 contacts from about 50 countries. You decide if it works or not!

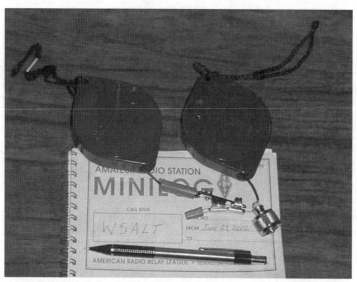

Walt's travel antenna spools up on to two plastic reels, ready for action when he gets to a hotel.

W5ALT TRAVEL ANTENNA

Walt does a lot of travelling and likes to take his Yaesu FT-817 QRP transceiver along with him. He says that he has found the perfect solution to carrying around a bulky antenna and ATU – he takes up the story: "While pondering the portable antenna issue and playing with some antenna modelling software, I stumbled on an interesting fact. Basically, if you take a 1/3 wavelength of wire and a 1/6 wavelength of wire mounted at an angle of 45° to each other and feed them at the intersection, the thing will resonate and show an impedance of 50Ω resistive. It's sort of a bent, off-centre fed doublet. Depending on how high it is and the quality of the ground, it can actually show some significant gain over a dipole.

"So with that information, we can leave the tuner at home and all we need is two pieces of wire that are 1/3 and 1/6 wavelength long on the bands of interest. Since I operate QRP, wire size isn't much of a concern and the wire can be rolled up when traveling and not in use. Some additional playing with *MultiNEC* seemed to indicate that the idea should work. So I got a couple pieces of copper wire, measured them for the 15m band, put them on a coax connector and attached them to an MFJ-269 antenna analyser. Sure enough, some minor adjustment of the lengths and angle gave a pure 50Ω resistive impedance.

"The next step, of course, was to try it out on the air. I pulled out my FT-817 and set it up on the dining room table using batteries, similar to how I would operate from a hotel room. Once again, a slight adjustment and the little rig thought the SWR was 1:1. I gave a call to an OK (Czech) station calling CQ on 15m, got a reply and got a report of 559. Not too bad with 2.5 watts from Venezuela. I tuned around a little and heard an HK0 (San Andres, Colombia) DXpedition, called and got a standard 599 report. That's not too far away, but those two contacts showed that the antenna does actually work," said Walt.

He spools his antenna onto some RadioShack 'reel' antennas, but you can use anything – how about a travel washing line reel?

Walt says: "So, now I have a portable antenna that can be wound up and stuffed in a shirt pocket or wherever else is convenient, works at least as well as a dipole, and doesn't require a tuner. Not too bad for an afternoon's playing around.

"Shortly afterwards, I made a trip to Puerto La Cruz, YV6 (Venezuela). I took my rig and left the tuner at home - that's confidence! I forgot the battery charger, so I only had about three hours operating off the batteries. I laid out the reels of wire in the hotel room on the fourth floor overlooking the Caribbean (a nice salt water ground plane helps). The short one was on the floor, the longer one ran up to the corner of the ceiling on a balcony. A slight adjustment of the lengths and the SWR was close to 1:1. The bands weren't very good in July, but I managed to work a handful of OM, OK, DL and UA stations on 15 and 20m using the antenna with 2.5W output. I'd say it works," he says.

Walt has some other tips:

- "Don't cut the wires. Just reel out the length you need and leave the rest inside the reels. It won't affect the performance enough to worry about.
- The angle between the wires isn't very critical. Just adjust the shorter wire length and position a little to get a match.
- The exact orientation of the wires isn't very critical, either. Droop one over a balcony, hang the end from the curtains, etc. The antenna is somewhat directional broadside to the plane of the wires.
- The higher the better. Both modelling and experience indicates that close to the ground a lot of the signal gets lost in ground losses. Stay above about the third floor of a hotel to get the best results.
- This isn't a good choice for camping, unless you are close to salt water. Note that the antenna will tune at low heights, but it won't work very efficiently.
- The distance from my fingers to my opposite shoulder is one metre. Knowing that saves having to carry something to measure the wires or having to mark them.
- There is nothing special about the reel antennas. Any type of wire could just as well be used. I used the Radio Shack product simply because I had them and they saved me from having to carry a bunch of wire in my luggage through airport security etc."

I modelled Walt's antenna design in *MMANA-GAL* and it works! Take two pieces of wire 7.05m and 3.53m long, arrange them at 90° and the SWR is less than 1.4:1 on 20m if they are at least 10m off the ground. If only 3m off the ground try lengths of 6.87m and 3.46m.

W0ES'S 'BIRD HOUSE' ANTENNA FOR 2M

Earl Schlenk, W0ES, recently moved into a house with severe limitations on external antennas. This wasn't going to stop him from having a station up and operating. He says: "A flyer came from the home owners' association suggesting the residents put up bird feeders with the provision that they must be off the ground and be 'squirrel proof'. Boy what a bit of synchronicity! This was the perfect ploy for using their suggestions to put up a 2m antenna.

The ultimate 'bird house' antenna – hiding a magnetic loop for 145MHz inside.

"I enjoy experimenting with magnetic loop antennas and I have a design that would fit inside a bird house / feeder, and I would build a bird house to enclose it. The dimensions were sized to enclose the loop and I added a roof for appearance purposes and decorative windows and a door.

"The basic loop was built using 3in wide copper strapping, 6in in diameter. This was mounted on a DC motor. I mounted limit switches, using lever switches, to stop the motor at its maximum rotation in the CW and CCW directions. I also mounted a home position indicator (for initial loop orientation reference) using an infrared opto-coupler and an LED.

"The capacitor I used was from my junk box and was a 2 to 10pF. The stepper motor was purchased from the Motion King Motor Industry [2] and was mailed directly from China. This was the smallest stepper motor I could find with enough torque to turn the capacitor and have enough resolution (1.8 degree) for the very fine tuning this loop requires.

"The stepper motor controller was bought as a kit and purchased from Cana Kit [3]. I used a LM350 regulator adjusted to turn the loop at a slow speed.

"The bird house was made from scrap material I had on hand, and I gave the 'house' a coat of paint to match the colour of the facade of the complex and coated

The 2m magnetic loop antenna inside Earl's bird house.

it with two coats of polyethylene. I purchased the 'door' and 'windows' from a dolls house company.

"The stepper motor is used to adjust the capacitor for resonance on the frequency that you want to use. You can use your SWR meter to tune for resonance by tuning for a 1.1 SWR. The loop is bi-directional and has good nulls off its sides. I mounted the 'house' on 1.5in diameter PVC pipe 11ft in the air. It is supported by a 6ft tall piece of two x four inch timber, attached to landscape timbers that were in the planting area around my patio.

"The coax and control cable were buried under the mulch in the planting area and ran into the shack through a board mounted in the bottom of the shack window. I am very satisfied with this antenna.

"I have received compliments from my neighbours about the 'Bird House' and no one knows it is an antenna. I was quizzed as to what the electrical wires were for and I replied that I am going to install a 'weather station' inside in the future. This ruse was to explain any future changes I may make or if repairs are necessary in the future. I could also have said it has a camera inside to observe the birds!"

THE CARPET LOOP ANTENNA

I first heard about this as an antenna for short wave listeners, but I don't see why it couldn't be adapted for QRP transmissions as well. The idea would be to put a loop of wire underneath your carpet and then bring the ends up to the edge and feed it with 300Ω ribbon cable or direct to a magnetic loop tuner.

If you were on a first or second floor it could work well. The overall size of the loop would depend on what bands you wanted to work and how versatile your loop tuner is.

A 10 - 15ft circumference loop would work on 10m - 20m. You could either use a commercial loop tuner like the MFJ-936B or build your own. I think this would have to be strictly QRP, though, as the proximity to house wiring would pretty much ensure EMC problems unless you are very lucky. You could just about get away with a 20ft circumference loop on 40m and 30m, but ideally it should be bigger, say 28ft. A loop for 80m would have to be very big indeed – up to 63ft in circumference.

At very low heights, close coupling to the ground causes detuning and losses due to current induced into a mirror image of the loop below the surface, with resistance of the image loop proportional to soil resistance. Another loss component is due to current flowing in the soil via capacitance between the loop and soil surface. Therefore it might work better upstairs or if you live in a high-rise flat.

Small transmitting and receiving loops, when properly designed, can approach the performance of a full-size antenna. Also, due to their high-Q nature, a well-designed loop antenna system can provide pretty significant rejection of undesired signals and noise. No ground or radials are needed, but tuning will generally be very sharp.

It won't be brilliant, but if you are stuck for space it might be worth trying.

THE FENCE-TOP ANTENNA

Do you have a wooden fence running around your property? If you do, you could fit a stealthy loop around the top and feed it with open-wire feeder. The chances are that it won't be resonant on any of the amateur bands, but that doesn't really matter – just don't feed it with coax.

It is likely to be around a full-wave at somewhere between 3.5 and 7MHz. That is, a total length of somewhere between 40 and 80m. Just load it up with a balanced ATU and see what you can work. Its proximity to the ground may help you with NVIS contacts on 80m, but it might not be a good DX antenna on the lower bands due to the high angle of radiation.

Martin, G8JNJ, converted a scrap washing line into a stealthy HF vertical.

The vertical uses Petlowany loading coils.

But the only cost will be a few tens of metres of insulated wire and a short length of ribbon cable or open wire feeder – just make sure that no-one can trip over it or decapitate themselves!

THE ROTARY WASHING LINE ANTENNA

You know those rotary washing lines? If that doesn't look like a vertical with a capacity hat, I don't know what does. On its own it wouldn't work too well, but with a little help. . .

The first thing to do is to put down some radials. Next thing is make a wooden or plastic centre insulating support to ensure that the washing line is insulated from the earth.

I would then wire all the various metal elements together to create a single structure. Connecting an analyser to the earth and the washing line would then let you know where it was resonant.

My guess is that it would more likely be towards 10m than 80m! You could then add series inductance (to bring it down in frequency) or capacitance (to move it up).

Let me know if you get it to work.

Martin Ehrenfried, G8JNJ [4], used Petlowany loading coils on his modified rotary washing line to get it to resonate on 80m. If you search for "Petlowany" on Google you'll see how Bill Petlowany, K6NO, used spiral loading coils to make small dipole antennas resonant on much lower frequencies.

Martin said: "The version with the three interwoven Petlowany loading spirals worked best on 80m, but even that wasn't too brilliant. I also tried one very long continuous spiral to try to make it directly resonant on 3.6MHz but that didn't work at all well. Overall I think it needed better radials. Unfortunately this lowers the resistive feed impedance, so it may be necessary to add an impedance matching device if you don't want to use an ATU.

"It did strike me that this would make a good multiband vertical, if it was used with a reasonable radial system, and an auto ATU at the base in place of the loading coil. The top loading would help on the low bands, whilst the overall height would be good for the range 5 to 30MHz."

G8JNJ 'FAT MAX' ® ANTENNA

Every now and again you see a design and think "that's brilliant!" This is one of those antennas. Martin, G8JNJ [4], has come up with a multi-band vertical that pays homage to another well-known commercial antenna. The difference is that this one uses a cheap retractable metal tape measure from a pound store.

Martin said: "I got the idea for this antenna when I wanted to make some field strength measurements, and needed to be able to quickly set up a number of quarter-wave vertical antennas in order to make reference measurements. The basic idea is to use a retractable steel tape measure as the radiating element, so that the length can be continuously adjusted to achieve resonance. The tape measure I used was a cheap 8.5m long one which I had obtained from a pound shop (Dime store). There are any number of tapes which could be used, including the Stanley Fat Max ® range (hence the antenna's name) which are available in lengths up to 100ft long.

"Several people have tried to make retractable antennas using a steel tape measure, but most have taken the design decision to mount the case of the tape measure at the bottom end of the antenna. The disadvantage of this method is that some way has to be found of providing a sliding contact with the steel tape as it spools out, as the wound steel tape on the internal reel does not provide a low enough impedance connection. The coiled construction also adds a large inductive reactance which is not desirable in this application. Purists may argue that a steel tape is also likely to have high losses when used for an antenna. However, I was not able to measure any difference between the steel tape and a copper wire, so this does not seem to be a problem in practice. I suspect this may be due to the broad width of the tape, but so far I have not been able to test this theory.

"During my tests I attached the case of a tape measure to one of the top sections of a 10m fibreglass fishing pole and connected my coax to the steel tape by means of a nut, bolt and solder tag at the start of the tape. I extended the tape from 8.5m to approximately 10m by adding an additional length of wire to connect it to the coax. I chose this length so that I could get the antenna to tune from 6m to 40m by simply extending the tape.

"This arrangement worked very well, and I quickly realised that it would be possible to operate it remotely by attaching a rope to the casing of the tape, which I could use to raise and lower it as required. The rope would run over a pulley which could be suspended from a non-conductive support pole, tree limb, house or anything else that was approximately 10m high. The other end of the rope could be brought into the shack and simply tied off at the required lengths, using loops or knots tied into the rope. Alternatively it could be wrapped around a cable drum which is arranged to be rotated by a surplus electric drill or screwdriver, ideally one which has a mechanical torque adjustment (see **Fig 8.8**). This could also be as simple or complex as required.

"With the addition of microswitch end stops and positional counters it could even be made fully automated in operation. Note that the antenna doesn't have to be used as a quarter-wave; with a suitable switched matching network at the base it could also be used as a half or 5/8 wave.

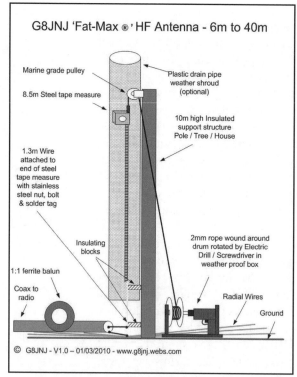

G8JNJ 'Fat-Max ®' HF Antenna - 6m to 40m

Marine grade pulley

8.5m Steel tape measure

Plastic drain pipe
weather shroud
(optional)

10m high Insulated
support structure
Pole / Tree / House

1.3m Wire
attached to
end of steel
tape measure
with stainless
steel nut, bolt
& solder tag

Insulating
blocks

2mm rope wound around
drum rotated by Electric
Drill / Screwdriver in
weather proof box

1:1 ferrite balun

Coax to
radio

Radial Wires

Ground

© G8JNJ - V1.0 – 01/03/2010 - www.g8jnj.webs.com

Fig 8.8: Martin's, G8JNJ, latest idea pays homage to a well-known commercial antenna manufacturer – can you work out which one?

"The only slight problem I encountered was that in high winds the tape could be blown sideways, so it would be best to use this antenna in a sheltered position. Alternatively it could be housed inside a 10m length of plastic drainpipe, which would make the whole antenna much stealthier. Spraying the tape a less distinctive colour with some car paint also helps to reduce visibility and improves durability. A rain cover made from the end of a plastic bottle slipped over the case of the tape also helps. If the tape proves reluctant to retract, adding some additional weight to the tape body may help.

"Finally, here's a whacky idea for those of you with HOA (Home Owner Association) restrictions on antennas. Why not build the base of this antenna into a bird table, and have the tape raised by some thin line run though a pulley attached to a tree branch? At night simply let the tape rise from the 'bird house' in the style of the *Thunderbirds* secret island base!" Martin said.

Hopefully there are some new ideas here for you to try. As one ham told me when I was writing the book: "I'd rather have a 55 report from a stealth antenna than no report at all."

REFERENCES

[1] *K3MT's HF Antenna Topics*, Michael Toia, K3MT, Jokalym Press. See http://f5ad.free.fr/Liens_coupes_ANT/G/K3MT%20Antenne%20gazon.htm
[2] Motion King Motor Industry (stepper motors): www.motionking.com
[3] Cana Kit: www.canakit.com
[4] Martin, G8JNJ, website: www.g8jnj.webs.com

Commercial stealth antennas

IN THIS CHAPTER we look at and test a wide variety of commercially-available antennas that are suitable for the stealthy operator.

THE I-PRO TRAVELLER DIPOLE FROM PRO ANTENNAS – TESTED

The I-Pro Traveller is from Carl Kidd, G4GTW [1], and promises great things for the portable DXer or home-based ham with little garden space. The antenna is a centre-fed half-wave vertical dipole with capacity hat end loading. Capacity hat loading was chosen to keep the inductive loading to a minimum and so minimise losses. The added benefit is that you have an antenna that can cover 10m - 40m without an ATU, but which stands only 3m tall. The other bonus is the antenna doesn't need any form of ground plane or radials to work. The I-Pro Traveller power specification is 1200W PEP on 10m - 20m and 1000W PEP on 40m.

The antenna comes packed in a sturdy cardboard box. Once everything is pulled out you are left with a selection of components, including the star-shaped quad-leg base, the two capacity hats and the multi-band centre matching section. You can opt for the 10 - 20m or 40m versions, or buy the separate optional loaded dipole centre piece and have two antennas in one.

The I-Pro Traveller can be erected in minutes and put away again when you have finished.

All of this fits neatly into a 1m long custom-built black nylon hold-all which can easily be carried around or put into a car boot. The I-Pro Traveller also lends itself to explore portable operation overseas as it is easily transported in its compact carrying hold-all.

The dipole pieces are made of high-quality anodised thick-walled aluminium stock, with right angle bracing and thumbwheels to enable a) the four legs to be adjusted on uneven ground and b) the lower capacity hat legs to be moved upwards to tune the antenna – this is especially important on 10 - 12m.

The antenna packs away into its own carrying case.

All nuts, bolts and screws are stainless steel with plating and anodising protecting bracketing and tubing. This means that it can be left outside as a permanent installation.

The quad-legged base allows the I-Pro Traveller to be used with the ground sloping by as much as 30°.

The bandwidth of the antenna is very impressive – on test I was able to get SWR lows of around 1.1:1 in the middle of each and concur with the I-Pro Traveller specifications that you should be able to get the following 1.5:1 bandwidths:

20m	300kHz
17m	500kHz
15m	900kHz
12m	1800kHz
10m	2200kHz

An antenna analyser is not required to set up the I-Pro Traveller - the built-in SWR metering in most radios will be fine. The choice of transceiver is made easy because no ATU is required.

If you wish to operate on 40m you remove the centre multi-band centre matching section and replace it with a dedicated 40m section, complete with loading coils. I was able to achieve a 1:1 match on 40m with about a 70kHz bandwidth between the 1.5:1 SWR points.

We first tested it against Chris Danby's, G0DWV, Cushcraft A4S triband beam, which had been lowered to around 25ft due to high winds. We also compared it against Chris's 132ft doublet at the same height. We then tested it against my dipoles and 132ft OCF dipole (Windom) at 25ft and a 65ft inverted-L with 9:1 unun and ground system.

At Chris's we found that the antenna performed pretty much the same as the 132ft doublet on 20m and 17m. Sometimes it was slightly better and sometimes slightly worse. What was gratifying was that the noise level was lower on the I-Pro Traveller by about 2 - 3 S-points. The similar reports on the two antennas was confirmed by a contact with a station in Italy who couldn't tell the difference between the two antennas.

We also listened to a CW station in 8P9 (Barbados) and there was no difference. Chris's beam was consistently 2 - 3 S-points better, which was to be expected.

With the 40m centre section fitted Chris was able to take part in our Norfolk Amateur Radio Club's 40m net with a station in Koblenz, one of Norwich's twin cities, receiving 59 reports each way with 100W. In these tests the I-Pro Traveller

You even get a spirit level to make sure that the base is level.

was down slightly on the 132ft doublet on 40m, but that is hardly surprising given that the antenna is only 3m tall – a fraction of the full 40m wavelength.

At my QTH the I-Pro Traveller was quite competitive on a closing 20m band. Signals were roughly equal to my dipoles and 132ft off-centre fed dipole, sometimes slightly weaker as propagation varied. The antenna was more than capable of working across the Atlantic to the USA, Canada and the Caribbean. It was around 2 S-points down on my 65ft inverted-L with 9:1 unun with the top at 9m, which is a good DX performer on HF.

On 17m the I-Pro Traveller was either equal to or outperformed all my other antennas by about 1 S-point.

We then took it to Walcott on the north Norfolk coast and set it up right next to the edge of the sea. Carl is a keen advocate of water-edge DXing and we soon saw why. The sea acts as a giant ground plane, which coupled with the take-off available stretching out to the horizon, guarantees Yagi-like performance. We were soon listening to VK (Australia) stations aplenty on 20m, and had a genuine 57 - 59 short-path QSO with Mike, VK3XL, near Melbourne, straight out across the North Sea.

We then swapped over to 40m and had solid 59+ QSOs with a lot of European stations. All this with an antenna just 3m high.

The multi-band I-Pro Traveller costs £279.95 for either the 20 - 10m or 40m version. You can add the other bands to either version by buying the alternative centre matching section for £119.95. The only other option is the custom-designed I-Pro Traveller branded nylon carrying hold-all at £19.95.

THE I-PRO HOME FROM PRO ANTENNAS - TESTED

The I-Pro Home Multiband HF Vertical Antenna, to give it its full name, is designed by Carl Kidd, G4GTW, of Pro Antennas. As it can be assembled quite quickly it can work as a stealthy antenna, which is only erected when you wish to operate.

The antenna is a centre-fed vertical dipole with capacity hat end loading, looking like an H on its side. Capacity hat loading was chosen to keep the inductive loading to a minimum and so reduce losses.

It is designed to be *non*-resonant on all of the amateur bands. A large unun transformer (of unspecified impedance transformation) is fitted to the centre of the dipole, which reduces the resultant SWR to something your rig's internal ATU can handle. The maximum power it can handle is 400 watts PEP.

The antenna is 5m long with the top and bottom elements spanning 2.5m. It comes with a heavy-duty

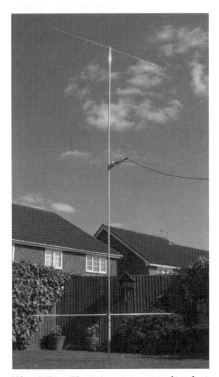

The I-Pro Home uses capacity hat loading to make it smaller.

The feedpoint and unun.

galvanised mounting bracket, suitable for posts of between 1.5 and 2 inches. Once mounted on a suitable stake (not supplied) it actually sits just under 6m tall and weighs in at 4.5kg.

Aerospace alloys are used throughout as are non-corrosive stainless steel fittings. Solid GRP rod is used for the important insulating sections. This material combines excellent dielectric properties with great structural strength.

The antenna will cover all five amateur bands from 20m to 10m. If you have an external ATU it can also be 'persuaded' to cover 40m and 30m (the average internal ATU will not handle the high SWR the antenna presents on these bands). There is no reason why the antenna shouldn't be used for short wave listening either, from about 5 to 30MHz.

Having assembled the antenna you then attach the coax, via a PL259, with suitable weatherproofing such as self-amalgamating tape, and drop it on to the mounting post.

The instructions say that for all-weather use the antenna should be guyed (not supplied). I would endorse this – if leaving it up for more than a few hours guying with nylon cord is essential as the antenna is quite top heavy.

The coax has to be arranged to come away from the antenna at about 45 degrees. This minimizes interaction.

An internal ATU should be able to find a 1:1 match on all of the bands 14MHz – 29MHz. My rig could also match 10MHz, but I know that other manufacturer's internal ATUs won't match much beyond an SWR of 3:1.

The benefit of the I-Pro Home is that it doesn't need a ground plane, which is reflected in the shorter setting up time. This shouldn't be underestimated as you will be up and running in an hour or so, whereas you could spend *days* putting a decent set of radials down for a ground-mounted vertical!

On 20m the antenna shone, with signals and noise levels similar to my doublet to UA3 (European Russia), EW8 (Belarus) and HG (Hungary). Compared with the five-band trap vertical signals from around Europe including Russia were generally better on the I-Pro by about 1 - 2 S-points. This was very significant as just about every European signal I found on 20m was better on the I-Pro than on a trap vertical (though on longer paths the difference was less marked).

The five-band trap vertical doesn't cover 17m, so I switched to my dipole / doublet. On 17m the I-Pro Home was better than my dipole / doublet, with RW3XZ in Moscow up 2 S-points. Other signal strengths pretty much matched my other antennas on this band, but sometimes the I-Pro Home bettered them by about 1 to 2 S-points. There were also some weak CW signals that were inaudible on anything other than the I-Pro Home.

On 15m the I-Pro Home bettered my doublet (which doesn't work well on 15m) and generally beat the trap vertical by about 2 S-points. Despite poor band conditions at the time, a number of stations were worked, each giving better reports on the I-Pro.

A station purporting to be T31A (Central Kiribati), but in reality a pirate, was much stronger on the I-Pro Home – shame he wasn't real! Imam, YB4IR, in Sumatra, Indonesia, was much louder on the I-Pro and would not have been workable on the trap vertical: the I-Pro Home is a good performer on 15m.

On 12m it was once again equal to, or slightly better than, my other wire antennas into Russia and Ukraine. 5B4AGQ (Cyprus) was better on the I-Pro than the doublet by 1 S-point. Once again the trap vertical doesn't play on 12m.

The 10m band was pretty dead at the time of testing, but with the few stations I did hear performance appears to be similar to 12m. The I-Pro Home and trap vertical were neck-and-neck on contacts into Spain and Italy and it easily beat the longer wire antennas. It was neck-and-neck with a dedicated 10m horizontal wire dipole around Europe.

In conclusion then, the I-Pro Home will give good service on 20m to 10m and, as pointed out in the specifications, reduced performance is to be expected on 30m and 40m. For more information about the antenna see www.proantennas. co.uk or tel: 07906 512459.

THE TAK-TENNA

New antenna designs don't come along too often. The spiral-coiled TAK-tenna [2] is unusual in that, although it is new, its design harks back to the early days of wireless. Look at any old photographs of radio equipment from the early 1900s and you will see a lot of spiral coils – even inventor Nikola Tesla used them for the primary winding on his famous high-voltage coils.

The TAK-tenna is a dipole with each quarter wavelength radiating element made of a spirally-wound coil of wire. This was the principle behind Bill Petlowany's, K6NO, design in the March 1998 edition of *WorldRadio* magazine. Less well known, but *the* most important person, is the original inventor A R Brown who patented his spiral version in 1969. Stephen Tetorka, WA2TAK, (hence the "TAK-tenna" name) in New Jersey, USA, is the developer of the newest version and has a patent pending with improvements to the previous designs.

The use of spiral radiating elements means the antenna can be made much smaller than the 'full-stretch' wire dipole for the same frequency. To give you an idea, the 40m TAK-tenna version, as tested, has a boom length of only 30in and weighed 5lb. To put that in perspective, a full-size half wave dipole for 40m is 66ft long. So the TAK-tenna is physically only 4% of the size of a half-wave wire dipole. There are TAK-tennas available for all HF bands from 80 – 10m.

The 40m version can be used as a multiband antenna on 30, 20, 17, 15, and 10m with a suitable ATU. There are many customer reviews on eHam [3] giving TAK-tenna performance reports. Some operators use balanced line, with low cable loss for off-resonance performance, in place of a lengthy coax run in order to

The TAK-tenna is a dipole with each leg made of a spirally-wound coil of wire.

The coils fit into grooves in the support arms and are held in place with mil-spec locking cable ties.

minimise power loss in the transmission line. Maximum performance is obtained when the TAK-tenna is resonated just as to be expected with the traditional wire version as resonance provides maximum efficiency for power transfer and it also provides more 'user friendly' impedance values when operated off-resonance in multiband operation.

Assembly is fairly straightforward. You insert the four coil supports into the boom ends and secure them with the black mil-spec UV resistant locking cable ties. Pre-cut notches on the coil supports ensure proper wire spacing and the neat spiral shape. You then add the mast mounting hardware and mounting screws for the coax connections / coil feed wires. You also need to solder three tags and two crocodile clips to the feed wires and (unsupplied) coax. The complete assembly took around one hour and it was ready for testing.

Once you have completed assembly, you use the crocodile clips to pick up the suggested tapping points on the coil for the intended resonant frequency of your choice. The resonating process involves moving the crocodile clips to tapping points around the spiral until you get resonance at your desired frequency. The clips are removed and the wire ends soldered to the spirals once it is resonated. Some users resonate with a rig at low power and its SWR meter to locate the resonant frequency although using an antenna analyser makes this process much easier.

The end result in my case at a low height was a minimum SWR of 1.1:1 at 7.080MHz with maxima of 3:1 at 7.000MHz and 2.2:1 at 7.200MHz. I could have moved the resonant point higher or lower, but as most UK operations appear to be below 7.100MHz this was deemed OK.

I connected the coax to my Icom IC-7400 to see how the TAK-tenna 40 performed. Conditions were not good in the middle of the day in July. The solar flux was 66, the A index 9 and the K index 1, but many Europeans were worked on 40m with 50 - 100W on SSB and CW. Compared with a W3EDP 85ft end-fed inverted-L and 40m half-wave dipole signals were generally down 1 - 3 S-points.

Raising the antenna height makes a difference for any antenna. At the manufacturer's recommended height of 20ft many signals on the horizontally-orientated TAK-tenna were within one S-point of the reference antennas. The resonant point moved higher in frequency as the antenna was raised and the tapping points had to be adjusted. The feedpoint capacitive impedance changes with the antenna's height above ground due to capacitance-to-ground effect.

The loss of 1 - 3 S-points is not all doom and gloom. On 40m at night there were many S9+20dB signals that were a still a perfect copy at S9+10 on the TAK-tenna. In the IOTA contest many "59 / 599" reports were exchanged, although that doesn't count for much!

In one QSO, Ike, DM3ML in Dresden, said that the TAK-tenna was only 1 S-point down compared with the end-fed. Another good point is that the noise levels were also down on the TAK-tenna – S5 on average versus S8 on the end-fed, which made for easier listening.

TAK-tenna recommends a statistical sample of at least 30 QSOs over a period of several weeks to assess performance under varying band and propagation conditions, and taking into account the antenna's directivity and changing antenna patterns as more lobes are generated in a dipole as the frequency increases.

As one happy TAK-tenna user put it: "It works at 13ft, better at 25ft, and is really awesome at 45ft! Imagine getting it up to 60ft? All with 100 watts." TAK-tenna reports that maximum signal report is achieved when the 'cold' spiral (the one connected to the coax shield) is pointing to the receiving station with reference to the boom centre.

Depending upon the specific site characteristics, vertical orientation may provide better results. It gives a lower angle signal suitable for DX, although mounting height is a factor. The instructions also state that you might be able to null local interference and peak signals by rotating the TAK-tenna directivity, although this wasn't tried.

On the TAK-tenna website [2] there is an installation photograph of Vince Grgic's, S52CC, TAK-tenna 40 jutting from his third floor balcony. With the MFJ-949E it tunes fine on eight bands from 80 to 10m. Using the Yaesu FT-450 transceiver he has logged over 925 QSOs and 118 DXCC entities from five continents, some of them even in serious pile-ups.

I tried the TAK-tenna 40 mounted vertically at about 20ft. The average noise level was higher (S6 against S5 when horizontal) but received signal strengths were generally only 1 S-point lower than the reference antennas and sometimes equal. GB5FI on Flatholm Island was preparing for the IOTA contest and gave me 59 on the end-fed and 58 on the TAK-tenna. In his words: "The end-fed has the slight edge." On CW some Europeans were equal to or 1 S-point stronger on the TAK-tenna. No comparison with each antenna's directivity was made.

At the time of writing, TAK-tenna has been in business three years and has maintained a customer satisfaction score on eHam of 4.7 / 5 - a 94% rating. That says a lot.

The TAK-tenna is a unique and useful antenna that would suit hams with little or no space for a full-size 40m antenna. Is it a compromise? Yes, signals were generally lower than on either full-size 66ft half-wave antennas or an 85ft end-fed, but then the TAK-tenna is only one sixtieth of a wavelength long on 40m. And then, try rotating a wire either 66 or 85ft long!

If you don't have the room for a full-size 40m wire antenna (or even if you do) it will get you on the air with satisfying results.

THE BILAL ISOTRON - TESTED

The Isotron range of antennas [4], by Ralph Bilal in Colorado, USA, have been around for over 30 years now and have a loyal following. They are the ultimate in small, stealthy HF antennas, but are not 'magical' in any sense of the word. Instead they rely on the known technique of combining a capacitor (the end plates) with a coil to give a resonant circuit. Looking like some kind of bird feeder, the Isotron has a capture area that equals or exceeds the area of a conventional half-wave dipole.

A test by Gilfer Associates in New Jersey measured the Isotrons to transmit as well as a half-wave dipole and be less susceptible to noise – up to 3dB less noise than a dipole at times.

There are Isotrons available for all bands from 160m (1.8MHz) to 6m (50MHz) and even combination models for 80 / 40m, 20 / 40m and 20 / 15 / 10m. You can combine up to three Isotrons on a single mast and feed them with a single piece of ladderline feeder between each one and 50Ω coax back to the radio.

You can mount up to three Isotrons on a single mast.

The topband model is not surprisingly the largest at 9.5ft long. The 6m version is the smallest at only 16.5in. In the middle of the range are the 80m and 40m models which are 32 and 22in high respectively.

John Smithson, N8ZYA, of Charleston, West Virginia, is featured in the first chapter of this book and uses an Isotron 80-40-20 combo. He sums his experience up by saying: "I have *fun* with it. . . and to me. . . that's *all* that matters."

If you read the reviews at eHam [3] you will see that people are divided. There are glowing reviews from people who think they are the best thing since sliced bread and others who have struggled to make them work. As always, the only way to find out is to try one, but the general consensus is that while they may not work as well as a beam at 50ft, they do work and let many people who would otherwise not be able to play radio get on the bands.

But how did our test go? I had been looking forward to testing the Bilal Isotron antenna. I have read about these for some time and given that they have been around for 30 years it was about time that we tested one. Now that Martin Lynch [5] in the UK is importing them from Colorado it seemed like a good opportunity. The antennas supplied were the 40m and 80 Isotrons.

The manual says that the antennas *must* be mounted on a metal pole, preferably earthed. It can be mounted in an attic or on a balcony, but even if you can't earth the antenna it should still be on a metal pole. The instructions say that if you mount them in the attic you could use the mains earth for your connection, but this seems like a recipe for RFI unless you are running QRP.

The antennas arrived in a very small cardboard box. Opening it revealed the two coils (one for the 80m version and one for the 40m). Also included were the aluminium top and bottom plates, the plastic / nylon insulators that hold the plates apart, plus all the hardware to assemble the antenna. The instructions came as a photocopied booklet, but were quite clear.

A close-up of the 40m Isotron.

It took about 30 - 45 minutes to assemble each antenna. I suggest you read the instructions very carefully and allow some time for mistakes. It wasn't until I went to connect up the coil that I realised that I had put the insulating spacers in upside down. You won't need much in the way of tools – I used a couple of 11mm spanners and a flat-head screwdriver.

The antenna uses two aluminium rods to suspend the resonating coil between the top and bottom capacitor plates. The 80m version also has two small square aluminium tuning plates on rods that can be moved to tune the antenna to the part of the band you are interested in. You are advised not to fit these until the antenna is in position and you have found the natural resonant point, but given that it is designed to operate out of the box at around 3.950MHz (the US 75m band) you may as well fit one or both tuning rods from the start. Bilal recommends one tuning rod and hat if you wish to operate from 3.675 – 3.8MHz and two if you wish to operate from 3.5-3.675MHz.

A close-up of the tuning rod on the Isotron antenna.

Once assembled the antenna is quite light (6lb / 2.7kg) and can easily be picked up with one hand. My only complaint was that the edges of the aluminium plates were a little sharp and it might pay to use some emery cloth on these to prevent cutting yourself. Once assembled I mounted it on a lightweight 18ft aluminium mast that has been living in my shed since I moved into this property three years ago. This was mounted temporarily on a ground post in the back garden and the antenna was fed with Mini 8 coax.

Without the two tuning rods the antenna resonated at around 4.0MHz – way too

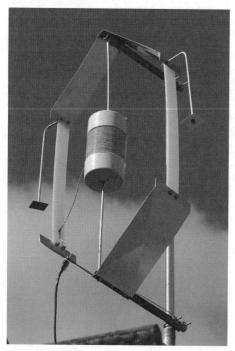

The 80m Isotron.

high. But putting both tuning rods on, with the small aluminium capacity hats facing down, saw the SWR come down to 1.8:1 at 3.610MHz, using an earthed MFJ antenna analyser. The 3:1 SWR bandwidth at this setting was 3.586 – 3.642MHz (56kHz).

Conditions on a May afternoon on 80m were not too good, but there were one or two SSB signals around. I compared the Isotron with my 132ft OCFD, which lies across the roof at about 30ft and the 85ft W3EDP end-fed that also goes over the same roof. Both antennas perform about the same on 80m. I live in a typical suburban location and the noise level on 80m is usually S8 - S9 all the time.

I found the noise level on the Isotron about 3 S-points lower than on my normal antennas as it was positioned further away from the house. This made listening much easier. In terms of signal strength, signals were generally down about 1 - 2 S-points on the Isotron. With the antenna tuned to 3.600MHz my rig's internal ATU was able to find a match at 3.500MHz and 3.700MHz, but couldn't find a match at 3.800MHz. So if you want to try to work the whole band make sure you set the resonant point at about 3.650, and you may need to use an external ATU.

Obviously, it is better all round to set the resonant point in the region of the band of most interest to you – SSB, PSK or CW. The fall off as you moved away from the resonant point was quite obvious, while at its resonant point the antenna was at times equal to my other antennas.

A CW QSO with Ray Fautley, G3ASG, showed that the antenna was OK until QSB kicked in, when it became a bit of a struggle. Switching to the W3EDP made life a lot easier. That evening it was the same story. Contacts with F5VLO, G6NKL, M0KVA and G6UUR showed similar results to the afternoon. This isn't quite as bad as it sounds because most signals in the evening on 80m are 59+10 – 59+20dB, so they become S8 - S9 on the Isotron. However, if conditions are marginal, the Isotron will lose out. It performed better on CW and PSK31 where absolute signal strength is not as critical.

I passed the antenna to Roger Cooke, G3LDI, who mounted it at 45ft and compared it with a low-ish 80m dipole at about 25ft. Roger found similar results to me – signal strengths were 10 - 20dB down with the Isotron and he found it noisier. He worked DO1DTA on 3635kHz getting a 59 report. Roger then switched to the dipole and received 59+20dB. Later he called CQ on the Isotron. G3OKA gave him 59, coming back to his first call too. Roger then switched to the dipole and he gave him 59+10dB.

If you are looking for a replacement for an 80m dipole you will be disappointed, but if you have no other way of getting on the band it will work well for you, just make sure that you operate as close to its resonant point as possible for the best results.

40m version

I then built the 40m version, which looks very similar, but is slightly shorter. The aluminium capacitor plates are also less wide than on the 80m version and it only has one tuning rod, not two. I fitted the tuning rod, complete with the small 1.5in-square aluminium capacity hat, and set it in the minimum capacitance position. I put the Isotron on the 18ft mast and found that it resonated out of the box at 7.050MHz with an SWR of 1.4:1. It also showed that it should be possible, by adjusting the tuning arm, to resonate the antenna in the CW portion of the band. I then took the tuning arm off completely and found that the antenna resonated at 7.3MHz, so it looks like you do need the tuning arm on, at least for the UK allocation on 40m.

Tuning arm back on, but with no capacity hat, and I eventually managed to get the antenna resonant at 7.1MHz with an SWR of 1:1. The SWR at 7.000 and 7.200MHz was then 2.5:1.

At the CW end of 40m the antenna was quite lively. Signals that were S9+10dB on the 132ft OCFD / W3EDP long wire were S8 on the Isotron, but then the centre of the dipole is 12ft higher. Some signals were only 1 - 2 S-points less on the Isotron, and quite a few were identical. In the SSB portion of the band, my first call was answered straight away by DL60DRC, a special event station in Germany. Other SSB signals were also either equal on the Isotron or down by no more than 1 - 2 S-points.

The 40m Isotron didn't strike me as too much of a compromise. If you have no room for a 40m dipole the antenna will get you on the band. Again, if your interests are CW or PSK31 the antenna will serve you well. If you prefer SSB, your signals are likely to be down by 1 - 2 S-points, but you will work the stronger stations.

So, in conclusion, the lightweight 40m and 80m Isotrons allow you to get on the bands when you don't have room for a full-size dipole or long wire. Yes, signal strengths are likely to be down a little, but you will be able to operate. It pays to get the antennas as high as possible and follow the installation instructions carefully to get the best results.

Are they pile-up breaking DX antennas? No. But that's missing the point. With many people living in houses with little or no gardens the Isotrons allow you to continue to enjoy the hobby. Isn't that what it is all about?

LNR PRECISION PAR ENDFEDZ

The LNR Precision Par EndFedZ [7] are full-length half-wave dipoles, but with an important difference. The coax connector is at one end of the dipole, where it is often more convenient. These antennas, available from 6 - 40m, can be mounted horizontally, vertically or as a sloper. No ground plane or counterpoise is needed and end insulators are supplied making suspension easy.

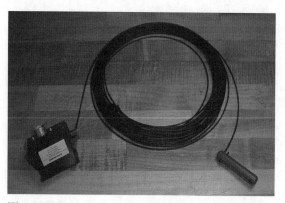

The UV resistant ABS plastic housing encloses an efficient matching network allowing the antenna to be fed with common 50Ω coaxial cable. All hardware is stainless and the SO239 connector is silver / teflon. The radiator wire is 18 gauge stranded Copperweld with a tough polyethylene jacket.

One end comes with a solder lug making attachment to the supplied matchbox simple and allowing the radiator portion to be replaced if ever necessary. Power rating is 100W and they are very lightweight. Because they are all black they are hard to spot as well.

The LNR Precision Par EndFedZ are ideal if you want to put up a single vertical antenna or mount the matching box next to your upstairs window.

The Par EndFedZ are single band antennas as the matching boxes are designed for one band. The company also has a three-band 10 / 20 / 40m version which is rated at 25W only and has a radiator length of 40ft.

They don't need earth stakes or counterpoises either, which makes them ideal for people with upstairs shacks who have problems running normal end-feds.

I was drawn to the antenna because people rave about them. The feedback on eHam [3] is always good and they work well. If you want to put up a single vertical antenna or mount the matching box next to your upstairs window and run the wire down the garden then the LNR Precision Par EndFedZ may be for you.

The AlexLoop uses a soft copper pipe loop of about 37in diameter.

ALEXLOOP SML 7-30 MAGNETIC LOOP ANTENNA

The AlexLoop SML 7-30 is a small magnetic loop antenna, designed by Alex Grimberg, PY1AHD [8], over a period of seven years. His field tests involved more than 800 QRP DX QSOs. Alex is pretty famous in the world of magnetic loop antennas (see the section on magnetic loops) and has produced the AlexLoop as a result of his experiments over the years. It uses a soft copper pipe loop of about 37in in diameter. This is mounted on a two-part pole that also holds the exciter loop and the matching / tuning box.

Designed for no more than 20W (10W continuous modes, such as AM / FM) the handheld antenna can be tuned by hand within five seconds to any frequency between 6.95 and 29.7MHz. It is ideally suited to small QRP transceivers like the Yaesu FT-817 and the Icom IC-703.

You just adjust the built in capacitor to peak the signal on receive and then fine tune on transmit for lowest SWR. It can be hand-held or mounted on a short mast. It can also be mounted on a window balcony with a small plastic clamp or used indoors.

Although Alex has designed the loop to be sent in the post throughout North and South America, he is happy to post it to buyers in the rest of world for the appropriate postage cost.

THE MIRACLE WHIP

Sadly, the inventor of the original Miracle Whip became a silent key after the first issue of *Stealth Antennas* was printed and the company is no longer in existence. I have, however, left this original write-up in place as they do come up quite often on eBay etc. Also, there are a number of clones and spinoffs around, including the 'Wonder Wand' and the 'Whizz Whip'.

The Miracle Whip, made by Miracle Antenna in Canada [9], is a self-contained, all-band (HF / VHF / UHF) 57in telescoping whip antenna with integrated tuner for receiving and transmitting that mounts straight on to your radio's SO239 antenna socket. The heart of the Miracle Whip is a continuously variable autotransformer that permits tuning throughout the entire HF range with a single control, achieving a match of better than 2:1 on almost all bands. A VHF spot on the dial allows you to drive the whip directly and adjust it for frequencies from 50 - 450MHz.

The controller uses a manually-tuned capacitor.

The antenna is designed for QRP use (up to 5W) and works well with one of the modern all-band radios like the Yaesu FT-817. Because of the continuous tuning, the Miracle Whip can be tuned in most cases without any additional counterpoise, although tests have shown that a counterpoise may help.

The Miracle Whip is designed for QRP use and works well with one of the modern all-band radios like the Yaesu FT-817.

Receive performance on the lower bands (80 / 160m) is good, but transmit performance is only fair, given that the antenna is only a fraction of a wavelength long. The antenna starts to shine as you head HF though. Initial tuning is done my rotating the knob for maximum band noise. You'll then find that you are within one or two clicks from the lowest SWR point.

I have owned a Miracle Whip since the day I bought my Yaesu FT-817 and it lives in the bag along with the radio. The combination has been used in hotel rooms and holiday villas around the world and I can't think of a more portable HF solution. I have worked across the Atlantic on 20m SSB in contests, and around the UK on 40m CW.

While it isn't as good as a dedicated antenna fitted outside you can forgive it for its sheer portability. If you are completely stuck for a stealth antenna solution, or like quick and easy portable operation, the Miracle Whip should be high on your buy list.

The Sandpiper MV7 multiband vertical.

SANDPIPER ANTENNAS

Sandpiper Aerial Technology Ltd [10] is based in Aberdare, South Wales, and has been designing and manufacturing aerials for more than 30 years. A regular on the UK radio show circuit, they have some excellent designs that might suit the stealthy operator. I have already mentioned their 2m delta quad beam, but their HF range includes some low-profile vertical antennas that might suit those people with smaller gardens as well.

The 'V27.5' range are approximately 8.5m high, and include monoband verticals for 40, 80 and 160m. There is also a triband vertical for all three bands. The MV10 range are compact verticals. They range from single band models to 10-band versions. These are ground mounted and need a minimum of one earth spike, although radials will help. The good news is that they are only 2.25 - 4m high, so are quite stealthy. There is also a lightweight version of the MV with a built in fibreglass tripod called the MVP.

The antennas get good reviews on eHam [3] and users report good results despite their small size.

If you have a little more space, the V9 range might suit you better. You can choose from single-band versions to nine-band variants.

The company also has some shortened dipoles for 40, 80 and 160m that are only around 3m long – ideally for stealthy or loft applications.

Sandpiper also offers a range of lightweight masts and tripods that could be used for temporary antennas, including one which will extend to 6m (nearly 20ft) in seconds. There are also more sturdy masts capable of extending to 10m (over 32ft).

The company's range of fibreglass fishing poles is also extensive, with lengths from 3m to 10m. I used their 10m pole to build the 20m (14MHz) half-wave end-fed antenna featured earlier.

If you want a lightweight beam antenna for HF the GM3VLB delta beam only weighs 2kg and is constructed with fishing rod-type telescopic poles. It has a turning radius of approximately 2.4m and covers 10, 15 and 20m. There is also a 4kg heavyweight version.

Sandpiper also has a range of two-element boomless quads for the higher HF bands.

If you like building your own antennas the company has a full range of antenna parts including dipole centres, insulators and tubing.

The screwdriver antenna can make a stealthy multiband aerial for the garden.

TARHEEL SCREWDRIVER ANTENNAS

There is a type of vertical mobile antenna known as a 'screwdriver', which uses an electric motor to tune it. As you change bands you adjust the overall inductance and bring the antenna to resonance. This got me thinking – if the antenna will work on a car could it be made to work in a loft or garden? It seems the answer is yes and Tarheel Antennas [11] in the USA have photographs on their website of just such installations.

The Little Tarheel II antenna when properly installed on a vehicle will provide continuous coverage from 3.5 to 54MHz with the supplied whip. If mounted over a decent ground plane or radials the same antenna can be made to work off the car.

Tuning can be accomplished manually or automatically. Change the radio to the frequency you want to operate. With the manual switch run the antenna up or down until you hear the noise level start to come up. Switch the radio into low power tune mode and continue to adjust the antenna in the same direction until the SWR dips on your radio.

You can even hide one in your garden birdhouse for the ultimate in stealth.

Tarheel's antennas come with the sensors already pre-installed so you can add one of its auto controllers (SDC-100 Simple Controller, SDC-102 Programmable Controller, Turbo Tuner, Antenna BOSS and BOSS II) now or later.

The antenna comes in standard colours of black, white, red or silver – the black is obviously the stealthiest. It comes with the whip, 20ft. of plug-and-play control cable, a manual control box, ferrite decoupling core and 3/8-24 stud for mounting.

If you have room for something a little bigger the company also has the 100A-HP with a 6ft whip right up to the 400A-HP, which will cover topband. As Tarheel's website shows, the antenna can be mounted outside on a tripod with radials or a dedicated base mount. They even have one disguised as a bird house!

FORCE 12 SIGMA-5

The Sigma-5 from Force 12 [12] is a small and unobtrusive vertical antenna offering low loss capability for five bands (20, 17, 15, 12, 10m). It is just 3.5m (9ft) high and has two capacity loading arms (top and bottom) that are 120cm (48in) long. The antenna works like a vertical dipole and is therefore unaffected by bad ground situations.

It needs no radials and no guy wires are normally required. The maximum power load is 1200W PEP or 700W on CW. Weighing only 3.5kg, the antenna is centre-fed with the supplied balun. Band switching is done with relays in the centre element and a 15m control cable and remote switch is included. The switching system requires 12V DC, 100mA. Without any power supplied the antenna is automatically switched to 20m.

Force 12 says that the antenna can be mounted in a five gallon bucket of cement, placed on the ground and guyed once. VSWR

The Force 12 Sigma-5 covers five bands in a 9ft package.

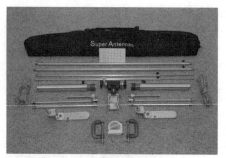

The Superantennas MP1.

is less than 1.7:1 maximum on 17, 15, 12 and 10m, and less than 2:1 on 20m. This is a great way to get on five bands in an antenna only 9ft tall.

THE SUPER ANTENNAS MP1

While writing this book I had to bear in mind that some hams don't have *any* form of garden and don't have lofts either. That's why I have also looked at antennas that could be used in flats or apartments. The portable Super Antennas MP1 [13] is such an antenna and will cover 40m (7MHz) to 6m (50MHz), from QRP to a maximum of 300W.

The MP-1 will fit into a briefcase with a K2, FT-817 or similar small rig. Its universal mount allows it to be set up on almost any object that is handy and at any angle.

It has a standard 3/8in mounting and a short (8in) vertical section, above which is a large diameter high-Q loading coil, tuned by moving a sleeve up and down. A 4ft whip section screws into the top of the sleeve. This whip breaks down into six lengths of rod which can be stored inside the coil for ease of transportation.

You can clamp the antenna to a table or balcony railing or use it on a kitchen or garden table using a tripod mount. The company will also sell you an 80m extension coil.

You tune the antenna by sliding the top section up and down on a loading coil. Once you have a low SWR you just tighten the band locking knob. Super Antennas also supplies the MP2, which is similar but has a servo motor to tune the antenna for you.

The antenna needs some form of ground plane, such as resonant radials, just like any other vertical – short or otherwise.

Other antennas from this company include the YP3 'Yagi in a Bag' which, as the name suggests, is a lightweight portable beam antenna, and the YP-1 rotatable six-band dipole. Accessories include a 21ft mast, which is collapsible to 5ft, and weighs just 4.5lb.

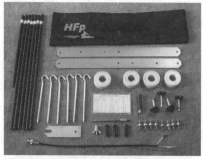

The HFp design consists of a series of 18in long elements, about 3/8in in diameter, with threaded brass inserts in each end.

VENTENNA HFP-VERTICAL

The Ventenna [14] HFp-Vertical kit consists of a series of 18in long elements, about 3/8in in diameter, with threaded brass inserts in each end. They screw together by means of brass connectors, which are called Inter-Element-Connectors. There are three different types of elements, which are electrically different from each other, and are also different end to end. Each of the elements is identified by a label at one end. The mix and orientation of the elements defines the resonant frequency.

The HFp comes with all the parts required to set the

antenna up on bands from 6 to 40m, including base plates, radial wires, guy lines, a coax pigtail, and a laminated card which shows the configuration for each band. Options include an add-on coil which allows the antenna to be tuned on 60m (5MHz) and 80m (3.5MHz). Other options are a clamp mount, a backpack mount, and a mobile mount adapter. There is also an upgrade available to allow the HFp-V to be set up as a dipole.

While the antenna was originally designed for backpack and portable use it works well as a stealth vertical for a back garden as well.

Ventenna has tested the HFp with a different numbers of radials and found that three seems to be the minimum number to be effective, and that more than three didn't seem to add much. Having the radials set to the correct 'tuned' length was much more important – note this is *not* the same as saying you need a quarter-wave length at, say, 20m. As we have said before, lying a radial on the ground detunes it, meaning it needs to be much shorter to be resonant. Ventenna found that for 20m a length of about 6 - 14.5ft was best on 20m. Longer than this and the radials were pretty much worthless.

The vertical antenna is probably too long to set up in an attic, but makes a very effective one-band-at-a-time vertical for a small garden. There is an HFp dipole that could be used in an attic.

MOONRAKER HF VERTICALS

Moonraker [15] is another British company that has a lot to offer the stealth operator. As well as supplying a full range of antenna accessories, including insulators, dipole centres, cables, baluns, masts and mounting hardware, it also has its own range of HF and VHF / UHF antennas.

Its EVX range includes four, five, six and eight-band trap verticals, covering from 10 - 80m. Power rating is a sturdy 2000W, reflecting their heavy duty design. The EVX4000 covers 10, 15, 20, and 40m and is 6.5m long. The EVX5000 adds 80m and increases the length to 7.3m. The six-band EVX6000 also adds 30m (10MHz) coverage as well, but the overall length is down to 5m. Finally, the top-of-the-range eight-band EVX8000 adds the other two WARC bands, 12m (24MHz) and 17m (18MHz), in a package that is 4.9m tall.

If you only want to cover 10, 15 and 20m, the company also offers the VR3000 vertical which stands just 3.8m in height.

All of these antennas need a decent ground plane or radial system to work.

Moonraker also has a wide-band, no-tune vertical antenna for 80 to 6m (3.5-57MHz). The GP2500 offers a 1.5:1 SWR and doesn't need an ATU. The max power is 250W, the overall length 7.13m and the weight 3kg.

The company has a range of HF mobile antennas as well as VHF / UHF mobile and base antennas. If you looking for a simple omnidirectional antenna for 6m (50MHz), 4m (70MHz) or 2m (144MHz) Moonraker has

Moonraker's website.

Tom's, G4TPH, magnetic loop for 40m weighs less than 700g.

three halo loops, which are ideal for loft or pole mounting. Other antenna options include Yagis and HB9CVs.

THE G4TPH MAGNETIC LOOP ANTENNAS

Tom Brockman, G4TPH (first licensed as K8VST in 1960) [16], bought an apartment in Spain and travelled a lot with work. He decided that he needed a portable antenna that would fit in a holdall and could be used in the apartment and hotels when travelling. Several commercial portable antennas were tried, but were not all that successful. He wanted a self-supporting magnetic loop so came up with the idea of using lengths of aluminium rail that could be set up and packed away easily.

After several prototypes the ML-40 loop was created. This consisted of 12 10mm-wide rails 400mm long with an air-spaced capacitor at the top and a ferrite ring inductive loading unit at the bottom.

The antenna tunes 20 to 40m and handles 20W. No ATU, ground wire or radials are required. The antenna is 1.2m in diameter and weighs less than 700g. (This antenna will actually also tune to 80m, but the efficiency is so low it is not marketed as an 80m antenna).

The ML-40 worked so well that Tom set up his website [15] to market the antennas for those who might need a stealth or portable antenna. Sales have now been made to more than 40 countries. Many are used free-standing in apartments in front of a window. G4TPH has successfully made contacts from a hotel with the antenna lying on the bed in a horizontal position since there was no suitable way to hang the assembled antenna on the curtain rail or window. Using 5W and the ML-40 antenna on 20m SSB from the south-east corner of Spain, Tom worked G4AKC bicycle mobile in Blackpool in the north-west of the UK.

Following the success of the ML-40, Tom designed a similar antenna for 20 to 10m: the ML-20. This antenna consists of eight 10mm-wide rails, 400mm long, and weighs less than 600g. In 2008 Tom packed 45 of these antennas in his checked luggage and attended the Dayton Radio Rally. The antennas were so well received that he sold out. At Dayton several people asked if there was a 100W version. On returning to the UK Tom started work on designing a 100W version and the ML-40HP was created.

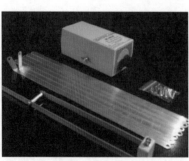

The ML-40HP uses eight 15mm-wide rails 500mm long. The antenna has a large air-spaced capacitor at the top and still weighs less than 1.2kg. Since there were problems developing the ferrite ring inductive loading to handle the higher power the tuning unit is by a gamma match.

The G4TPH antennas are all very portable, do not require ATUs and make the ideal stealth antenna. The efficiency of a magloop antenna can come close to that of a full-size

The ML-40HP loop disassembled for travelling.

dipole and are more effective than many small antennas that compromise performance for size.

MFJ LOOP TUNERS

The MFJ [17] Loop Tuners (MFJ-935B, MFJ-936B and MFJ-933) are small devices that turn any wire loop into a multi-band transmitting antenna system. They are designed for 150W maximum input. The MFJ-932 QRP loop tuner is a much smaller, lower-powered, unit rated at 50W maximum.

The tuners use a low-loss butterfly capacitor with no rotating contacts in this circuit and no ground, radials, or counterpoise system is required. You can tune a circle, square, rectangle or any odd shape of wire, but the circle is best. You can also fit a circular length of wire or copper tubing that you supply yourself.

The loop tuners use a low-loss butterfly capacitor with no rotating contacts for minimum losses.

The most efficient is a wire that approaches a quarter-wave long at the operating frequency. This is actually no different to conventional magnetic loops (such as the MFJ-1786x) where the loop is normally about 0.25 of a wavelength at the highest frequency of operation and significantly less at the lower extremes of the tuning range.

The loop tuners use fixed wire lengths, which cover about 1.5 to 1 frequency ranges (i.e. 28 – 18 or 10 – 7MHz). MFJ can supply a PVC cross which mounts on the top of the unit's cover and lets you fix an insulated flexible wire loop to the unit.

To use the tuner just connect the wire or tubing to the back and adjust for lowest SWR.

The instruction book that comes with the tuner has quite a lot of information about RF exposure, suggesting that you do not get closer than about 2ft when operating with 100W on 7MHz and not closer than 7.5ft on 28MHz at the same power level. In any case, you do not want to touch the loop when you are transmitting as you could get a severe RF burn. Safety advice over, the loops are a great way of operating HF from a small space and the reviews for the tuners on sites like eHam [3] show that users get good results.

MFJ-1621 40-10M PORTABLE AND MFJ-1622 40-2M APARTMENT ANTENNAS

MFJ [17] has two more solutions for those who have no room for external antennas. The MFJ-1621 Portable Antenna covers 40 to 10m. It comes with a matching box / ATU and is designed to let you work HF from anywhere. The MFJ-1621 is designed for where a regular antenna may be difficult to set up and it does not require a ground plane. A field strength meter is built in for ease of tuning. With the MFJ-1621, you can enjoy operating your rig in remote locations (camping, motels, field day, etc). MFJ says that you should keep in mind that this antenna is not intended to permanently replace or

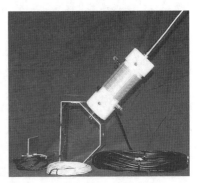

The MFJ-1622 Apartment Antenna covers 40 to 10m on HF as well as 6m and 2m on VHF.

outperform a regular full-size antenna (dipole, beam, etc). It is designed to allow you to operate when no other antenna is available.

An SWR below 2:1 can be obtained in most cases and 50ft of RG-58/u cable is provided to allow you to locate the antenna where it is best for operation.

The MFJ-1622 Apartment Antenna covers 40 to 10m on HF as well as 6m and 2m on VHF. Its universal mount / clamp lets you easily attach it to window frames, balconies, and railings. It also works indoors mounted to a desk, table, or bookshelf.

The antenna features a highly-efficient air-wound 'bug catcher' loading coil and telescoping 1.67m radiator. The radiator collapses to 762mm for easy storage and carrying. It includes coax RF choke balun, coax feed line, counterpoise wire and safety rope. The operating frequency is adjusted by moving the 'wander lead' on the coil and adjusting the counterpoise for the best SWR.

The design of the antenna allows it to be installed in many ways. It can be easily attached to a window frame, window box or balcony railing. A wooden fence is another common location for mounting.

MFJ says that the best performance will be obtained by placing the antenna outside, although the antenna may be used indoors if necessary. The base plate may be attached to a table, book shelf, or other suitable support. The counterpoise is simply placed on the floor and you're on the air. Some installations may require the use of a C-clamp or vice-grips to secure the base plate. Always remember to keep the antenna away from metal objects and out of reach to prevent injury – you must not touch the radiating element while transmitting.

THE ALPHA ANTENNA MICROTUNE MAGNETIC LOOP

Alpha Antenna from the USA [6] has a lightweight magnetic loop (or more correctly a small transmitting loop, STL) antenna that comes in its own carrying case and which tips the scales at just 6.6lb (3kg).

The Alpha Loop is a magnetic loop antenna that is easy to tune, has acceptable bandwidths, and offers coverage on 40, 30, 20, 17, and 15 metres. Alpha Antenna also includes a small feed loop that has been optimised for 12 and 10 metres, for use after you make a small alteration to the larger loop.

The antenna appears to your transceiver as a large resonant circuit, consisting of a large single turn inductor tuned with a single-section variable air-dielectric butterfly capacitor.

It is rated at 30 watts PEP SSB maximum and uses a 6:1 reduction drive to make tuning easier.

The antenna comes in a very smart nylon holdall for its field bag, which is just under three feet (87cm) long. The holdall, which has the manufacturer's name and logo neatly embroidered on the side, includes a zip-fastened

The Alpha Loop is ideal for temporary or travel use as it can be transported in its own case.

side pocket that is handy for carrying instructions. The pocket also contains a shoulder strap that can be affixed to the holdall.

Once completely assembled, the antenna mounts on the included tripod by screwing securely in place on a ¼ x 20 thread. The whole assembly is reasonably sturdy, but it might be worth guying if using it outdoors in windy weather. It is not designed for a permanent outdoor installation as it is not really weatherproofed.

The Alpha Loop antenna is well built and is easy to assemble with no tools required. It can be assembled in less than 10 minutes and works from 40 to 10m (once you have removed two of the aluminium segments and swapped the feed loop). Tuning is easy, but very sharp, and hand capacitance effects are evident.

In terms of the Alpha Loop antenna's performance, it will work better for you on CW and data modes where all-out signal strength is not as important.

It can be ordered from the Alpha Antenna eCommerce website at www. AmateurRadioStore.com

M0CVO OFF-CENTRE FED DIPOLES - TESTED

Off Centre Fed Dipoles (OCFDs), sometime inaccurately called Windoms (which technically only have a single wire feeder) are 'Marmite' antennas – people seem to either love them or hate them.

I have had reasonable success with a 132ft 80m version, so I was interested to see how the M0CVO's HW-20P performed. The antenna is 33ft (10.14m) long and is split one third / two thirds (6.76m and 3.38m) where it is fed with an impedance transformation balun (more of that later). I mounted mine on the top of a fishing pole pushed into a tree for a 'stealthy' appearance.

This is obviously a half-wave dipole for 20m. The idea is that the feedpoint is located where the impedance on the antenna's fundamental resonant frequency is between 200 and 300 ohms, so giving a low SWR when fed through a 4:1 or 6:1 balun. You can normally also expect the antenna to work on 28MHz (2 x 14MHz) with a low SWR.

Nigel, M0CVO, says that his antenna will also work on 15m, 12m, 11m and 10m without an ATU and on 17m and 6m with an ATU.

He says: "The balun is based loosely around the Ruthroff design, but has been varied somewhat from the available designs into one of my own. I believe that the transformer action of this then also helps somewhat in the operation of the HW-20HP on the 15m band."

The antenna was installed as an inverted-V for the test with the apex at 10m and the ends sloping down so that one ended up about eight metres above ground and the other at about five metres. It was fed with about 25m of RG213 coax.

The antenna can be used on many bands without a tuner, although I would recommend using one. In

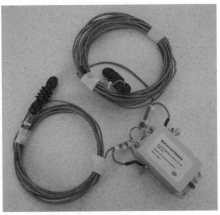

The M0CVO HW-20P Windom and balun box.

practice any internal ATU will match this antenna to an SWR of 1:1 very easily on any of the bands from 20m to 6m. You will no doubt find that your actual SWR results are different, and possibly higher if a shorter length of coax is used.

So how did it perform? When compared with conventional half-wave dipoles at the same height the antennas were pretty much neck-and-neck, as you would expect. A long list of stations worked would not really tell you anything. Sometimes the HW-20HP would have the edge, sometimes my dipoles would, as they are orientated in different directions. At no time did I find a signal that was way down on the OCFD.

It also seemed to work equally well on all of the bands under test. What it *did* do was outperform my longer doublet at times, which confirmed my fears that these are not always optimal for the higher bands. Nothing was heard on 50MHz during the test period.

So, overall, the antenna is a cost-effective way of getting on the five or six higher HF bands. It is inevitably a bit of a compromise, but not as much as you might think.

Nigel has other models available. I also tested a version that would work from 40m to 10m and which was also quite effective. See www.m0cvoantennas.eu

REFERENCES
[1] Pro Antennas: www.proantennas.co.uk
[2] TAK-tenna: www.TAK-tenna.com
[3] eHam: www.eham.net
[4] Bilal Isotron antennas: www.isotronantennas.com
[5] Martin Lynch & Sons: www.hamradio.co.uk
[6] Alpha Antennas: www.http://alphaantenna.com
[7] LNR Precision Par End-Fedz: www.lnrprecision.com/endfedz
[8] AlexLoop: www.alexloop.com
[9] Miracle Antenna Clones: www.wonder-wand.co.uk/ and
    www.moonraker.eu/the-whizz-whip-qrp-hf-vhf-uhf-antenna
[10] Sandpiper Aerial Technology Ltd: www.sandpiperaerials.co.uk
[11] Tarheel Antennas: www.tarheelantennas.com
[12] Force 12:   www.force12inc.com
[13] Super Antennas: www.newsuperantenna.com
[14] Ventenna: www.ventenna.com
[15] Moonraker: www.moonraker.eu
[16] Tom Brockman, G4TPH, magnetic loop antenna: www.g4tph.com
[17] MFJ equipment: www.mfjenterprises.com

NOISE IS GETTING to be a massive problem in suburban areas. So much so that you often hear of amateurs going QRT due to interference from switched mode power supplies, plasma TVs, broadband over power line devices and much more.

At my own QTH (in the middle of a modern housing estate) I have a constant noise level of S9 on 80m (3.5MHz), S7 on 40m (7MHz) and even S5 on 20m (14MHz). And yes, that is with the rig's pre-amp switched off. The noise appears to be coming up through the mains and being re-radiated – and I can't see things getting any better.

One solution to the noise problem is to have a separate receiving antenna, especially for the lower bands, such as 80m and 160m.

There are a whole host of different designs available including the Beverage, K9AY, EWE, Flag, Kaz and many others. But what if you haven't got much space? Here are two designs that take up very little room and work well. And in the case of the Miniwhip it is almost completely invisible, only being six inches long!

By using a separate receive antenna you might be able to get around noise problems caused by using a transmitting antenna close to or inside your house. And, if all else fails, or you unable to put up *any* transmitting antenna (especially for the lower bands), one of the following will still allow you to continue your hobby as a short wave listener.

THE WELLBROOK ALA1530 ACTIVE RECEIVING LOOP ANTENNA

The lightweight Wellbrook ALA1530 is an antenna with a massive reputation. Andy Ikin at Wellbrook has built up a world-wide following with his active receiving loops and quickly responded to my request for a review model. So what do you get for your money and how well does it work?

The Wellbrook ALA1530 is a one-metre aluminium loop with a built-in wideband preamplifier. A note of caution before we go any further: *it is a receiving antenna only. Do not transmit RF through it: if you do you will blow the preamp.*

The ALA1530 has been specifically designed to reduce intermodulation products

Andy Ikin's Wellbrook loops have a fantastic reputation.

to a minimum, so you are unlikely to find sum and difference products from strong broadcast stations.

It is an untuned loop, so really it is fit and forget – you don't need to twiddle anything as you scan the bands. It is designed to work from 50kHz to 30MHz and over the past 10 years has been re-engineered to increase the gain on long wave and medium wave by approximately 10dB and 3dB respectively.

The antenna comes with its own power supply interface and a small regulated PSU. The interface feeds 12V at 150mA via the coax to the BNC connector on the antenna (maximum recommended length 100m). A one-metre lead fitted with a PL259 goes from the antenna interface to your receiver.

The loop itself is one metre in diameter and has the built-in wideband preamplifier fitted in a plastic box at the base. The preamp is actually embedded in epoxy resin, so you can't see much of it. This helps with weatherproofing and mechanical strength.

You can mount the antenna directly to a piece of wood or other non-conducting surface, or use the supplied aluminium mounting flange and a short aluminium tube to mount it on a rotator or mast.

Wellbrook recommends the use of a rotator as the antenna is directional in the plane of the loop.

It has significant rejection off the sides in the order of about 35dB that can be used to null out local interference or interfering stations.

If you do mount it without a rotator then you will have to put up with its directional characteristics and / or align it with stations you wish to listen to, but more of that later. Wellbrook recommends that it should be positioned approximately 5m away from buildings, metal objects and sources of interference. If using it as a receiving antenna in conjunction with a transmitting antenna you should keep the two as far apart as possible.

The company suggests that you can mount the antenna at ground level and my tests were done with it on a short four-foot aluminium pole to see if this was

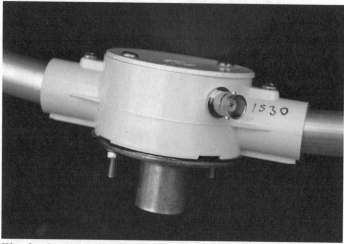

viable. No foliage or branches were allowed to brush against the loop and it was fed with about 20m of Mini8 50-ohm coax.

You may also mount the antenna higher if you wish and this may improve HF performance, but might not improve LF / MF reception. There is nothing to stop you installing it in your loft, but a) it is unlikely to fit through the access hatch and b) this is not the best option in terms of reducing noise. To get around

The feedpoint of the Wellbrook loop.

the first problem Wellbrook offers the LA5030 semi-rigid loop for indoor use and this will fit through a loft opening.

So how does the ALA1530 perform? I first started around 70kHz. The Wellbrook brought in time signals that were virtually inaudible on a 100ft doublet. Moving up to long wave and many strong signals were also found during daylight, including 153kHz (Deutschlandfunk), 162kHz (France), 183kHz (Saarlouis), 198kHz (BBC Radio 4) and many others. These were generally clearer than on my wire antennas.

Further up the bands a host of non-directional beacons (NDBs) from around Europe were heard, such as 387kHz ING in St Inglevert, France, and 395kHz OA, in Schiphol, Netherlands.

Onward to medium wave and the surprise to me was how easily the ALA1530 would pick up distant stations, even in broad daylight. BBC Radio Scotland (810kHz) was perfectly audible in Norfolk.

The directional effects of the loop were made apparent when I tuned to BBC Radio Wales on 882kHz from Washford, Somerset, and heard absolutely nothing. But rotating the antenna from its NW / SE orientation to SW / NE made BBC Radio Scotland disappear and BBC Radio Wales appear at a very clear S5.

Further afield, and Boston, USA, AM station WWZN on 1510kHz was heard easily at 0330UTC in late August with the loop orientated NW / SE. This was followed by CFRB Toronto on 1010kHz and WWKB in Buffalo, New York, on 1520kHz. There were traces of these on the doublet, but nothing more.

On topband (160m) the Wellbrook turned a noisy S9 mess on my wire antenna into a perfectly quiet band. During daylight in September, a continental SSB station in Germany could be heard on 1850kHz on the loop that was totally inaudible on the wire antennas.

It was a similar story on many stations from around the UK on topband. At 0350UTC I heard W0FLS, K4EJQ, K0ONF and K2JO on the loop on 160m – admittedly very weak, but there was no chance of hearing them on the wires. Listening to topband on the loop was an absolute pleasure – no noise, just pure CW signals.

On 80m weak CW stations in the Netherlands could be heard clearly during the day on the Wellbrook that were barely audible on the wire antennas. The ALA1530 made them a lot easier to listen to.

The antenna also works well up to 30MHz, although its low-noise characteristics are not so important on the higher frequencies. But to have a single effective antenna for short wave listening that will cover 50kHz to 30MHz in a simple one-metre package mounted at ground level makes the ALA1530 a Godsend.

In conclusion then, if you are a shortwave listener looking for a single, small antenna to cover everything you may ever wish to listen to, the Wellbrook ALA1530 could prove very useful. To get the most out of it I highly recommend that you use a rotator, otherwise you may miss out on a lot of signals. You will also miss the ability to null out interference.

But this is really all dependent upon your particular location. If you suffer

S7 - S9+ noise across the lower bands, and can locate the Wellbrook well away from your house, you will notice a big difference and most likely hear weak signals that are inaudible on your wire antennas.

It is relatively easy to connect the ALA1530 to a transceiver with a separate RX antenna input, such as the Icom IC-7600, Yaesu FT-2000 or Kenwood TS-590S. If your transceiver doesn't have a separate RX antenna input you will need to fabricate or buy a switching box to handle two antennas. One such commercial product is the MFJ-1707 automatic RF sense antenna switch.

Recent developments from Wellbrook include its Imperium loop with an additional 9dB gain, plus a very high OIP3 of +55dBm.

The rigid Wellbrook loops also now have separate amplifier modules for improved reliability and for ease of repair. The low-cost ALA100M, using a 2 x 2m home-made wire loop, can be used as a stealth antenna too.

For more information see www.wellbrook.uk.com

PA0RDT MINIWHIP

This has to be the ultimate in small antennas – one that will receive everything from VLF to HF in a package less than six inches long! The antenna was conceived after Roelof, PA0RDT, had several attempts to make an active loop work in a city environment.

What he discovered was that the electric field from local noise sources was generally contained within his house. But, the magnetic field of noise sources was not, making weak signal reception at LF virtually impossible. From that he decided that an antenna mounted outdoors that was receptive to the electric field, rather than the magnetic field, might be useful.

After extensive tests he said it became clear that at LF an active whip is effectively a "capacitance coupled to the electric field".

Roelof added that in practice the 'whip' can be tiny, such as a small piece of copper clad printed circuit board, and his Miniwhip was born. Roelof's practical design is only 100mm long and 40mm in diameter yet will receive from 10kHz to 30MHz.

It is an active antenna and the power to the antenna is fed via the coax and a bias T circuit.

The antenna details and schematic are available on the Internet in order for you to make one yourself, but Roelof also makes them to order (you can e-mail him at

The circuit is actually quite simple to build.

roelof@ndb.demon.nl. At the time of writing the cost was €48 including shipping within Europe.

Roelof was kind enough to supply one for review, complete with its bias T power supply that feeds 12V up to the antenna via the coax feed. When the postman delivered the antenna I was quite surprised – the box was so light. On opening it I found the antenna and was equally taken aback. It actually weighs just 84 grams and is only about 4 inches (10cm) long.

The antenna and its amplifier circuit are built into a sealed grey plastic pipe leaving you only to connect a suitable length of coax via its BNC socket. You will need to provide a 9 - 15V supply, such as a small 'wall wart' PSU, though note that it must be a 'clean' supply: some of these 'wall wart' supplies can be electrically noisy.

Extensive tests with the antenna showed that it is very prone to receiving noise (which I had been warned about). In my shack it picked up all manner of interference, from switch mode power supplies to a low-energy light bulb. Even a TV on standby in a room 20ft away caused problems. To be fair, this was to be expected: Roelof says it is an excellent noise sniffer! He has used it extensively to investigate several local noise sources.

It is best mounted outdoors and as high as you can get it. In fact, I mounted mine on a telescopic fibreglass pole so that I could test it at different heights up to 8m.

Extensive use of ferrite chokes might also be useful. I found that my two PCs produced a lot of interference which was picked up on my Perseus SDR receiver. Using my Icom IC-756 Pro 3 - with the PCs switched off - made a big difference, especially on the LF / MF bands. Roelof says that grounding the shield of the coax before it enters the house or at the bottom of the mast is also important.

What happens is that local noise is received on the shield of the coax inside the house and travels to the antenna. By grounding the shield, the noise will 'flow' to earth and this can make a considerable difference to the level of noise picked up. He has also included an RF isolating transformer in the power bias T box. A jumper is used to select between isolated and connected grounds.

What also soon became apparent was that the higher I mounted it, the better the Miniwhip worked. In fact, at about 5m it almost matched the performance of my existing HF antennas, despite its tiny size. Roelof says that moving the antenna from 1.2m to 4.8m could increase the received signal strength by up to 8dB on the lower bands and I would agree.

I tested it on everything from non-directional beacons (NDBs) at LF, long wave, medium wave and all ham and broadcast frequencies up to 30MHz and it worked very well indeed. Mounted on a fibreglass pole the antenna

To say the PAØRDT Miniwhip is tiny is an understatement.

My own 'homebrew' attempt at a Miniwhip.

merrily received aircraft NDBs down in the 300kHz range – signals that were considerably weaker on my main doublet antenna.

It was a similar story with medium wave stations, with the tiny antenna pulling in stations from all over Europe in August. My usual test is to see how well I can pick up BBC Radio Wales on 882kHz from Washford, Somerset, here in Norfolk. It did this with flying colours.

Moving up to topband (160m) and although there wasn't a lot of activity I did pick up some DL and PA CW signals that were at least as loud as those received on my W5GI antenna over the roof.

It was a similar story on 80m (3.5MHz) where the little antenna worked reasonably well, but was down on a dedicated 80m antenna - noise levels were a lot lower though. On 40m (7MHz) the antenna also picked up signals, but the signal levels were down quite significantly. Interestingly, in some instances, the overall signal-to-noise ratio was no different, so in terms of copying the signals there was little difference.

Roelof says that he has his antenna mounted at 4m on a non-conductive mast to get clear of bushes in his garden, but he has also had excellent results in an open field at a height of only 2m.

The Miniwhip makes an excellent SWL antenna, as long as you spend some time calming all the various noise sources in your shack. I even mounted it in the loft, where it worked, though the noise levels were higher.

In the interests of experimentation I also decided to build one myself from the plans I found on the Internet. The antenna is made on a piece of single-sided PCB, with the top half acting as the antenna and the lower half holding the circuit. I made my circuit board by carefully cutting away the copper with a Dremel-type tool. I then built the circuitry 'ugly-style' (very ugly actually!) on the board, using Superglue to mount some of the components securely with their wire leads being used for the interconnections. The end result was a little Heath Robinson, but did it work? The answer was a resounding 'Yes'.

As a test I also tried it on VHF and found it was a reasonably effective little antenna for airband and 2m signals.

Overall then, if you have no means of putting up an antenna for topband, and are also interested in LF, NDBs and medium wave, this tiny antenna will let you listen to all the action. While testing the antenna I couldn't help but think that for hams and SWLs living in care homes and the like it would let them continue to enjoy their listening hobby without having to use a conspicuous antenna. For hams living in flats, putting the lightweight miniwhip out of the window on a fibreglass pole would also let them listen to the lower bands.

Is it worth building your own? To be honest it is hard to source all the components you need for less than Roelof charges to supply the whole antenna. If you like 'home brewing' equipment then go ahead – it is a fascinating little antenna and you'll have fun building it. If not, buy one direct from Roelof.

THE BONITO BONI-WHIP

The Boni-Whip is another active E-field antenna that is both tiny and powerful. Made by Bonito in Germany, it is derived from the PA0RDT Miniwhip, but uses a small 'whip' antenna instead of a PCB and offers an extended frequency range of 20kHz – 300MHz.

Despite its size (about 17cm long), it offers excellent reception results on long wave, medium wave and short wave, with the added bonus of VHF coverage.

The active antenna circuitry is encased in a weather-resistant box and the voltage supply is delivered via the antenna cable and the included bias-T module. You just need to provide a 12V DC supply.

Because of its interchangeable antenna element (which just unscrews) the Boni-Whip can be used for experimentation with different whip lengths.

Just as with the PA0RDT Miniwhip, the antenna is very sensitive to noise sources and works best when mounted outside – generally the higher the better. My own tests, and those by Fernando (Fenu) on his site at www.fenu-radio.ch show that the original Miniwhip and the Boni-Whip are virtually neck-and-neck when it comes to sensitivity, up to 15MHz at least.

The antenna allowed reception of a whole host of signals, including my local NDB (NWI) on 342.5kHz, long wave stations, both here and in Europe, medium wave and short wave broadcast stations and radio amateurs on 80, 40m and 20m.

On an A-to-B comparison it often matched my dedicated HF antennas on 20m signals – pretty amazing considering its size.

Above 15MHz the Boni-Whip mostly had the edge over the original Miniwhip, as Fenu's Perseus SDR screengrabs and MP3 files show on his website.

But what about reception up to 300MHz? Is it possible to design an antenna with such a wide bandwidth? Well, it looks like it is. I connected the Boni-Whip up to my Uniden Scanner and was able to hear VHF airband traffic out as far as Heathrow and

The Bonito Boni-whip is another tiny receive-only antenna.

Stansted, marine and local air ambulance operations on VHF and also GB3NB, my local 2m repeater.

The gain wasn't quite as good as my dedicated 2m collinear, but it worked and allowed a wide number of signals to be received. All this with the antenna mounted in the loft.

This makes it a powerful little antenna for SWLs. Chris Taylor, from Taylor Made RF Limited (who supplied the antenna for review) said that he has sold a number to people who can't put up outside antennas but who want to continue their short wave listening hobby. I can see why.

You can find out more from www.tmrf.co.uk (tel: 020 8953 3861) or see Bonito's website at www.bonito.net

Topband antennas

IS IT REALLY possible to have a stealthy topband antenna? Well, yes and no. It is possible to put up a stealthy 160m antenna that will get you on the band, but don't expect to run around winning contests with it as it may not be too efficient.

The biggest problem is that effective topband antennas are huge. With a wavelength of 160m that means a half-wave dipole is around 83m (272 feet) long. Even a full size quarter wave vertical is 41.7m (136 feet) tall.

So to come up with anything that is remotely useful we need to add loading or use some other technique to get the antenna down to something that is manageable.

In this chapter we'll look at some of the options that will at least get you on the band, even if they are not world beaters.

OPTION 1 – USE YOUR EXISTING 80M ANTENNA

This really is the easiest way to get on to topband but it won't be a stunner. However, it is fairly easy to put together and will make you contacts.

A couple of years ago I fancied taking part in a topband contest. The way I did it was to use my existing W5GI dipole that spans the roof and rests on the tiles. I connected the inner and outer of the coax feed together at the rig and treated it as a Marconi T antenna. I then fed it against a single earth stake and while it worked it wasn't brilliant.

I then ran a single quarter-wave counterpoise wire out of the window and around the garden at a height of about four feet. The counterpoise was about 136 feet long and I didn't realise just how long this is until I had to try to 'lose' it around a suburban garden!

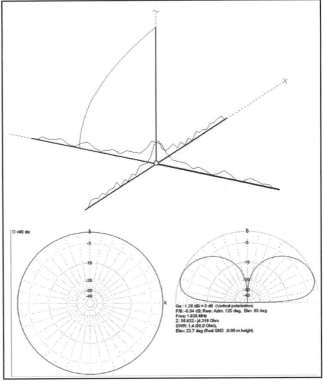

A full-size quarter wave vertical for topband is just a dream for most of us.

It went all the way around the garden and then down the side of the house before coming back around the front. If I had had burglars that night they would have been broken their necks to be honest!

The whole lot was tuned with my ATU and I set about taking part in the contest. The end result was that I was able to make contact with quite a few UK and European stations using CW. If they were louder than about S5 I could usually get through. Anything much less than that and they just couldn't hear me.

To improve the station it would have helped to have run a large number of ground radials out from the earth stake – as long as possible really as you'll see later. But at least it got me on the band.

OPTION 2 – USE A BILAL ISOTRON OR CROSS FIELD / EH ANTENNA

I have never tried their 160m model but Bilal makes an Isotron for 160m. If you are not familiar with the Isotron range, take a look at the chapter on commercial stealth antennas.

The 160m model is 9.5 feet (2.9m) tall, which is still small for a topband antenna. The manufacturer claims a bandwidth of 100kHz between 2:1 SWR points and it will take up to 1000 watts PEP.

Daniel, KC7UBS, in Wyoming, has one, admittedly at 30ft, but he says that it works well. "For a nine foot antenna on 160m, it is great," he said. "It works as well as my ugly home-brew reduced super sloper did. I use it on 1838kHz JT65 with 15 to 20W and I have worked Canada, Mexico, and about 25 states so far. What *is* critical is a metal mast, an earth connection, whether or not the mast is connected to the ground rod, and the tuning rod position.

The Bilal Isotron for topband is only 9.5ft tall.

"I finally settled on: earth strap connected, mast grounded to the ground rod, and tuning rod almost all the way up. The SWR is 2.8:1 at 1850kHz with a tiny bandwidth. When I disconnect the ground wire at the bottom of the mast I get 1:1 at 1910kHz with about 35kHz bandwidth. Have fun – it is ham radio!"

Other options to consider are the EH and Crossed Field antenna (both featured in the book). Many years ago I made an experimental one metre diameter Crossed Field Loop from RG213 coax. It was tuned using a similar circuit to the one I outline in the book, but used two variable capacitors instead of a coax capacitor. After a lot of fiddling I eventually made a 160m SSB contact with a station about 150 miles away using about 10W. He gave me a 59 and was amazed when I told him what I was using – and so was I.

Subsequent to that I fiddled with the matching circuit to try to 'improve' it, but never managed to get it to work as well again. I do think that there is still room for experimentation with Crossed Field antennas on topband.

There is also scope to experiment with larger magnetic loops and EH antennas. To be efficient on 160m a magnetic loop really needs to be about 3.4m in diameter or bigger, but it could be hidden in a tree. I have seen one ham who built one in his garage using coax. It was invisible from the outside and got him on the band.

OPTION 3 – USE A VERTICAL WITH A CAPACITY HAT

If you just build a short vertical with a massive loading coil in the middle you may be disappointed. Yes, you might be able to get the SWR down, but it won't be a good performer. A way of improving things is to include a 'capacity hat' on the top of the antenna, which makes it look longer electrically.

One antenna I tested for *RadCom* wasn't too stealthy, but it managed to get an 18m high vertical resonant on 160m using four capacity hat wires running from the top. In effect, it used the guy wires as the capacity hat and worked quite well with a little bit of loading at the bottom.

By using the *MMANA-GAL* antenna modelling software I tried to see if you could do something similar with an 8m fishing pole (using a 10m pole and taking the two top sections out to give it added strength). I started off by modelling a full size 40m (132 feet) high vertical with four quarter-wave radials. This gave 1.2dBi gain at a take-off angle of 25 degrees. Very nice if you could fit it into your garden!

By changing the height to just 8m *MMANA-GAL* can work out what we would need to add to the middle of the vertical wire to bring it to resonance. The answer is an inductor of 268μH. This is quite big and would need around 350 turns of 1mm wire on a 4cm former, giving you a coil 70cm long. This would no doubt be quite lossy and the lowest SWR is still poor - so back to the drawing board!

Connecting two pieces of wire 5.56m long to the top of our vertical as a capacity hat, attaching nylon cord to their ends and

This electrically "small" 18m topband vertical was not exactly stealthy!.

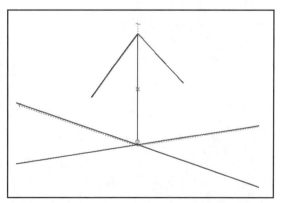

Adding a capacity hat lowers the amount of inductance needed to resonate the antenna.

175

guying them 8m away from the antenna, so that they come down at 45 degrees, lets us reduce the inductor size dramatically. The coil required now drops to 76μH. According to *MMANA-GAL* you still have a poor SWR of 17:1 though (3.06R+10.46jX). If you are interested you would need a shorted stub of RG213 about 24m long, or a 0.14H inductor in parallel with a capacitor of 6832pF.

Let's be honest, this antenna is very tricky to match with a very low impedance, but I never said it was going to be easy!

The model shows that a capacity hat can be very helpful, but we really need to keep the antenna as tall as we possibly can to make matching easier and to keep its efficiency up.

Another option is to wind a vertical helically (a small capacity hat too will help). As a guide you need to wind about half a wavelength (about 83m / 273ft) of wire on to a PVC or fibreglass tube about 25ft tall to get it to resonate as a quarter wave. You'll still need an extensive earth system.

So is there an easier antenna to build and match?

OPTION 4 – USE A SHORTENED INVERTED-L

If you are really serious about topband we need to think about longer antennas. Michael, G7VJR, achieved DXCC on topband, but only after spending a lot of time optimising his antenna design and going through the same 'loaded vertical' experience that we have outlined above.

Michael eventually settled for a loaded inverted-L antenna, which stretches the term stealthy to the limit, but shows what you can achieve. The idea of an inverted-L for topband is not new. The late Stew Perry, W1BB, topband's greatest advocate, recommended the inverted-L as a good antenna for newcomers to the band.

Michael said: "In my quest for nine-band DXCC, I needed to put up an antenna for 160m which would let me work 100 entities. The available space and planning restrictions for this project left me little choice - with a few modest

trees, but no space to spread out, it would need to be an inverted-L with considerable base loading.

"As I live in the centre of a village this design had two advantages; firstly, I was able to lay many radials, knowing that these would be unnoticeable, and secondly, by using very thin wire I would be able to conceal the main element in the trees and foliage. I was determined to try, and was, in the end, rewarded by this simple antenna."

Michael says that for the antenna to work efficiently you

Michael G7VJR is passionate about 160m operation.

must be prepared to bury many long radials. "Although the antenna is stealthy above ground, it is only efficient with a good ground plane," Michael said. "In actual fact, you may think of it as having the vast majority of its mass (by wire) underground. In my case, I laid 32 radials of approximately 1/8 to 1/4 wavelength (up to 40m long each) as evenly as possible, about one inch under the soil. That's perhaps 1000m of radial wire!

"I used any wire I had lying around - this is not critical except, perhaps, if you have animals grazing or many rabbits gnawing at your installation. In my case, the radials extend beyond the boundary of my property into a small paddock that is very seldom occupied, so I was bold and used the cover of darkness and a sharp spade when laying the wires. After approximately three days there was no visible evidence.

"The wires emerge from the ground at the base of the antenna, where I crimped them to eye-hole connectors and bundled them together for quick connection to the feed point."

Michael says his radiating element rises directly from ground near to the base of a convenient tree, which is about 40ft tall. The wire is a strong, light, dark coloured type that he acquired from dx-wire.de. This is very low profile, so it suited his needs in terms of its stealthy properties and mechanical strength.

"It is only 1mm or so in diameter. I would advise against hard-drawn wire as you will be pulling wires through branches for this project, and you need flexibility in the element," Michael said. "I raised the wire through a mini-pulley situated near the top of the tree. It's important to use a pulley because the wire element of the antenna will need to move in the wind. One tip - the pulley was raised using a continuous loop of thin Kevlar cord which I installed with a catapult.

"As you pull the element up, try to start away from the main trunk, and keep the wire a little bit away from the tree, as it is likely to interfere with the antenna each time you let the wire touch a branch or foliage. You may otherwise have issues with arcing if you run full legal power.

"At the top of the tree, the element runs a further 60ft horizontally to the next tree along (at a similar height of 40ft) to create a total element length of roughly 100ft. This length is not critical.

"Do make sure the tip never comes close to the second tree. Instead join on a thin insulating line which comes back down to tie within easy reach. The tip of the wire is at extremely high potential when transmitting, and almost any contact at all with the tree will result in the antenna wire burning through, bringing the antenna down to ground and spoiling your hard work," he said.

Michael said he formed a substantial coil of insulated car battery wire on a nine-inch diameter bucket. The number of turns was picked experimentally by temporarily using a needle connected from the element, which he could poke into any point on the coil (through the insulation) to get a quick reading from his Mini-VNA analyser. This saved a lot of time and effort forming or cutting the coil to length, which had around 15 turns.

Michael added: "Avoid using thin wire, where your losses will be far too great. Aim for thick insulation coated on to thick wire, which is ideal in terms of spacing and insulation, and is quite typical of car battery wire or car audio cabling, so is less expensive than you might expect."

He fed his 50-ohm coax to a 1:2 (*note:* it is 1:2, not 2:1) unbalanced-to-unbalanced transformer (unun) from balundesigns.com, and connected the radials directly through a large nut and bolt. He used Contralube (a waterproof electrical connection protector) to stave off any corrosion and then connected the centre of the coax on the output of the unun to the coil.

Michael added: "The reason for the unun is that like all inverted-L antennas on 160m, the feed point is likely to be between 22.5 ohms (theoretical) and perhaps 30 ohms. By using a step-up transformer we get closer to 50 ohms for the feeder, and therefore obtain efficient power transfer. The unun has a small effect on the resonance of the antenna (in my case dropping it lower by about 25kHz).

"Another tip, if your antenna impedance looks like 50 ohms without an unun, you do not have enough radials! Add more radials, and you'll see the impedance falls to this range. Otherwise, you are simply warming the ground with your RF transmissions," he said.

Michael's antenna has a deep 50 ohm resonance around 1825kHz. The bandwidth of the antenna is only 15kHz either side, so it is quite specific to CW, although it can be tuned for SSB.

The receive performance is very good. With much of the antenna being horizontal its noise characteristics are lowered at the expense of its transmit efficiency at low angles.

Michael worked 125 entities in one season with this antenna, including New Zealand, Clipperton Island, Alaska, and many Japanese stations.

"No complaints were made and I truly suspect that no-one was aware I had installed it," he said. "Although it was eventually blown down by wind, the antenna gave me great pleasure and the 160m band delighted me all winter.

"Although unusable on other bands due to the large coil, if you bypass the coil you may find the antenna performs well on 80m as well as 160m," Michael concluded.

Playing with Michael's design in *MMANA-GAL* shows how much easier it is to match on 160m than our capacity hat vertical. It really only requires an inductor at the feed point with little or no capacitance. Also, by making the antenna larger and the coil former bigger you don't end up with having a coil with a large number of turns, so reducing the losses.

If you want to take this idea further in terms of stealth operation, you could reduce the height of the antenna to about 8m, shorten the horizontal leg and perhaps add an inductor in the middle of it, or perhaps angle the leg down so that you could attach it to a suitable fence post. The SWR will increase and the efficiency will go down, but as long as you have a decent earth system you should make contacts.

Avoiding interference and EMC issues

IF YOU ARE A radio amateur, sooner or later you are going to come up against
EMC issues. EMC stands for Electromagnetic Compatibility, although I think
it should really be called EMI (for 'Incompatibility')! EMC really breaks down
into three main areas:

* **Breakthrough**
   Interference to neighbouring electronic and radio equipment caused
   by the relatively high field strength of the amateur transmission.

* **Interference caused by spurious emissions**
   This is where the amateur station causes interference (usually to radio
   or TV) by generating unwanted emissions.

* **Interference *to* amateur reception**
   This is generally called radio frequency interference or RFI.

If you use outside antennas and reasonable power levels you are unlikely to
experience any more EMC problems than any other ham. But if you use indoor or
loft-mounted antennas, or antennas in close proximity to your house, you are more
likely to suffer problems – even
with relatively low power levels.

One again, both the RSGB
and ARRL have sections on
their websites devoted to EMC
issues and I recommend that you
visit them.

INTERFERENCE BEING
CAUSED BY YOU

The biggest problem with
stealth or hidden antennas is their
relative proximity to household
wiring and domestic equipment.
With electromagnetic fields varying
according to the inverse square law
you can see that halving the distance

**Freezing, blocking or a lack of signal are all possible
symptoms of RF interference to a digital TV or set-top
box.**

Make sure that all your antenna connections are tight. A loose PL259 can cause interference.

from your antenna to a device such as a TV results in the field strength going up by a factor of four. Put another way, using 50W to an indoor loft-mounted dipole may have the same effect as someone running 400W to an outdoor antenna.

So what can you do about any potential interference problems?

Firstly, keep your antennas as far away from household wiring and domestic devices, such as TVs, hi-fi equipment, telephones etc. If possible keep them away from your neighbours too.

Secondly, if you are causing interference to you or anyone else, stop transmitting – at least until you can determine what the extent of the interference is and what is causing it.

Check your own station to make sure that it is wired correctly, that all PL259 plugs are securely tightened and that there are no breaks in your coax or other antenna cabling. I have seen loose PL259 plugs on the back of ATUs cause TVI and a break in a G5RV antenna, where the twin feeder was joined to the coax, that was arcing on transmit.

If possible make sure that your transmitter is working properly and not generating unwanted spurious emissions. There is usually an expert in your local club who can check this.

If the interference is caused by spurious emissions or harmonics using an ATU can help as it will attenuate out of band and unwanted signals. Certain types of antennas are better than others too – magnetic loop antennas, for example, are very good at only radiating the frequency upon which you are operating.

In the UK keeping an amateur radio station log is no longer compulsory, but it is useful to have a record of when

Wrapping your TV antenna lead through a ferrite ring might help to eliminate interference. Or try a high-pass filter.

and where you have been transmitting. This helps you and your neighbours decide if you are responsible for any interference and, if you are, what band(s) and / or antenna(s) were responsible.

The first action you can take if you are found to be causing interference is to try to move the antenna away from the affected item.

I found that I was causing interference to my main television while using 2m FM, even though I was only running about 5W. The digital picture would freeze as I transmitted. I found that my moving the loft-mounted vertical antenna just six feet away did the

Some cheap computer speakers are notoriously bad at picking up RF.

trick. I can now run 25 - 40W with no problems, although the problem shows itself again at higher levels (which I don't run). If the problem still persists don't presume that it is your 'fault'. It could be that the TV antenna connections have deteriorated or the cable has broken. If all else fails, a high-pass TVI filter can be fitted into the back of the TV set. These are available from most good amateur radio retailers or the RSGB.

Breakthrough on to hi-fi units can usually be cured by winding the loudspeaker wires and mains leads on to ferrite rings – as close to the device as possible.

Some cheap computer speakers are notoriously bad for breakthrough and I had one pair that resisted all attempts at silencing them. I borrowed another pair which showed no signs of breakthrough whatsoever, so replaced them with the same make.

If a telephone is sold by BT, and suffers RF breakthrough while under warranty, the customer can return it to the point of sale. In this case, BT retail outlets will, if possible, replace such a telephone with another model offering higher RF immunity. Alternatively, they may supply a 'plug-in' RFI filter free of charge if appropriate. If a telephone was sold by BT, but is out of warranty and is not covered by a maintenance contract, there is a standard charge for the sale of a 'Freelance' plug-in RFI filter, LJU 10/14A, BT Item Code 877596. These are sold by BT PhoneShops for less than £10 but may not be effective in all cases.

If you find you are causing interference to more than one device in your house the chances are that you could be injecting RF into the mains wiring.

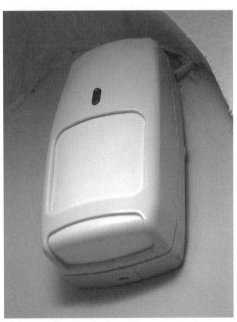

Some alarm PIR detectors are also prone to being triggered by stray RF.

If so, reduce your power or relocate your antenna. Wrapping every mains lead in the house around a ferrite may seem to make sense, but what about your neighbours?

Interference to burglar alarms is also possible, but the good news is that the RSGB's EMC Committee has never known a case of alarm RF triggering that could not be cured by fitting RF-immune PIRs or occasionally a more immune control panel. If your transmissions set off the neighbour's alarm system, it is advisable to tell them as soon as possible, otherwise that they may be charged for a visit by the installer or maintenance engineer who may find no fault. If the system is centrally monitored, the monitoring service could be withdrawn if there are too many false alarms.

Some installers have come across RF triggering before (not necessarily from amateur transmissions) and may realise the cause if they see your aerials (if visible). Others claim that it has never happened to one of their installations before and assume that it must be the radio amateur's fault - which is isn't.

If the installer does not have sufficient technical knowledge to deal with the problem, you will need to give some technical advice otherwise they may waste time trying things which are unlikely to work. Again, the RSGB has a technical document that you can download at www.rsgb.org.

If you find that you are killing your broadband Internet connection when using 80m the solution may be to reduce power and / or move the antenna further away form the telephone points. If that doesn't work it is possible to remove the ring wire from the master socket. The ring wire induces an imbalance in the phone wiring and removing mine cured the problem once and for all. It has no effect on modern telephones and the ring wire is a hang over from days of old. If you have a BT NTE5 Master socket with a removable bottom half, instructions for removing this wire can be found on the Internet, but if in doubt call in a professional.

If you cannot resolve a persistent case of interference your first stop might be another local ham with more experience.

Following a change of procedure in mid-2010, the BBC is now responsible for investigating complaints of interference to domestic radio and television. The Ofcom [1] website has more detail, but the BBC has an interactive diagnostic website [2] where you answer questions and will be presented with guidance on the possible causes of the problem you're experiencing and advice on what you could do.

This should take up to 10 minutes to complete. If the guidance and advice don't help, you are then given the option to proceed through a webform and send the BBC an e-mail. They will then investigate and, if they believe you are suffering from an interference problem, may contact you for further information to help resolve the problem. If, following the investigation by the BBC, there is evidence of interference caused by something outside your control and which is unlawful, the BBC may refer your case back to Ofcom for possible enforcement action.

Ofcom does not currently investigate problems with cable television or baby alarms, nor any equipment that is not intended to receive radio signals such as hi-fi systems, computer speakers or telephones.

INTERFERENCE BEING CAUSED *TO* YOU

Increasingly nowadays this is getting to be a major problem. Years ago, amateurs only had to worry about noisy electric motors and car ignition systems, but the rise in microcomputer-controlled circuitry and switched-mode power supplies has resulted in us living in a veritable fog of electrical noise.

Amateur Radio is an 'unprotected service' in the UK, which means that radio amateurs do not have a right to interference-free reception. Radio services such as emergency services, Private Business Radio (PBR, formerly PMR) and broadcasting are examples of 'protected' services whose users can ask Ofcom to investigate any interference. For protected services, a minimum usable signal level is defined but radio amateurs often receive weak signals which are only just detectable and may therefore suffer interference from sources which would not affect other services.

If there is interference to amateur bands, it is worth checking whether it also affects the UHF TV band or the 88 - 108MHz FM broadcast band, particularly classical music stations in stereo. If it does affect a TV or FM broadcast station, which is intended to serve your area and you are using an adequate outdoor TV or FM aerial, go to the BBC website [2], click on the "reception problems tool" link at the top of the page and complete the interactive web form. After answering a series of questions the site will offer suggestions as what could be causing the problem. Otherwise you will be invited to submit an e-mail to the BBC for further investigation.

It is worth keeping a log of exactly when the RFI occurs as this can give a clue to the possible source. Tuning across the affected band or bands can also give some clues about the source of the interference. Here are some common sources of interference:

Television line timebase harmonics

The line timebase frequency of 625-line television systems in the UK is 15.625kHz. Harmonics may be heard as narrow band signals on multiples of this frequency, for example, 3500.000kHz, 3515.625kHz, 3531.25kHz, etc. As the line frequency is 1MHz divided by 64, harmonics are found on multiples of 125kHz. If the TV is receiving an off-air programme, the harmonic will usually have a sound which changes with picture content when heard on an SSB or CW receiver.

To prove that a TV set is the source, try watching another TV set (with low RFI!) and select different channels until you find one where changes in the picture coincide with changes in the sound heard on the radio.

Sometimes a braid breaker filter fitted in the antenna lead can help reduce timebase harmonics as it prevents them being re-radiated by the TV antenna and coax. It is worth trying.

Switch-mode power supplies

A switch-mode power supply (SMPS) generates a square wave at a frequency of 30 - 90kHz or more. On the LF, MF and lower HF bands, harmonics from an

SMPS can produce broad band RFI with broad peaks and 100Hz modulation. The peaks are spaced at multiples of the switching frequency. On the higher HF bands and at VHF, the peaks may merge together. These are becoming more and more common and are used to power all sorts of things, from laptops computers to portable radios.

I have even seen a mobile phone charger wipe out 2m (144MHz) completely when it was being used about 10ft away from the shack.

It is relatively easy to find out if an SMPS is responsible for the noise – just switch it off, wait a few seconds and the noise should vanish. If you do find a noisy SMPS the solution is usually replacement. I also make sure that all SMPSs that are not actually being used in the house are actually switched off and not left connected to the mains.

TV power supplies

When heard on an AM or SSB receiver, the sound from a TV switch-mode power supply usually changes with picture content (see also TV line timebase harmonics above), but is broad band and may peak at a certain frequency such as 14 - 18MHz.

The switch-mode power supply also runs when in standby mode and its characteristics may change so that interference is only noticeable in standby mode. Emissions in standby mode are normally continuous, but in some sets sold since 1999, the noise is modulated at about 8 - 10Hz in standby mode. This produces a 'chuff-chuff' noise like a fast steam train. These are mainly 28-inch Bush models although there are some other brands that use a similar chassis.

Video recorder power supplies

Video recorder power supplies normally operate continuously and may be linear or switch-mode. Some video recorders not intended for the UK market have been personally imported from the Middle East and have inadequate mains filtering. These are likely to be multi-standard models with PAL and MESECAM and can be very noisy on the 1.8MHz and 3.5MHz bands.

TV 'set-top boxes'

There are various types of TV 'set-top box' for satellite TV, cable TV, digital terrestrial TV or video on demand via ADSL (Asymmetric Digital Subscriber Line). These normally have switch-mode power supplies that run continuously.

Lighting

If the RFI occurs mainly after dark, does it appear when a light is on in a room nearby?

I have seen a mobile telephone switch mode charger that wiped out 2m reception.

Electronic transformers - For lighting which uses 12V halogen spotlights, the transformers may either be a conventional type or an 'electronic transformer' which is a switch-mode power supply with AC output.

Compact fluorescent lamps (low energy lamps) - Most types are electronic and contain a small switch-mode power supply. There are also larger non-electronic types such as the Philips SL range which generate less RFI, but have a heavy iron-cored choke.

Computer power supplies

In a desktop computer, the SMPS is normally in a screened box with a mains filter and may therefore produce much less RFI than a computer monitor, where the SMPS may be unscreened. Laptop computers have an external mains power supply unit / charger which is normally an SMPS without screening.

Fax machines

The power supply runs 24 hours a day and it is almost always a switch-mode type.

Electric motors

RFI from an AC or DC electric motor with brushes and a commutator is broad band without peaks. Its pitch varies as the motor speed varies. The variations in speed and the pattern of use can give clues about the source. For example, this might be a washing machine or drier, sewing machine, electric lawn mower, food mixer, electric drill, hair dryer or even a model railway. It is not likely to be a refrigerator because they normally use induction motors which do not produce RFI.

Thermostats

Faulty thermostats can arc for 1 - 30 seconds or more producing broad band RFI with no peaks and 100Hz modulation. This may be heard on a number of HF and / or VHF bands. The most common source is a faulty gas central heating boiler thermostat and it is likely to be worse in winter. The arcing may occur every 5 - 20 minutes although in some cases it could be as often as two or three times per minute.

Conventional fluorescent lights

RFI from fluorescent lights is broad band with no peaks and

Interference that is there 24 hours a day could be caused by a fax machine and its PSU.

is modulated with a 100Hz buzz, mainly on the LF, MF and lower HF bands. Fluorescent lights have been required to include RFI suppression since 1978 although most met the relevant standard long before this date. If the tube is worn out and flickering at 50Hz, this can increase the level of RFI.

Dimmer switches

RFI from dimmer switches is similar to that produced by fluorescent lights and is stronger when the lamp is dimmed than when on full brightness. Dimmer switches sold in the UK have been required to include RFI suppression since 1978 although most met the relevant standard long before this date. They seldom cause problems to amateur reception unless they are faulty or are a type not designed for the European market.

Computers

Various oscillators in a computer and its associated components such as the keyboard and mouse can produce narrow band radiated emissions. Some are crystal controlled and generally have no drift or modulation while others use a ceramic resonator which drifts and may have slight frequency modulation which can be heard as a 'warbling' noise on an SSB or CW receiver. Such modulation may sound like someone typing on a keyboard or playing a game.

Intruder alarm systems

Intruder alarm systems normally contain a microprocessor and can radiate signals from the wiring to the sensors on the HF and / or VHF bands. As they normally use a ceramic resonator, the harmonics drift slightly and may have

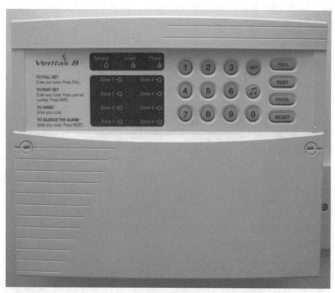

slight modulation which can be heard on an SSB receiver. This modulation may change if the alarm ever goes off and may also change when the user presses keys on the control panel. I had an alarm panel once that put a very powerful carrier signal on 18.140MHz. The solution was to replace it.

I had an alarm panel once that put a strong intermittent carrier on 18.140MHz – it sounded like someone tuning up. A replacement cured the problem.

Other digital electronic devices

Digital electronic circuitry can radiate narrow band signals on certain frequencies such as harmonics of the clock frequency and may also produce broad band signals. Such sources include NICAM decoders and other digital electronics in TV sets, video recorders and satellite receivers/decoders. Many of these devices are connected to long cables which can radiate RFI on HF bands as well as VHF.

Cable TV

Many modern cable television systems use vision carriers from 128MHz upwards on multiples of 8MHz although some frequencies such as 144.000MHz are not normally used. The street cabinets normally contain a switch-mode power supply which may produce detectable emissions on the HF bands due to common-mode signals conducted along the coaxial cables.

Telephone equipment

Fax machines contain a microprocessor which runs continuously. If a computer is connected to a modem, this can allow RFI from the computer to be radiated via the telephone line. If the modem can receive fax or voice calls, the owner may leave the computer running all the time.

'Touch Lamps'

These are table lamps with a touch-operated switch which turns the lamp on and off and selects several levels of brightness. They contain a saw-tooth oscillator which operates continuously and produce emissions which are similar to an SMPS but with a fundamental frequency of around 190kHz. Some models sold before 1996 contain no RFI suppression.

Garage door openers

The super-regenerative receivers for some 173MHz remote-controlled garage door openers manufactured in the late 1980s radiate broad band noise on 430 - 440MHz. They can also receive VHF radio paging and rebroadcast it at a number of frequencies on the 430 - 440MHz band!

Water conditioners

Electronic water conditioners are claimed to reduce deposition of lime scale. Some types such as the 'Water King' and 'Water Imp' use a sequence of audio frequency tones which have harmonics up to 28MHz in some cases. The radiated emissions have a very unusual characteristic as the tone changes about once a second in a sequence which repeats every few minutes.

Electric fences

RFI from an electric fence is a regular clicking noise. The source is likely to be sparking at a faulty insulator rather than the electric fence unit itself. Try looking for flashovers in the dark (with the landowner's permission).

Overhead power cables

Overhead power cables can radiate broad band noise with 100Hz modulation. High voltage cables always produce a certain amount of RFI due to corona discharge from the cable itself but RFI can be greatly increased due to arcing at a faulty insulator, in which case the level of RFI may reduce in dry weather.

Radio Paging

This sounds rather like packet radio but usually starts with a tone. Strong signals from nearby radio paging transmitters may be heard on the 2m band or other bands but in most cases such breakthrough is caused by shortcomings in the amateur receiver. Transceivers with extended receive coverage are more likely to be affected than those which only cover amateur bands. Hand-held transceivers connected to an outdoor aerial can be particularly susceptible.

Power Line Adaptors / Telecommunications (PLA / PLT)

Power line telecommunications (PLT) apparatus uses a technology that can carry data on mains wiring around the house and is used to connect computers or other digital devices. They use shortwave frequencies to transmit their data. At the time of writing there are about 25 brands of PLT apparatus on the market in the UK. The largest supplier is British Telecommunications plc (BT). BT includes Comtrend UK Limited's PLT apparatus as part of its BT Vision package.

PLA units can cause broad-band interference right across the short-wave spectrum, although some units (include the BT Vision ones) have their output notched at the amateur frequencies, so cause less interference.

However, this doesn't stop them causing extreme interference to the short-wave broadcast bands and they generally add to the overall high noise floor we experience in urban and suburban areas.

If you think you are suffering from PLA interference first tune your receiver to a frequency like 13 or 27MHZ AM and sweep up and down the band. PLA interference sounds like a constant, but modulated, digital buzz – a bit like electronic mosquitoes. When I suffered with PLA interference a check up and down the street with a Yaesu FT-817 soon tracked down the culprit.

If you lodge a complaint with Ofcom they will ascertain the cause of the interference and push for the PLA units to be removed. BT will often replace the PLA units with a hard-wired Ethernet solution.

Keep an eye on the RSGB website as there will be lots of developments in the field of PLA interference and how we can combat it over the next few years.

SEARCHING FOR THE SOURCE

First of all, don't forget to check everything in your own home! If you have a receiver that can run on battery power, switch off the all the mains power at the fuse box. If the receiver needs mains power, unplug each item from the mains in turn. If the noise vanishes when you switch off the power you know the problem lies in your home. If not, it must be elsewhere.

If the interference remains you need systematically to go around the house switching things off – a portable short-wave receiver can help at this point, but do bear in mind that just about every electronic device will emit some signals if you get close enough. You are just looking for the major culprits!

Don't forget to unplug appliances such as a video recorder, TV set or fax machine which may be in a 'standby' mode even when they appear to be switched off. It may not be possible to check an intruder alarm system by disconnecting the mains supply as this may cause the alarm to sound and in any case, some systems have a battery back-up.

A cheap portable short-wave radio can be used to track down interference sources.

On the HF bands, interference can enter your home via the mains supply, whether underground or overhead, and can be radiated by your mains wiring. In such cases, switching off a double pole main switch at the fuse box will probably reduce it although this depends on the exact layout of your mains wiring. Pick-up of mains-borne interference on the HF bands can often be reduced by moving your aerial further from mains wiring if possible, or by using a balanced aerial such as a dipole instead of an end-fed wire.

If it is not in your own home, the next step is to go out and search for it using a portable receiver, or get someone to help you if you are unable to do this yourself. In the case of HF mains-borne interference, the source is likely to be on the same phase as your own mains supply. In a street of houses, every third house is normally on the same phase. On VHF, if you have an aerial on a rotator then it should be possible to get some indication of the direction of the source. RFI that occurs continuously or frequently can often be located without a directional aerial, simply by going around searching for the strongest signal. For RFI that only occurs intermittently such as an arcing thermostat, a portable directional aerial is very useful. In either case, the receiver should have an 'S' meter, preferably a moving coil type. It is also useful to have an attenuator to reduce the sensitivity when you get closer to the source.

For cases where you can't thread a cable through a ferrite ring you can buy clip-on ferrite instead.

189

One possible problem is that RFI which is quite strong when using your main station aerial cannot be heard at ground level on a portable receiver. For a narrow band source, the maximum sensitivity is achieved by using CW mode with the narrowest possible bandwidth such as 500Hz. For broad band sources such as arcing, greater sensitivity is achieved by using a receiver with the widest possible bandwidth – AM is useful.

The first thing to establish is whether the source of the RFI is nearby (within about one hundred metres, for example) or further afield such as the next street or even the next town. Getting someone to drive you around the local roads in a car with a portable receiver connected to the car aerial may show a clear peak at a certain point which is not apparent when walking. If interference is being conducted along telephone wiring or mains wiring, there may be a number of peaks which coincide with telephone poles, overhead power lines or lamp posts.

Lower HF bands

If interference affects the 1.8MHz amateur band, it may also be audible on a medium-wave broadcast receiver. Alternatively, a ferrite rod aerial with an MW coil can be tuned to the 1.8MHz amateur band and connected to a portable HF receiver using a two-turn coupling winding to match into a 50Ω receiver input. For 3.5MHz, the main winding on the ferrite rod should be about 20 turns tuned with a 200pF variable capacitor. A one or two turn coupling winding should be used.

A ferrite rod aerial is recommended for DFing RFI on the 1.8 and 3.5MHz bands because it can be held right down on the ground to detect the magnetic field from RFI propagating along underground cables as a common mode signal (that is, on all conductors together relative to earth).

If properly balanced, a ferrite rod aerial gives a minimum signal when the rod is pointing towards or away from the source but this direction finding property can give misleading results in built-up areas or near overhead cables because MF / HF interference can travel for hundreds or thousands of metres along mains wiring or telephone wiring (particularly if overhead). Standing waves can cause the signal strength to rise and fall at intervals along the line.

With any RFI from overhead cables, it is best to search for it on the highest frequency possible, moving higher as you get closer. If you want to follow overhead power cables across land without a public right of way, permission should be obtained from the landowner before entering. If you can identify which pole is responsible, make a note of its number and report it to the electricity company.

Higher HF bands

The tendency for interference to travel along wiring decreases as frequency increases so it is better to search for interference on the highest frequency on which it can be heard. In practice, it will probably be necessary to listen on a frequency above the MUF where the HF bands are quiet.

CONTACTING THE OWNER OF THE SOURCE OF THE RFI
Residential property

If you decide to approach the occupier of a house or flat where you think the source of the interference is, bear in mind that the occupier will probably want to be sure of your identity and your motive before letting you in. It is a good idea to write or telephone first to gain their confidence and arrange a convenient time for a visit. Remember that the source may not actually be where you think it is so you should say that there *may* be something in the house or flat which is causing interference. In most cases, the only way to prove what is causing the RFI is to ask the owner to switch off various electrical equipment until the source is found.

In most cases, there is no fault in the equipment in question and only amateur bands are affected. A diplomatic approach is therefore essential as the owner of the equipment is under no obligation to do anything about the RFI, so it can only be reduced with their co-operation. Any RFI reduction should be restricted to measures that can be fitted by the owner without the need for you to touch or dismantle the equipment in question.

Some new TV receivers, digital set-top boxes and plasma screens have also been found to cause interference on the amateur bands.

In some cases, for example a faulty thermostat, the RFI is likely to interfere with the owner's broadcast radio or TV reception and may affect neighbours.

Commercial or industrial premises

If RFI appears to be coming from an office, shop, factory or other commercial premises, some effort may be required to make contact with the right person. In the case of a large company, there is probably an office services manager, building services manager or technical manager whom you could contact. If you are lucky, there may be a licensed radio amateur working on the site somewhere and he or she could be a very useful contact. In any case, it is best to write or telephone first and ask to make an appointment to see the appropriate person. With luck and a diplomatic approach, they may be prepared to take you around the site to look for the source. You will need to take a portable receiver as it probably won't be possible for equipment to be turned off.

REDUCING THE RFI
Contacting manufacturers

If you prove conclusively that a certain piece of equipment is producing RFI, it is worth trying to find out full details of the make, model number and date of purchase so that a complaint can be made directly to the manufacturer or importer. A polite and technically well-informed approach is recommended when dealing with manufacturers. The equipment probably met all necessary standards at the date of manufacture so the only way forward is on a good will basis.

The best approach when dealing with manufacturers is usually to phone first and find out the name of the person responsible for EMC then follow up the phone call with a letter, fax or e-mail. It is also worth finding out whether a newer model is available with reduced RFI. In some cases, the manufacturer may be prepared to provide a filter or exchange the equipment in question for a newer model at a reduced price.

An exchange of a faulty new unit by the supplier, or a visit by a service engineer may be the answer. Some new TV receivers, digital set top boxes and plasma screens have also been found to cause interference on amateur bands and it may be possible to trace the source to a particular neighbour. In most cases the device or equipment manufacturer will take a responsible attitude and provide a fix – often free of charge.

However, do act diplomatically when making an approach, as your neighbours may well not understand why you are concerned if their equipment appears to them to be working normally - you may even find the complaint turned back on you and your antenna system, however innocent or irrelevant that may be! Most of us want to live peacefully with our neighbours and this often means a degree of give and take.

RSGB assistance

If you can't find the source or you find you are getting nowhere with the owner of the offending equipment, the Society's EMC advisers may be able to offer advice, although they will not normally make home visits. If they cannot help, or if the problem has some complex or novel aspects, the EMC Committee may become involved and investigate further. They may ask if they can take measurements of the radiation or ask the official services to intervene. A list of the EMC advisers and further information about EMC matters can be found on the Society's website www.rsgb.org.uk - Leaflet EMC04 in particular gives examples of types of in-bound interference and how to trace them.

Official intervention

In persistent cases Ofcom field operations staff can investigate the interference for you, subject to resources as described above. There is no charge for this. If necessary they have enforcement powers against interference under the Wireless Telegraphy Acts, although these do not

In persistent cases of interference that you can't sort out yourself you can call Ofcom.

normally need to be employed. As an example, an amateur found he had a continuous very high noise level across several HF bands. It got worse when it rained. Investigating officers traced the source to a cracked insulator on an electricity pylon, which was subsequently replaced by the power company.

Ofcom also enforces the EMC and the Radio and Telecommunications Terminal Equipment (RTTE) Regulations, which implement EU Directives about electromagnetic radiation from new electrical, radio and telecommunications equipment placed on the market. Local Trading Standards Officers also have powers under these regulations. However, interference in the amateur bands could have a wider effect on other radio services, so Ofcom should normally be approached first on matters where interference affects the radio spectrum.

There is also a TV licence condition, which forbids a person to let their TV receiving equipment interfere with any other radio or TV reception. Ofcom has powers to enforce this condition. There have been several examples where spurii from digital set-top boxes have triggered alerts on distress frequencies. Ofcom has acted very quickly in these instances.

The RSGB EMC Committee recommends that you make your complaint to Ofcom in writing or by e-mail. Ofcom prefers that you approach the Head Office first [1] otherwise contact your local office, whose address can be found on their website.

LEAFLETS AND FURTHER INFORMATION

The following leaflets are freely available from the RSGB's website:

- *Radio Transmitters and Domestic Electronic Equipment* - General EMC information sheet about breakthrough on TV, radio, hi-fi, etc.
- *Radio Transmitters and Home Security Systems* - An information sheet for neighbours or alarm installers about RF triggering of intruder alarms.
- *Dealing with Alarm EMC Problems* - Advice to members on how to deal with RF triggering of an intruder alarm.
- *Locating Sources of Interference to Amateur Radio Reception* - Advice on how to identify and find sources of RFI in amateur bands.
- *Radio Transmitters and Telephones* - All about RF breakthrough on telephones.
- *Automotive EMC for Radio Amateurs* - Advice on installation of mobile amateur radio equipment in vehicles.
- *Protective Multiple Earthing (PME)*
- *TV Distribution Amplifiers* - For neighbours and TV aerial installers about solving breakthrough on home TV distribution amplifiers.
- *Handling In-bound Interference*
- *Avoiding Interference to Nearby Electronic Equipment*
- *The Ofcom Procedure for the Measurement of the Field-Strength of Amateur Stations*
- *Part P and the Radio Amateur*
- *RF Safety and the Radio Amateur*
- *Interference from In-house PLT*

REFERENCES

[1] Ofcom, Riverside House, 2a Southwark Bridge Road, London SE1 9HA; tel: 0845 456 3000 / 020 7981 3040; e-mail: contact@ofcom.org.uk; website: www.ofcom.org.uk

[2] BBC Help Receiving TV and Radio: www.bbc.co.uk/reception and click on "reception problems tool"

BY NOW YOU should have a pretty good idea of what sort of antenna solution will work for you. We've looked at indoor and outdoor antennas, conventional antennas and new ideas. We've also looked at cost-effective ways of putting up efficient antennas like the dipole, and derivatives like the off-centre fed and trap dipole.

What we have also shown is that if you have stealthy antennas in or near to your property you might have to reduce power to ensure you are not causing interference.

What I want to do now is to make sure that you are not throwing away precious power by the inappropriate use of the wrong feeder for your antenna.

MATCHED LOSSES ON COAX

Most people reading this book will feed their antennas with coax and, as I am about to show, this isn't a bad idea, but there are some issues to bear in mind. If you have a perfectly-matched antenna then coax losses will be at a minimum. For example, **Table 11.1** shows the losses on a 20m length of RG58C coax where the antenna represents a 50Ω load to the coax. That is, it is showing a 1:1 SWR. These were derived from an online calculator - just search for "coax loss calculator" on the Internet. Please note that actual loss figures may vary from manufacturer to manufacturer.

Usually we say that 6dB equals one S-point (which is a kind of industry standard), although many transceivers differ from this and some have been calibrated at 3dB per S-point. However it is calculated, you can see that you lose

Frequency	Matched loss
3.5MHz	0.446dB
7MHz	0.638dB
14MHz	0.917dB
21MHz	1.136dB
28MHz	1.325dB
145MHz	3.295dB
433MHz	6.323dB

Table 11.1: Typical losses for 20m of RG58, 1:1 SWR.

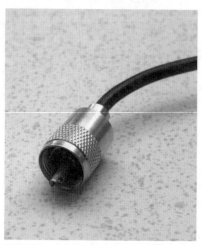

less than half an S-point by using 20m of coax on 21MHz or 28MHz, if you have a perfect match with a 1:1 SWR.

At VHF (e.g. 145MHz) and UHF (e.g. 433MHz) the losses start to get very significant. And these are representative figures only – one brand of RG58 being advertised in the UK when this book was being written was actually far more lossy than this, although the company selling it only quoted loss figures for 100MHz and 1000MHz.

So the moral is, if you are operating into a 1:1 SWR (perfect) load:

- If you are only interested in operating on the lower bands, e.g. 3.5 or 7MHz, short runs of RG58 are fine.
- Losses at 28MHz are worse, but not disastrous. If you wish to have the best performance think about using the thicker RG213 instead.
- RG58 is lossy at VHF and very lossy at UHF – use RG213 or better.

RG58 coax is easy to handle, but if you are feeding a VHF or UHF antenna, or an HF one with a high SWR, there are better alternatives.

But what if we used the thicker RG213 coax on HF instead? What would the loss figures be then? **Table 11.2** has the answers.

From this you can see that the losses at 28MHz, 145MHz and 433MHz are around half what they were with RG58. Although the cable is harder to work

Frequency	Matched loss
3.5MHz	0.238dB
7MHz	0.34dB
14MHz	0.486dB
21MHz	0.601dB
28MHz	0.699dB
145MHz	1.716dB
433MHz	3.207dB

Table 11.2: Typical losses for 20m of RG213, 1:1 SWR.

with, on HF it is worth the effort if you are able to use it. On VHF and UHF it is pretty much essential. You *can* use RG58 for VHF and UHF installations, but you are throwing away a lot of power. If you only use these bands for local contacts and / or repeaters you can get away with it, but if you are serious you need to install better coax.

Now let's see what happens if we use antennas that are not matched properly.

Unmatched losses

You may be tempted to use an antenna cut for one band on another band. I want to show you that this isn't always a good idea. What happens if we use, say, a 10-15-20m trap dipole on 17m (18MHz). The *MMANA* antenna modelling software says that we would expect to see an SWR *at the antenna* of about 1.4:1 if we use the antenna on 14MHz. But if we try to use it on 18MHz it predicts an SWR of about 64:1.

Now, in reality, if you try this with about 20m of RG58 coax and measure it at the rig end you will likely see an SWR closer to 10:1. Why? Because losses in the coax will make the SWR at the rig look a heck of a lot better than it is at the feedpoint. This is why when setting up antennas it is always best to use an antenna analyser with a short length of coax from the feedpoint. That way you are getting a better indication of what the antenna is *really* doing.

The sure sign that our trap dipole isn't working on 18MHz is that there is no dip in SWR as we move from the lower edge of the 17m band, 18.068MHz, to the top edge at 18.168MHz.

So what sort of losses do we get by using our RG58 coax with an SWR of 64:1? We have to add the unmatched losses to the matched losses we calculated earlier to give the total loss. Let's take a look at **Table 11.3**.

Frequency	Matched loss	Unmatched Loss	Total Loss
3.5MHz	0.446dB	5.888dB	6.334dB
7MHz	0.638dB	6.944dB	7.582dB
14MHz	0.917dB	8.02dB	8.936dB
21MHz	1.136dB	8.642dB	9.778dB
28MHz	1.325dB	9.074dB	10.398dB
145MHz	3.295dB	11.174dB	14.469dB
433MHz	6.323dB	11.948dB	18.271dB

Table 11.3: Typical losses for 20m of RG58, 64:1 SWR.

Wow! The term "total loss" seems very justified. The losses now are high. In fact the losses caused by using our 10-15-20m trap dipole on 17m (18MHz) equate to 9.454dB. Let's put it this way, if you fed 100W to your antenna with an SWR of 64:1 like this around 10W would actually arrive to be radiated.

In a test, I tuned in the 5Z0H DXpedition to Kenya on 17m (18MHz). On my dedicated 18MHz dipole they were just audible at about S1. But on the 10-15-20m trap dipole they were inaudible. Other signals on the 17m band were a good 2 - 3 S-points down as well, which correlates well with the calculated loss.

So the moral is this:

- Coax is fine if you are using your antenna on the band that it is designed for, providing the line length is not too long and you are using the correct coax for the job (see earlier).

- But if you are using an antenna with a high SWR, such as a badly-tuned antenna or on a band that it is not designed for, the losses will be large.

Luckily, there is a way around the problem, which leads us on to the next section

OPEN WIRE FEEDER

Open wire feeder has been used in the radio industry for donkey's years. In fact, go to a commercial HF transmitting station and open wire feeders will be in evidence all over the place. Why? Because it is cheap, can handle large amounts of RF and is very low loss, even when subjected to a high SWR. We can prove this quite easily. Again, search for "open wire feeder calculator" on the Internet to find a suitable tool (the one I used was at www.ocarc.ca/coax.htm but URLs do change).

If we take our model from the previous section, that is, trying to use our 10-15-20m trap dipole with a 64:1 SWR, but this time with 20m of generic 450Ω windowed ladder line, which you can buy in good radio stores, what do the losses look like? Well, they are down to just 1.98dB – that's an 8.8dB improvement. In

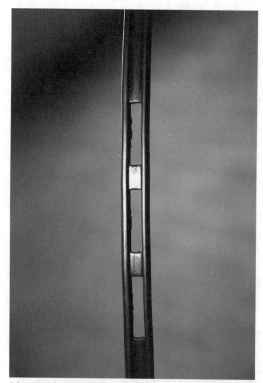

fact, if we use true 600Ω ladder line – the sort you can make yourself – the losses come down to just 1.4dB.

While I don't suggest that you start feeding your trap dipole with ladder line it does show the merits of the doublet antenna. Just fit the largest length of wire that you can. Split it in the middle and feed it from a balanced ATU with ladder line or open wire feeder. It will work well on all bands. That is, on a band where it is about half a wavelength long and then on higher frequencies too. Obviously the radiation pattern will change, depending upon the band you are on, but you do not need to worry about line losses. This is also why I think the G5RV concept is flawed. As I showed earlier, the antenna only shows a low-ish SWR on one band, 20m (14MHz). On every other band it exhibits a high SWR. Now add about 20m of coax to the bottom of the antenna and your losses go up badly. But cut off the coax connector at the bottom and run ladder line all the way back to the balanced ATU and the losses virtually disappear.

Slotted 300Ω ribbon feeder is the stealthiest form of open wire feeder you can get and is a similar price to RG213.

We may think that the doublet and open wire feeder are old fashioned, but they continue to be used for a very good reason!

ANTENNA MODELLING WITH *MMANA-GAL*

Throughout this book I have made reference to the *MMANA* antenna modelling software [1]. To give it its full title, the latest version should really be called *MMANA-GAL*, which is even more of a mouthful! It is a free antenna-analysing tool based on the moment method, which was introduced in *MININEC*. The program was written by Makoto Mori, JE3HHT; Alex Schewelew, DL1PBD; and Igor Gontcharenko, DL2KQ (the 'GAL' part refers to the abbreviation of the first names of DL2KQ and DL1PBD). It is available in English (default), Russian, Bulgarian, German, Japanese, Spanish, Serbian and Czech.

MMANA-GAL is capable of working out lots of useful information, such as the impedance and SWR of an antenna design, the gain, the azimuthal and elevation radiation patterns, the current distribution and much more. It can handle simulated loading coils and traps and help you work out the best LC combinations for the latter.

You can model antennas in free space or over simulated ground and compare the radiation patterns of one design with another. I have found it invaluable in understanding how my antennas work and it is useful for odd questions like "why does my W3EDP end-fed work so well to the south on HF?" Once you have seen the predicted radiation patterns and the big lobe in the direction in which the antenna points it all makes more sense.

The software can be a bit daunting when you first download it, but it does come with a lot of sample (.mma) antenna files. You can modify these or start from scratch. All antennas are built from "Wires" that are specified in terms of their start and end points in terms of their X, Y and Z coordinates (**Fig 11.1**).

This is easy until you start modelling antennas that are at an angle, like inverted-Vs. The answer then is to use Pythagoras's theorem to work out the X, Y and Z coordinates of a sloping wire. For example, a 10m long wire at an angle of 45° can have a start point coordinate of 0 (X), 0 (Y) and 7.07m (Z) and an end point of 0 (X), 7.07m (Y), 0(Z). Just square the 10m length, divide by two and then take the square root. I find it best to sit and work out the coordinates with a pen and paper before starting to build the antenna in *MMANA-GAL*.

Open wire feeder, such as used on the G5RV can be modelled by putting two wires very close together – perhaps 10mm apart to model 300Ω feeder and further apart for 450 and 600Ω.

Once you have the antenna design you then add a "source". This is the equivalent of a feedpoint and can be added to the beginning, end or centre of a wire. If you have open wire feeder a shorting wire between the ends of the

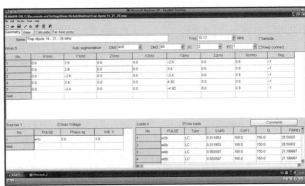

Fig 11.1: MMANA-GAL lets you build antennas by specifying "Wires".

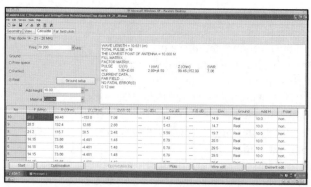

Fig 11.2: After running a calculation you get a table of SWR, impedance, reactance and gain.

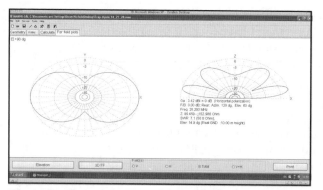

Fig 11.3: The great thing about antenna modelling is that you get to see the expected radiation pattern for your design.

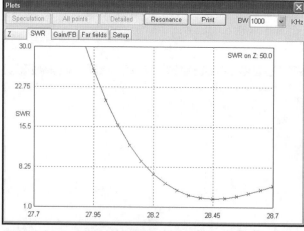

Fig 11.4: You can get simulated SWR curves so that you can see how changing various parameters affects the matching.

feeder and a source in the middle of that wire works well.

Going to "View" lets you see what your antenna looks like and then you can go to the "Calculate" section, specify the frequency to be tested and the height above ground and run the program.

You then end up with a table showing the frequency, calculated $R + jX$, the SWR, gain and maximum radiation angle (**Fig 11.2**).

Moving to the "Far Field plots" shows you the radiation pattern as seen from above and to the side of the antenna (**Fig 11.3**). You can also move this around and zoom in. This pattern can be modified for different radiation angles, so you check your design's DX potential at less than 10°. The patterns can also be saved for later and compared with each other.

MMANA-GAL lets you model antennas built with copper or aluminium wire or tubes. But if you are using insulated wire, do bear in mind that your modelled lengths will be longer than the actual lengths. I forgot this when I built a trap dipole and had to shorten each segment quite a bit.

Moving to "Plots" lets you run a plot of impedance, SWR, gain, and far field information across a range of frequencies to get the familiar SWR curves (**Fig 11.4**).

There is even more to *MMANA-GAL*, including an optimisation routine that will help you try out different parameters. For example, you can design a Yagi, say that you want to maximise forward gain and the program will automatically work out what needs to be done in terms of lengths and spacings to do just that.

You can do the same with impedance, SWR, gain, front to back ratio, elevation angle etc.

In all, there is a lot to like about *MMANA-GAL*, but do bear in mind that this is a *simulation* and cannot replicate your real-life garden or surroundings, complete with trees, shed, electrical wiring and other conducting elements. Nevertheless, I have found it invaluable in designing antennas and working out how to improve them.

There is also a PRO version of *MMANA-GAL*. To maintain compatibility with existing files, much of the original *MMANA-GAL* functionality has been incorporated into the new software. The PRO version has been specifically developed to handle very complex antenna designs. The personal licence for the software costs 99 euros and you can find out more on the *MMANA-GAL PRO* website [2]. However, if you are only interested in dipoles, verticals and Yagis you will probably find the free version of *MMANA-GAL* just fine.

MMANA-GAL uses the NEC (Numerical Electromagnetic Code) engine. There are lots of other antenna simulation tools that use the same engine, including NEC itself [3], *4NEC2* [4], and *EZNEC* [5].

If you are interested in finding out more about *MMANA-GAL* I recommend my book "An Introduction to Antenna Modelling", which is available from the RSGB.

REFERENCES

[1] *MMANA-GAL*:

    http://mmhamsoft.amateur-radio.ca/pages/mmana-gal.php

[2] *MMANA-GAL PRO:*   http://hamsoft.ca/pages/mmana-gal.php

[3] *NEC*:   www.nec2.org

[4] *4NEC2*:   www.qsl.net/4nec2/

[5] *EZNEC*:   www.eznec.com

Appendix
Glossary and abbreviations

THIS GLOSSARY provides a list of terms used frequently in amateur radio conversation and literature about antennas, and a list of common abbreviations. It is based on the glossary in the *ARRL Antenna Book* and is given here with the ARRL's permission.

With each item is a brief definition of the term. Some of the terms given here are discussed more thoroughly in the text of this book, and may be located by using the index.

A index:	A measure of the geomagnetic disturbance caused by the sun on a scale 0 to 400.
Actual ground:	The point within the earth's surface where effective ground conductivity exists. The depth for this point varies with frequency and the condition of the soil.
Antenna:	An electrical conductor or array of conductors that radiates signal energy (transmitting) or collects signal energy (receiving).
Antenna analyser:	See 'SWR analyser'.
Aperture, effective:	An area enclosing an antenna, on which it is convenient to make calculations of field strength and antenna gain. Sometimes referred to as the 'capture area'.
Apex:	The feed-point region of a V-type of antenna.
Apex angle:	The included angle between the wires of a V, an inverted-V dipole, and similar antennas, or the included angle between the two imaginary lines touching the element tips of a log-periodic array.
Array:	A group of radiating elements spaced some distance apart, with the current in each element having a particular amplitude and phase to increase the gain.
ATU : *(Antenna Tuning Unit)*	A device containing variable reactances (and perhaps a balun). It is connected between the transmitter and the feedpoint of an antenna system, and adjusted to 'tune' or resonate the system to the operating frequency. Also known as an 'ASTU' (antenna system tuning unit). In the USA an ATU is normally referred to as a 'transmatch'.
Balanced line:	A symmetrical two-conductor feedline that has

uniform voltage and current distribution along its length.

Balun: A device for feeding a balanced load with an unbalanced line, or vice versa. May be a form of choke, or a transformer that provides a specific impedance transformation (including 1:1). Often used in antenna systems to interface a coaxial transmission line to the feedpoint of a balanced antenna, such as a dipole.

Bandwidth: The current taken by a resonant antenna, and hence the radiation, falls off as the frequency is varied away from resonance. There will be two frequencies, one above and one below resonance, at which the power will be reduced by half. The difference between these frequencies is termed the 'bandwidth' of the antenna.

Base loading: A lumped reactance that is inserted at the base (ground end) of a vertical antenna to resonate the antenna.

Bazooka: A transmission line balancer. It is a quarter-wave conductive sleeve (tubing or flexible shielding) placed at the feedpoint of a centre-fed element and grounded to the shield braid of the coaxial feedline at the end of the sleeve farthest from the feedpoint. It permits the use of an unbalanced feedline with balanced-feed antennas.

Beamwidth: Related to directive antennas, the width, in degrees, of the major lobe between the two directions at which the relative radiated power is equal to one half its value at the peak of the lobe (half power = -3dB).

Bridge: A circuit with two or more ports that is used in measurements of impedance, resistance or standing waves in an antenna system. When the bridge is adjusted for a balanced condition, the unknown factor can be determined by reading its value on a calibrated scale or meter.

Broadside array: A broadside source has maximum radiation normal to its axis. A representative broadside array is a collinear array of horizontal array dipoles.

Capacitance hat: A conductor of large surface area that is connected at the high-impedance end of an antenna to effectively increase the electrical length. It is sometimes mounted directly above a loading coil to reduce the required inductance for establishing resonance. It usually takes the form of a series of wheel spokes or a solid circular disc.

Capture area:	See 'Aperture'.
Centre-fed:	Transmission-line connection at the electrical centre of an antenna radiator.
Centre loading:	A scheme for inserting inductive reactance (coil) at or near the centre of an antenna element for the purpose of lowering its resonant frequency. Used with elements that are less than a quarter wavelength at the operating frequency.
Characteristic impedance:	The relationship of current and voltage on a transmission line caused by the distributed inductance and capacitance. Most coaxial cable has a characteristic impedance of 50Ω.
Coaxial cable (coax):	Any of the coaxial transmission lines that have the outer shield (solid or braided) on the same axis as the inner or centre conductor. The insulating material can be air, helium or solid-dielectric compounds.
Collinear array:	A linear array of radiating elements (usually dipoles) with their axes arranged in a straight line. Popular at VHF and above.
Common mode signal:	Signal of similar amplitude and phase on both wires of a transmission line or input to an amplifier (as opposed to the normal anti-phase signal).
Conductor:	A metal body such as tubing, rod or wire that permits current to travel continuously along its length.
Counterpoise:	A wire or group of wires mounted close to ground, but insulated from ground, to form a low-impedance, high-capacitance path to ground. Used at MF and HF to provide an RF ground for an antenna. Also, see 'Ground plane'.
Cross(ed) Field Antenna (CFA):	An antenna that purports to synthesise an electromagnetic wave by bringing together an E and an H wave. Also, see 'EH antenna'.
Current loop:	A point of current maxima (antinode) on an antenna.
Current node:	A point of current minima on an antenna.
D-layer:	The lowest of the ionised layers of the ionosphere.
Decibel:	A logarithmic power ratio, abbreviated to 'dB'. May also represent a voltage or current ratio if the voltages or currents are measured across (or through) identical impedances. Suffixes to the abbreviation indicate references: dBi isotropic radiator; dBd dipole; dBm milliwatt; dBW watt.
Delta loop:	A full-wave loop shaped like a triangle or delta.
Delta match:	Centre-feed technique used with radiators that are not split at the centre. The feed line is fanned near the radiator centre and connected to the radiator

	symmetrically. The fanned area is delta shaped.
Dielectrics:	Various insulating materials used in antenna systems, such as found in insulators and transmission lines.
Differential capacitor:	Similar to split-stator capacitor, but arranged so that the capacitance on one side increases and the other side decreases as the moving vanes are rotated.
Dipole:	An antenna that is split at the exact centre for connection to a feedline. A resonant dipole is usually a half-wavelength long. A multi-band dipole is usually fed with tuned feeders.
Directivity:	The property of an antenna that concentrates the radiated energy to form one or more major lobes.
Director:	A conductor placed in front of a driven element to cause directivity. Frequently used singly or in multiples with Yagi or cubical-quad beam antennas.
Doublet:	A dipole, usually fed with open wire or balanced feeder.
Driven array:	An array of antenna elements, which are all driven or excited by means of a transmission line, usually to achieve directivity.
Driven element:	An element connected to the transmitter / receiver via a transmission line.
Dummy load:	A resistor used to provide a non-radiating substitute for an antenna for testing transmitters or transmission line test equipment.
E-layer:	The layer of the ionosphere nearest the earth from which radio signals can be reflected to a distant point, generally a maximum of 2000km (1250 miles).
E-plane:	Related to a linearly polarised antenna, the plane containing the electric field vector of the antenna and its direction of maximum radiation. For terrestrial antenna systems, the direction of the E-plane is also taken as the polarisation of the antenna. The E-plane is at right-angles to the H-plane.
Effective Radiated Power (ERP):	For a lossy low-frequency antenna the power dissipated in the radiation resistance when other losses have been taken into consideration. For omnidirectional vertical antennas the more common term is 'EMRP' (effective monopole radiated power). For HF, and particularly VHF / UHF, the power supplied to the antenna multiplied by the relative gain of the antenna in the direction of maximum radiation. The term 'EIRP' (effective isotropic radiated power) is also used, taking the gain of the antenna into account as referenced to an isotropic antenna.

Efficiency:	The ratio of useful output power to input power, determined in antenna systems by losses in the system, including in nearby objects.
EH antenna:	An antenna that purports to synthesise an electromagnetic wave by bringing together an E and an H wave. Also, see 'Cross Field Antenna'.
Elements:	The conductive parts of an antenna system that determine the antenna characteristics. For example, the reflector, driven element and directors of a Yagi antenna.
End effect:	A condition caused by capacitance at the ends of an antenna element. Insulators and related support wires contribute to this capacitance and lower the resonant frequency of the antenna. The effect increases with conductor diameter and must be considered when cutting an antenna element to length.
End-fed:	An end-fed antenna is one to which power is applied at one end, rather than at some point between the ends.
End-fire antenna:	An end-fire source has maximum radiation along the linear axis; a representative end-fire array is the Yagi antenna.
EZNEC:	Computer program for calculating the performance of an antenna.
F-layer:	The layer of the ionosphere that lies above the E-layer. Radio waves can be refracted from it to provide communications distances of several thousand miles by means of single- or double-hop skip.
Feed impedance:	The impedance of an antenna at the point where it is connected to the feeder.
Feeders:	Transmission lines of assorted types that are used to route RF power from a transmitter to an antenna, or from an antenna to a receiver.
Feedline:	See 'Feeders'.
Feedpoint:	The point where the feeder is connected to the antenna element.
Field strength:	The intensity of a radio wave as measured at a point some distance from the antenna. This measurement is usually made in microvolts per metre.
Free space:	A term used where antenna performance calculations are simplified by ignoring the effect of ground.
Front-to-back (ratio):	The ratio of the radiated power off the front and back of a directive antenna. For example, a dipole would have a ratio of 1, which is equivalent to 0dB.
Front-to-side:	The ratio of radiated power between the major lobe

	and that 90° off the front of a directive antenna.
Gain:	The increase in effective radiated power in the desired direction of the major lobe compared with a reference, such as a dipole or an isotropic source.
Gamma match:	A matching system used with driven antenna elements to effect a match between the transmission line and the feedpoint of the antenna. It consists of a series capacitor and an arm that is mounted close to the driven element and in parallel with it near the feedpoint.
GDO:	Grid (or Gate) Dip Oscillator, an instrument for measuring element resonance.
Ground plane:	A system of conductors placed beneath an elevated antenna to serve as an earth ground. Also see 'Counterpoise'.
Ground screen:	A wire mesh counterpoise.
Ground wave:	Radio waves that travel along the earth's surface.
H-plane:	Related to a linearly polarised antenna, the plane containing the magnetic field vector of an antenna and its direction of maximum radiation. The H-plane is at right angles to the E-plane.
Hairpin match:	A U-shaped conductor that is connected to the two inner ends of a split dipole for the purpose of creating an impedance match to a balanced feeder.
Harmonic antenna:	An antenna that will operate on its fundamental frequency and the harmonics of the fundamental frequency for which it is designed. A 7MHz dipole operating on 21MHz is an example.
Helical:	A helically-wound antenna, one that consists of a spiral conductor. If it has a very large winding length to diameter, it provides broadside radiation. If the length-to-diameter ratio is small, it will operate in the axial mode and radiate off the end opposite the feed point. The polarisation will be circular for the axial mode, with left or right circularity, depending on whether the helix is wound clockwise or counterclockwise.
Impedance:	The ohmic value of an antenna feed point, matching section or transmission line. An impedance almost always contains reactance, and is normally expressed as R 'jX, which means resistance and either + reactance (inductive) or - reactance (capacitive).
Inverted-V:	Any antenna erected in the form of an upside-down V; normally with the feedpoint at the apex.
Isotropic:	An imaginary or hypothetical point-source antenna

that radiates equal power in all directions. It is used as a reference for the directive characteristics of actual antennas.

K index: A measure of the geomagnetic disturbance caused by the Sun on a scale 0 to 9.

Lambda: Greek symbol λ used to represent a wavelength with reference to electrical dimensions.

Line loss: The power lost in a transmission line, usually expressed in decibels.

Line of sight: Transmission path of a wave that travels directly from the transmitting antenna to the receiving antenna.

Litz wire: Stranded wire with individual strands insulated from each other. Used to reduce RF losses in lower-frequency inductors.

Load: The electrical entity to which power is delivered. The antenna system is a load for the transmitter.

Loading: The process of a transferring power from its source to a load. The effect a load has on a power source.

Lobe: A defined field of energy that radiates from a directive antenna.

Log periodic antenna: A broad-band directive antenna that has a structural format causing its impedance and radiation characteristics to repeat periodically as the logarithm of frequency.

Long wire: A wire antenna that is one wavelength or greater in electrical length. When two or more wavelengths long it provides gain and a multi-lobe radiation pattern. When terminated at one end it becomes essentially unidirectional off that end.

Magnetic loop: (*magloop, or small tuned loop*) A small loop antenna, usually tuned with a capacitor.

Marconi antenna: A shunt-fed monopole operated against ground or a radial system.

Matching: The process of effecting an impedance match between two electrical circuits of unlike impedance. One example is matching a transmission line to the feedpoint of an antenna. Maximum power transfer to the load (antenna system) will occur when a matched condition exists.

MMANA-GAL: Computer program for calculating the performance of an antenna.

Monopole: Literally, one pole, such as a vertical radiator operated against the earth or a counterpoise.

Null: A condition during which an electrical unit is at a

minimum. The null in an antenna radiation pattern is that point in the 360° pattern where a minimum in field intensity is observed. An impedance bridge is said to be 'nulled' when it has been brought into balance, with a null in the current flowing through the bridge arm.

OCFD (Off-centre fed dipole):
A dipole fed at a point other than the centre – usually around one third from one end.

Open-wire line:
A type of transmission line that resembles a ladder, sometimes called 'ladder line'. Consists of parallel, symmetrical wires with insulating spacers at regular intervals to maintain the line spacing. The dielectric is principally air, making it a low-loss type of line.

Parasitic array:
A directive antenna that has a driven element and at least one independent parasitic element (director or reflector), or a combination of both. A Yagi antenna is one example of a parasitic array.

Parasitic element:
An element which is not connected directly to the transmitter / receiver via a transmission line, but which receives its energy by the coupling due to the proximity of other elements.

Phasing lines:
Sections of transmission line that are used to ensure the correct phase relationship between the elements of a driven array or between bays of an array of antennas. Also used to effect impedance transformations while maintaining the desired phase.

Polarisation:
The sense of the wave radiated by an antenna, by convention aligned with the E-field of an electromagnetic wave. This can be horizontal, vertical, elliptical or circular (left- or right-hand circularity), depending on the design and application.

Q section:
Term used in reference to transmission-line matching transformers and phasing lines.

Quad:
A parasitic array using rectangular or diamond shaped full-wave wire loop elements. Often called the 'Cubical quad'.

Radiation pattern:
The radiation characteristics of an antenna as a function of space coordinates. Normally, the pattern is measured in the far-field region and is represented graphically.

Radiation resistance:
The ratio of the power radiated by an antenna to the square of the RMS antenna current, referred to a specific point and assuming no losses. The effective resistance at the antenna feedpoint.

Radiator:
A discrete conductor that radiates RF energy in an

	antenna system.
Random wire:	A random length of wire used as an antenna, fed at one end and resonated by means of an ATU.
Reflector:	A parasitic antenna element or a metal assembly that is located behind the driven element to enhance forward directivity. Hillsides and large man-made structures such as buildings and towers may act as reflectors.
Refraction:	Process by which a radio wave is bent and returned to earth from a layer of the ionosphere or other medium after striking that medium.
Resonator:	In antenna terminology, a loading assembly consisting of a coil and a short radiator section. Used to lower the resonant frequency of an antenna, usually a vertical or a mobile whip.
Rybakov antenna:	Vertical antenna made using a fibreglass fishing pole and fed with an unun. Designed by IV3SBE.
Shunt feed:	A method of feeding an antenna driven element with a parallel conductor mounted adjacent to a low impedance point on the radiator. Frequently used with grounded quarter-wave vertical antennas to provide an impedance match to the feeder. Series feed is used when the base of the vertical is insulated from ground.
Solar flux:	A measure of solar activity, on a scale 66 to 300, obtained by measuring the noise from the sun on 2800MHz.
Split-stator capacitor:	Variable capacitor with two sets of fixed plates and one variable set. Often used for tuning small loop antennas.
Stacking:	The process of placing similar directive antennas atop or beside one another, forming a 'stacked array'. Stacking provides more gain or directivity than a single antenna.
Stub:	A section of transmission line used to tune an antenna element to resonance or to aid in obtaining an impedance match.
Surge impedance:	See 'Characteristic impedance'.
SWR:	Standing Wave Ratio on a transmission line caused by the line being mismatched. When the line is perfectly matched the SWR is 1:1. Where only the voltage component of the reflected wave is measured (i.e. when using a neon indicator) it is called 'VSWR' (voltage standing wave ratio).
SWR analyser:	Self-contained instrument for measuring SWR. Some

	models are also able to measure impedance.
T-match:	Method for matching a transmission-line to an unbroken driven element, attached at the electrical centre of the driven element in a T-shaped manner. In effect it is a double gamma match.
Tank circuit:	A parallel-tuned circuit in a power amplifier or ATU.
Top loading:	Addition of a reactance (usually a capacitance hat) at the end of an antenna element opposite the feedpoint to increase the electrical length of the radiator.
Transmatch:	See ATU.
Trap:	Parallel LC network inserted in an antenna element to provide multi-band operation with a single conductor.
Tuned feeder:	A transmission line that provides a designed degree of impedance transformation, in addition to its primary purpose of conveying RF energy with minimal radiation.
Unun:	An unbalanced-to-unbalanced impedance transformer. Usually used to lower impedances of end-fed antennas.
Valve:	Thermionic amplifying device, known as a 'tube' in the USA.
Velocity factor:	The ratio of the velocity of radio wave propagation in a dielectric medium to that in free space. When cutting a transmission line to a specific electrical length, the velocity factor of the particular line must be taken into account.
VSWR:	Voltage standing wave ratio. See 'SWR'.
WARC bands:	Frequency bands 10.100-10.150MHz, 18.068-18.168MHz and 24.890-24.990MHz.
Wave:	A disturbance or variation that is a function of time or space, or both, transferring energy progressively from point to point. A radio wave, for example.
Wave angle:	The angle above the horizon of a radio wave as it is launched from, or received by, an antenna.
Wavefront:	A surface that is a locus of all the points having the same phase at a given instant in time.
Windom antenna:	More correctly called an off-centre fed dipole (see 'OCFD') unless it is fed with a single wire feeder.
Yagi:	A directive, gain type of antenna that utilises a number of parasitic directors and a reflector. Named after one of its two Japanese inventors (Yagi and Uda).
Z-match:	A multi-band ATU derived from the link-coupled PA tank circuit.
Zepp antenna:	A half-wave wire antenna that operates on its

fundamental and harmonics. It is fed at one end by means of open-wire feeders. The name evolved from its popularity as an antenna on Zeppelins.

ABBREVIATIONS

A	ampere
AC	alternating current
AM	amplitude modulation
ARRL	American Radio Relay League
AWG	American wire gauge
Az-el	azimuth-elevation
Balun	balanced to unbalanced
BC	broadcast
BCI	broadcast interference
BW	bandwidth
Coax	coaxial cable
cm	centimetre
CT	centre tap
CW	continuous wave power (Morse code mode)
dB	decibel
dBd	decibels referenced to a dipole
dBi	decibels referenced to isotropic
dBm	decibels referenced to one milliwatt
dBW	decibels referenced to one watt
DC	direct current
deg	degree
DF	direction finding
DPDT	double pole, double throw
DPST	double pole, single throw
DVM	digital voltmeter
DX	long-distance communication
E	ionospheric layer, electric field
EIRP	effective isotropic radiated power
ELF	extremely low frequency
EMC	electromagnetic compatibility
EME	Earth-Moon-Earth
EMF	electromotive force
ERP	effective radiated power
f	frequency
F	farad
F/B	front to back (ratio)
F1	ionospheric layer
F2	ionospheric layer
F-layer	ionospheric layer
FM	frequency modulation
ft	foot or feet (unit of length)
GDO	grid- or gate-dip oscillator
GHz	gigahertz
GND	ground capacitance
H	henry
H	magnetic field
HF	high frequency (3 - 30MHz)
Hz	hertz (unit of frequency)
I	current
ID	inside diameter
IEE	Institution of Electrical Engineers
IEEE	Institute of Electrical and Electronic Engineers
in	inch
ITU	International Telecommunication Union
j	vector notation
kHz	kilohertz
km	kilometre
kW	kilowatt
kΩ	kilohm
L	inductance
lb	pound (unit of mass)
LF	low frequency (30-300kHz)

LHCP	left-hand circular polarisation	RLC	resistance-inductance-capacitance
Log	common logarithm	PMR	private mobile radio
LP	log periodic	RMS	root mean square
LPDA	log periodic dipole array	RSGB	Radio Society of Great Britain
LPVA	log periodic V array		
LUF	lowest usable frequency	s	second
m	metre (unit of length)	S	siemen
mA	milliampere	S/NR	signal-to-noise ratio
max	maximum	SINAD	signal-to-noise and distortion
MDF	medium-density fibreboard	SPDT	single pole, double throw
MF	medium frequency (0.3 - 3MHz)	SPST	single pole, single throw
		SWR	standing wave ratio
mH	millihenry	TPI	turns per inch
MHz	megahertz	TR	transmit-receive
min	minimum	TVI	television interference
mm	millimetre	UHF	ultra high frequency (300 - 3000MHz)
ms	millisecond		
mS	millisiemen	UTC	Universal Time, Coordinated (= GMT)
MUF	maximum usable frequency		
mW	milliwatt	V	volt
MΩ	megohm	VF	velocity factor
NBS	(US) National Bureau of Standards	VHF	very high frequency (30 - 300MHz)
NC	no connection, normally closed	VLF	very low frequency (3 - 30kHz)
nF	nanofarad	VOM	volt-ohm meter
NiCd	nickel cadmium	VSWR	voltage standing-wave ratio
NO	normally open		
OD	outside diameter	VTVM	vacuum-tube voltmeter
P-P	peak to peak	W	watt
PC	printed circuit	WARC (ITU)	World Administrative Radio Conference (now WRC)
PEP	peak envelope power		
pF	picofarad		
Q	tuned circuit figure of merit	WPM	words per minute
		WRC (ITU)	World Radiocommunication Conference
R	resistance, resistor		
RF	radio frequency	X	reactance
RFC	radio frequency choke	Z	impedance
RFI	radio frequency interference		
RHCP	right-hand circular polarisation		

SYMBOLS AND GREEK LETTERS

°	degree(s)
λ	wavelength
μ	permeability or micro
μF	microfarad
μH	microhenry
μV	microvolt
Ω	ohm
π	3.14159

Index

An Introduction to Antenna Modelling

By Steve Nichols G0KYA

For many years, the only way for most radio amateurs to work out how well an antenna design would work was to build it and find out. The arrival of computer based antenna modelling programs has changed this. This book looks at the Free MMANA-GAL antenna modelling program that will let you design and optimise a whole host of antennas, and all on your PC.

An Introduction to Antenna Modelling has been written by antenna guru Steve Nichols, G0KYA and shows you step-by-step how to input antennas designs into MMANA-GAL, how to adapt designs you are given and how to optimise your designs for the best performance. By the time you have finished you should be able to model a whole host of antennas including dipoles, the G5RV, the W3DZZ trapped dipole, verticals, off-centre fed dipoles (OCFD), magnetic loop antennas and many more.

An Introduction to Antenna Modelling provides an easy way to design and 'test' your antennas without ever lifting a saw or picking up wire cutters

FREE CD
This book is enhanced by the inclusion of CD that not only contains the MMANA-GAL software so you can get started immediately but much more. There are sample antenna files and event other antenna modelling software including EZNEC, MININEC Pro and 4nec2. There are also over 30 other amateur radio programmes included.

Size 174x240mm 80 pages ISBN: 9781 9101 9300 6

RRP £9.99

E&OE All prices shown plus p&p

Radio Society of Great Britain www.rsgbshop.org
3 Abbey Court, Priory Business Park, Bedford, MK44 3WH. Tel: 01234 832 700 Fax: 01234 831 496